DATE DUE

JAN. 2 8 1969			
APR. 8 19			

GAYLORD

PRINTED IN U.S.A.

Tool

Engi

S. E. RUSINOFF

Professor of Mechanical Engineering
Illinois Institute of Technology
Industrial Engineering Consultant

Member of
American Society of Mechanical Engineers
Society of Automotive Engineers
American Society of Tool Engineers
American Society for Quality Control
American Society for Engineering Education
American Ordnance Association
Society of American Military Engineers

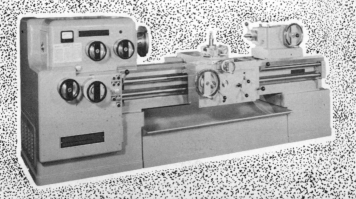

neering

1959

AMERICAN TECHNICAL SOCIETY
CHICAGO, U.S.A.

Dedication

To my dear wife Beatrice

Preface

The success of mass production is directly responsible for the emergence of *tool engineering* as a new field in manufacturing. Almost from its inception, mass production required men who were specialists in such areas as tool design, machine selection, cost estimating, or methods engineering. As the degree of specialization increased, however, another kind of specialist was born.

The qualifications this man needed were considerable. He had to have a working knowledge of all the technical phases of production— a knowledge that in the early days of mass production could only be gained through long and diverse experience. He had to be cost conscious, a good co-ordinator, and a student of exact methods. Today this man is commonly called a *tool engineer*. Wherever mass production techniques are used, his services are indispensable.

But it would be impossible, even if it were desirable, to fill the demand for such engineers from the limited number who have acquired the vast knowledge necessary from on-the-job experience. Men must be TRAINED to become tool engineers. To this end the field of tool engineering has undergone close scrutiny in recent years. Those qualifications essential to the tool engineer in his work have been isolated and organized so that they can be readily learned. Because of studies like this the tool engineer has acquired a professional status.

This book tells about the tool engineer—his job, the problems he encounters, his relationship to others in production. We shall see that his responsibilities are threefold: (1) to plan the processes of production, (2) to develop the tools, and (3) to integrate the facilities of manufacture. In explanation of this, Professor Rusinoff uses a simple, step-by-step narrative, many practical examples, and carefully selected illustrations. Throughout the text economical production is stressed. In fact, we shall learn that economy is the keynote in tool engineering.

Professor Rusinoff's book can be used profitably by those in colleges and universities, in technical institutes, or in industry. It makes valuable reading for anyone who must know more about tool engineering, especially in relation to what is actually practiced in manufacturing today.

THE PUBLISHERS

Acknowledgments

The author expresses his appreciation to the following organizations, tool equipment manufacturers, and industrial concerns for their generous cooperation in supplying illustrations and technical information used in this book. These contributors are given acknowledgment in illustration credits throughout the text:

Acme Industrial Co.
Allis-Chalmers Mfg. Co.
American Automatic Typewriter Co.
American Brake Shoe Co.
American Society of Mechanical
  Engineers
American Society of Tool Engineers
American Zinc Institute, Inc.
The Aro Equipment Corp.
Baird Machine Co.
Bakelite Corp.
Barber-Colman Co.
Bay State Abrasive Products Co.
The Bodine Corp.
Brown & Sharpe Mfg. Co.
Buhr Machine Tool Co.
Buick Motor Co.—Div. of General
  Motors
The Bullard Co.
Camfield Mfg. Co.
C. E. Johnson Gage Co.
Cincinnati Milling Machine Co.
Clearing Machine Corp.
The Cleveland Universal Jig Co.
Colonial Broach and Machine Co.
Commander Mfg. Co.
Consolidated Machine Tool Corp.
Convair
The Cooper-Bessemer Corp.
The Cross Co.
DeVlieg Machine Co.
Do-All Co.
Drop Forging Assoc.
The Dumore Co.

Ex-Cell-O Corp.
Fairfield Mfg. Co.
Federal Products Corp.
Greenlee Bros. & Co.
Hammond Machinery Builders
Hartford Special Machinery Co.
Heald Machine Co.
Hydraulic Press Mfg. Co.
Lake Erie Engineering Corp.
Landis Machine Co.
Link-Belt Co.
Machinery and Allied Products
  Institute
Magnaflux Corp.
Mechanical Handling Systems, Inc.
Mohawk Tools, Inc.
Multra Corp.
National Machine Builders' Assoc.
National Safety Council, Inc.
Norton Co.
Osborn Mfg. Co.
Reynolds Metals Co.
Rockford Engineered Products Co.
Scully-Jones & Co.
The Sheffield Corp.
Snow Mfg. Co.
Snyder Tool & Engineering Co.
South Bend Lathe Works
Sundstrand—American Broach Div.
Syntron Co.
Verson Allsteel Press Co.
Warner & Swasey Co.
W. F. & John Barnes Co.

The author also expresses thanks to W. Rahy Paul for sound appraisal of the manuscript, to Thomas Elliott for technical editing of the manuscript and for valuable suggestions relating to content, to Arthur E. Burke for page makeup and excellent rendering of many line drawings, and finally to Margaret Hultquist and Virginia Meagher for typing the original draft and final manuscript, respectively.

S. E. Rusinoff

Contents

Contents

Drafting room of design department.

Consults with designers

Table of comparable machine costs.

Studies costs

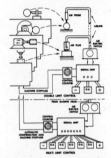

Diagram of gaging system.

Plans processes

TOOL ENGINEER

Drill used in machining of steel.

Analyzes equipment and operations

Hydraulic broaching machine.

Selects equipment

Turret lathe attachment to give added production.

Improves equipment

Typical operation sheets.

Develops operations

Functions of the modern tool engineer. In all phases of his job he strives for economy.

CHAPTER ONE

Introduction to Tool Engineering

Since the advent of modern mass production a new field in engineering has become more and more apparent. Today it has attained a professional recognition comparable to that of older fields in engineering. This new field is called *tool engineering.*

THE DEVELOPMENT OF TOOL ENGINEERING

Modern mass production dates from the first decade of this century. It replaced the long-established factory system, which was a mere massing of men and tools with little emphasis on planning and engineering principles. At first this new system caused bitter social and political hostility, but its basic worth was soon recognized. This led to an efficiency movement in industry, and time-study and similar methods became prominent.

As the techniques of mass production were advanced, tool engineering came naturally into its own. Mass production is a multi-phase operation requiring careful planning and coordination for its success. Before the emergence of tool engineering, planning was often inexact, coordination shoddy. As a result the cost of operation often rose above initial estimates, thereby reducing the manufacturer's return on his investment. From the beginning economics was inherently a part of tool engineering.

This new field is essential in metalworking industries, such as automobile and aircraft manufacture. It is also important in industries that manufacture plastic and textile goods, and other non-metal products. Furthermore, mass production is no longer necessary for its application. Now in moderate production good use can be made of the methods of tool engineering. In fact, different branches of industry are constantly applying these methods for better efficiency and greater profit.

In this age of specialization, the tool engineer has broad and vital duties, although he is considered a specialist. His importance makes him a respected member of the engineering profession. Most significantly, the field of tool engineering is never static. It is constantly improving, and the tool engineer must grow with it or risk becoming a liability.

WHAT IS TOOL ENGINEERING TODAY?

According to Webster's New International Dictionary, second edition, tool engineering is:

> a division of industrial engineering whose function is to plan the processes of manufacture, develop the tools and machines, and integrate the facilities required for producing given products with minimal expenditure of time, labor, and materials.

This definition was arrived at through consultation of the dictionary's editors with officials of the American Society of Tool Engineers, an organization founded in 1932.

Let's analyze this authoritative definition. There are three basic parts that require expansion.

Planning the processes of manufacture includes:

1. Studying the design of the product with a view toward improving the product's economical manufacture.
2. Determining the most suitable materials for the product.
3. Roughly developing the best arrangement of equipment and sequence of operations for efficient processing of the product.
4. Estimating the rough costs of materials, tools, machines, and production techniques, and holding them to a minimum.

Developing the tools and machines includes:

1. Determining if machines and tools on hand can be used or adapted for efficient processing of the product.
2. Adapting those machines and tools found usable.
3. Designing new machines and tools as necessary for the job.

4. Investigating the market for machines and tools necessary to the job, and purchasing them.

Integrating the facilities required for producing given products with minimal expenditure of time, labor, and materials includes:

1. Developing detailed arrangements of equipment and sequence of operations.
2. Scheduling rate of production and significant dates, including starting and completion dates.
3. Making route sheets that completely describe the sequence of operations and desired flow of work.
4. Making operator instruction sheets that completely describe the steps of operation of each machine.
5. Assembling bills of material that give all the information necessary for purchasing or drawing from stock.

Although the duties listed above are in the realm of tool engineering, they overlap into other fields as well. Product engineering, machine, tool, and gage designing, metallurgical engineering, cost accounting, purchasing, plant layout and methods engineering are all distinct activities in quantity manufacturing, yet the tool engineer has a hand in each. He must therefore have a working knowledge in other fields, especially in plant layout and applied mechanics, besides having a thorough background in the design of tools, machines, and other production equipment, and their many applications.

THE TOOL ENGINEER'S DUTIES—FROM DESIGN TO FINISHED PRODUCT

At this point a brief narrative of the tool engineer's duties is necessary to show his relationship with others in production and to emphasize his overall importance.

An idea for a product is conceived and presented to the product engineer, who designs a product based on the idea. The idea may come from a member of the sales force, engineering staff, production department, or from any responsible source. Arriving at a decision as to whether the proposed product has a market is a subject in itself. Surveys of the public are usually conducted and information gathered concerning competitive products, existing patents, and any available technical data. Even at this early stage the tool engineer may be brought in for technical advice.

The design of products nowadays entails a great amount of research and development. During the latter stages of development the tool engineer is usually consulted. After studying the design of the product he may suggest changes to promote a more economical manufacture; for example, standardizing hole dimensions or gear sizes. He may call for a standardization of materials, or suggest a material more readily available or at less cost. He may even advise that manufacture of the product would not be wise, due to excessive production costs.

This conclusion is based on a rough estimate of such costs as tools, machines, and other production equipment, and raw materials. Also involved is a rough layout (on paper) of the best equipment arrangement and sequence of operations. With the help of the plant layout engineer, methods engineer, and others, an experienced tool engineer can readily collect the data on which to make this decision.

Providing the Equipment

Once a product is designed and considered economical to manufacture, the tool engineer must then provide the tools and machine equipment to process it. This phase of production is crucial and complex. Two major factors affect the tool engineer's judgment: (1) The ultimate total volume of the product and (2) its quality, meaning the degree of tolerance and grade of material desired. Knowing volume and quality, he can decide whether or not new machinery and tools better suited for production than what he has on hand are warranted.

For instance, high volume requirements would mean he could purchase comparatively expensive equipment which would process the product more efficiently and economically in the long run than his own equipment. On the other hand, if high quality is also desired, perhaps the tool engineer would decide he must adapt the machines and tools at his disposal to keep overall production economical. His next problem then would be to adapt his equipment to meet the high quality requirements. If he can't do this, he is forced to purchase what he needs.

Again, no outside source may be able to meet his specifications and he must draw up plans for the manufacture of new-design equipment. Sometimes he might not find an outside source to build his new-design equipment, so he must make do with what he has by adroit arrangement and modification. Many other problems arise during this phase of production that require the tool engineer to bring all his experience and knowledge into play. This will be stressed again and again throughout the pages of this book.

Planning the Final Phase

After the necessary equipment has been provided, the final phase of production planning begins. Adequate floor space, lighting, and power are allotted. A detailed arrangement of machinery and sequence of operations is established, and the equipment installed. Here the tool engineer works with the process engineer. Their chief aim is to build in coordination so that neither time nor manpower is wasted. Working plans, bills of material, operator instruction sheets, route sheets, etc., are drawn up and distributed. Men are selected and, if necessary, given training.

Actual production can commence when the raw material for the product, and all other needed materials, are on hand. The tool engineer's duty now is to follow up on his work, making changes wherever he sees room for improvement, until he is fully satisfied.

THE TOOL ENGINEER'S DUTIES—SELECTING THE EQUIPMENT

All equipment used in the manufacture of a product is called *production equipment*. Power-driven machinery is an outstanding

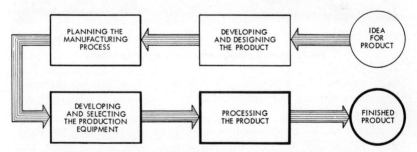

Fig. 1. Flow of operations from the initial idea to the finished product.

example of production equipment. Fig. 2 shows a power-driven machine which employs a metal-removing technique to work the material being processed into the designed product. Fig. 3 shows a sectional view of a machine that works a material by forcing it through a die under pressure, called extrusion. Either of these machines may have

Brown & Sharpe Mfg. Co.

Fig. 2. Straddle milling, using half side-milling cutters.

been designed for a special job, although the milling machine has adjustable control features. A unit of machinery is also called a *machine tool*.

Tools are called production equipment. Besides machine tools, they include jigs, fixtures, patterns, molds, dies, cutting tools, tool holders, checking fixtures, gages, and a number of small auxiliary tools necessary for a complete tooling-up operation. Later chapters will treat each class of tools separately.

Material-handling equipment, such as hand trucks, cranes, hoists, and conveyors is also classified as production equipment.

As explained earlier, development of machines and tools is based initially on product volume and product quality desired. When these

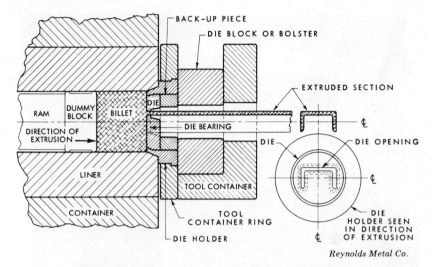

Fig. 3. Steel tools for producing aluminum shapes by extrusion.

factors are decided upon—usually by management—and a range of equipment, based on cost and general performance, is thereby determined, selection of equipment within this range can be made.

Influencing Factors

In his selection, the following considerations greatly affect any decision the tool engineer makes. Does the equipment:

1. Have sufficient production capacity? In the case of power-driven machinery especially, careful study of setup, loading, and cycling time is indicated.

2. Operate in the best possible way? In other words, is the equipment as simple and functional as it can be, with a minimum of moving parts?

3. Provide the necessary accuracy? Will it meet the tolerances required by the product designer?

4. Have acceptable depreciation and upkeep costs?

5. Have adaptability for future processing of products with a different design?

6. Require a minimum of labor, especially skilled labor? For many applications nowadays, machines are sought that have a maximum number of automatic devices, thereby reducing the chance of human error.

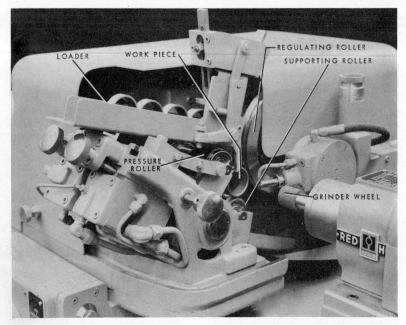

Fig. 4.   Automatic centerless internal grinder in operation.

Making Concessions

Seldom can the tool engineer either purchase or adapt production equipment to suit all his initial requirements. He must always be prepared to make concessions. A detailed analysis will usually show what requirements can be overlooked without seriously raising the overall cost or threatening the quality of the product. Since there are a host of variables involved, a good tool engineer must exercise careful judgment and, again, rely on his knowledge and long experience. Later chapters will present the variables and problems facing the tool engineer.

Fig. 4 shows an automatic grinding machine selected for its ability to mass produce. It has many automatic and time-saving features. Operation of the machine does not require a skilled mechanic. Since the machine has few moving parts, the upkeep and depreciation cost is low. The machine is used in centerless internal grinding operations. This class of equipment is capable of producing straight cylindrical or tapered holes.

EMPIRICAL VS. ANALYTICAL APPROACH TO TOOL ENGINEERING

The emergence of tool engineering as a field unto itself implies the use of exact methods in solving problems within its sphere. The passage of time and division of job responsibility will tend to cause the development of exact methods. In the early years of mass production, shop supervisors, toolroom foremen, master mechanics, and the like, acted as tool engineers as a matter of course. In general, what they accomplished they did not call tool engineering, nor did they recognize that their collateral work could be approached analytically. In that respect they were *not* tool engineers.

As a result production planning was often incomplete, inexact, and devious, especially as compared to present standards. Coordination among the various shops and on the assembly line itself was often less than smooth, with much wasted motion and loss of time. This inefficiency and lost time meant rising costs. We must remember, however, that thirty and forty years ago total quantities produced weren't nearly so great, nor labor so costly, as today. Also, men in industry then didn't have the means at their disposal to measure and compare with a view towards improving their production equipment and processes.

Recognition of Planning and Analysis

When problems arose in tool engineering before it became a distinct field, the men involved would rely on their experience and knowledge in their own specialties to solve the problems. Although sometimes these solutions were excellent, often they were makeshift, and good solutions weren't recorded in detail. But as time passed this all changed. Slowly the values of careful planning and analysis were recognized. It became economical to do what the tool engineer proposed. He presented figures and plans that clearly showed why one production process or machine was better than another for manufacturing the product under consideration. He reduced guesswork to a minimum and removed most of the gamble in production planning. When management found he could even improve the quality of the product with no increase in cost, tool engineering was here to stay.

Naturally we are indebted to the pioneers in tool engineering for advancing the analytical approach to quantity production. Today, however, the tool engineer has not abandoned the empirical approach.

Greenlee Bros. & Co.

Fig. 5. Typical transfer machine, which can be modified with a minimum of redesign.

Sometimes it is more advantageous for him to experiment than analyze. For example, when adapting his production equipment it might
prove simpler to try various setups than work them out on a drawing
board. Fig. 5 shows a transfer machine which has been modified
several times to accommodate different product designs. Changes on
this machine would probably be easier to make by practical experiment than by plan redesign.

Since tool engineering is comparatively new, any gaps in analytical methods must be bridged by using empirical methods. Also,
there may be some production problems where solution by detailed
planning and analysis isn't warranted. An approximate solution by
practical methods might be more satisfactory. Cost is usually the
reason, since more expense is involved in conducting the analytical
method.

Combining the Analytical and Empirical

Today the wise tool engineer combines the analytical approach with the empirical. Always, of course, he strives to manufacture his product to the quantity required as economically as possible without endangering its quality. By whatever means this manufacture can best be accomplished, is the duty of the tool engineer.

The following figures serve to illustrate the approach of the tool engineer to various process problems. Fig. 6 (left) shows a manually-operated turret lathe, which is unsuitable for quantity production. The tool engineer is told moderate production of a certain product is desired without a substantial outlay of money. After a thorough investigation, he decides to adapt the turret lathe by installing an automatic device.

Fig. 6 (right) shows the machine after an electro-hydraulic control has been attached. Now turret lathe versatility is combined with the automatic features of a chucking machine. Essentially, the control attachment is a hydraulic device which connects to the rear of the turret slide. Electronic control of the hydraulic cylinder's motion allows the feed rate for each turret position to be varied from 0 to 240 inches per minute in infinite increments.

While the basic control is directed toward actuation of the turret slide, auxiliary outlets on the electrical panel allow the addition of

Acme Industrial Co.

Fig. 6. Adapting a turret lathe. At the left is the lathe with manual control only. At the right is the lathe after an electro-hydraulic attachment has been installed.

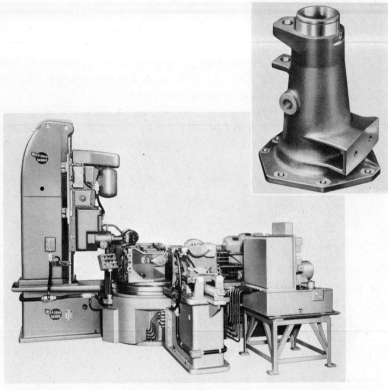

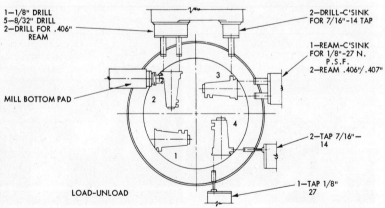

1—1/8" DRILL
5—8/32" DRILL
2—DRILL FOR .406"
    REAM

2—DRILL-C'SINK
FOR 7/16"–14 TAP

1—REAM-C'SINK
FOR 1/8"-27 N.
P.S.F.
2—REAM .406"/.407"

MILL BOTTOM PAD

2—TAP 7/16"—
14

1—TAP 1/8"
27

LOAD-UNLOAD

W. F. & John Barnes Co.

Fig. 7.   Machining a transmission housing, shown at the top. The special machine is shown at the upper left ;   the sequence of operations at the bottom.

attachments to open and close collets, feed bar stock, actuate cross slides, or change spindle speeds. Any standard turret lathe, therefore, may be used as a chucking machine. This changeover does not make it more difficult to set up, yet it greatly increases the machine's capacity while providing better surface finishes.

A Machine for Volume Production

Fig. 7 (upper left) shows a special machine a tool engineer may purchase if large-scale production is desired, and where changes in design are not anticipated for some time. The relatively high cost of this machine is justified, since it processes the product (or components thereof) at a unit cost lower than less complex machines. High output capacity of the machine and elimination of unnecessary labor through the employment of automatic controls are the main reasons unit cost is less.

Fig. 7 (top) shows the product, an aluminum transmission housing. Note the variety of machining required. Fig. 7 (bottom) shows a diagram of the operational setup. A total of seventeen machining operations are performed on the product continuously at three machining stations, while a single operator handles the loading and unloading. A 48-inch diameter hydraulic table indexes the work from station to station. The gross production rate is 118 pieces per hour.

As illustrated in Fig. 7 (bottom), station one is the load-unload point. At station two, one milling operation is performed on the bottom pad of the housing and eight holes drilled. At station three, two drill-and-countersinking, one ream-and-countersinking, and two reaming operations are performed. At station four, three tapping operations are performed. This gives a total of seventeen machining operations.

Besides offering high output at low unit cost over an extended period, this machine is compact to conserve floor space. Because of the substantial outlay of money initially, however, the tool engineer must analyze the machine's advantages and disadvantages carefully to assure management the machine will ultimately pay for itself.

CHAPTER TWO

Analysis of Manufacturing Costs

One basic problem always confronts the tool engineer: manufacturing any kind of product at the lowest possible cost. This statement implies (1) the tool engineer has the knowledge and experience necessary to manufacture any kind of product, and (2) he has the ability to estimate costs with a view towards economical production. Indeed, the good tool engineer *does* have these attributes; moreover, because of the wide range of modern production equipment and methods at his disposal, he is in a splendid position to select the most suitable equipment and arrange it to cut costs.

ECONOMY THROUGH COST ANALYZING

In the next few years many products will become increasingly complex in substance and function. The demands of the market for some products may increase to the point where new production techniques are indicated. It will be the tool engineer's duty to find the best methods of processing these products. Already he is using electronic computers, "tape controlled" machinery, intricate transfer equipment, and other wonders of automation to process his product smoothly and economically. However, economic production cannot be fully realized until the tool engineer knows how to determine costs in a reliable, systematic manner.

Later chapters will deal with the technical aspects of tool engineering. In this chapter we will be concerned with an analysis of manufacturing costs from the tool engineer's standpoint. As products become more complex, a logical and orderly breakdown of their component costs is essential, since complexity means a greater expenditure

Landis Machine Co.

Fig. 1.   A thread rolling machine.

for production equipment and a more expensive product, especially at first. A high investment to cover the initial expense often makes the job of cost estimating critical. The tool engineer must present estimates to management that are complete and accurate. Furthermore, his estimates must be realistic and in a language the non-technical men of management can understand.

The Outcome of Cost Economy

Figs. 1, 2, and 3 show three products where a realistic approach was used to produce them economically. The thread rolling machine in Fig. 1 was selected for its greater output of double-end studs. Both threads of the stud are rolled in a single threading cycle instead of separate cycles for each end as was done previously. The manufacturer of this machine claims a maximum production rate of 160 double-end studs per minute with satisfactory roll life. Here economy was realized by reducing the stud's unit cost to a minimum.

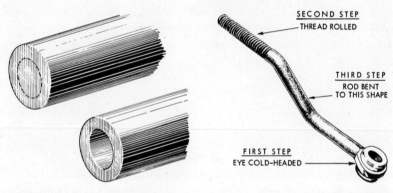

SECOND STEP
THREAD ROLLED

THIRD STEP
ROD BENT
TO THIS SHAPE

FIRST STEP
EYE COLD-HEADED

Fig. 2. Using tubing instead of solid round stock saves a machining operation.   **Fig. 3. A redesigned mounting bolt for a power lawn mower.**

Fig. 2 shows a solid bar and a length of seamless steel tubing. By using the tubing instead of the bar for internal thread rolling, a machining operation was eliminated. There is no hole to drill, less metal is wasted, and tubing is stronger than a bored-hole bar. Economy was realized by eliminating a machine operation.

Fig. 3 shows a mounting bolt for a power lawn mower. This bolt was redesigned to suit a new manufacturing process that would produce it at a cost substantially lower than the old process. The redesigned bolt is stronger yet it costs ⅔ less and eliminates a machining operation. It was made originally by welding a forged eye to a threaded rod, and bending the rod to the proper shape. The new process produces the bolt by first cold heading a ball on the end of a length of steel rod, flattening the ball, drilling a hole through the flattened portion, rolling the thread, and bending the rod to the required shape. Economy was gained by utilizing a better manufacturing process and redesigning the product to suit.

The examples above illustrate how economy can be achieved. Sometimes the advantages of one process or piece of production equipment over another are not immediately apparent. A systematic, detailed analysis of costs must be made before the tool engineer can see where and how he can economize. What course he follows depends ultimately on whether or not overall economy is possible.

DIMINISHING RETURNS

When we say a major aim of the tool engineer is to manufacture a product in the most economical manner, *overall* economy is always meant. Partial economy gained through a good choice of production equipment or adroit processing has no justification if an overall, long-run economy is not realized.

The replacement of existing production equipment with equipment of greater capacity would appear to insure a product with a lower unit cost. However, the initial investment must always be considered. If it is too high there can be no overall economy in spite of economical production. Equipment with electronic controls and other automatic features has many assembly line advantages, but its high initial cost may prohibit its use. Moreover, regardless of market possibilities, the tool engineer cannot assume that increasing production will eventually overcome these initial costs. Some equipment may require a number of years to pay for itself, which might not be feasible despite a current demand for the product.

Other factors of production may also introduce prohibitive costs. Redesigning production equipment, using one material instead of another, rearranging machinery and equipment, retooling, and other factors are never incorporated into a manufacturing process by the tool engineer without considering its effect overall. You will see we have now encountered a basic problem in economics, one where investment costs are only a part.

The Law of Diminishing Returns

In other words, in quantity production, an optimum point is reached whereby the greatest overall economy for a given set of conditions is attained. Striving for economy beyond this point will not be successful. Economists call the principle this relationship is based upon *the law of diminishing returns*. For our use the law may be stated as follows: If one or more of the factors involved in a manufacturing process should be held constant and the others increased, a point will be reached beyond which an increase in the variable factors will not result in a proportionate increase in the output.

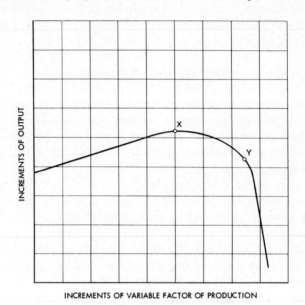

INCREMENTS OF VARIABLE FACTOR OF PRODUCTION

Fig. 4.   Graph showing law of diminishing returns.

Fig. 4 expresses this relationship graphically. Assuming all factors of a given manufacturing process are constant except one, increasing that factor will cause the output to increase until a point *X* is reached. Thereafter, increasing the variable factor results in a steadily decreasing output until a point *Y* is reached. From this point on the output diminishes rapidly due to an almost complete breakdown of the manufacturing process. Note that to study the law of diminishing returns more effectively, as many production factors as possible should be held constant.

A Practical Example of Diminishing Returns

To illustrate diminishing returns, let's consider a hypothetical case of an assembly line in an automobile plant. With 100 men on the line, 50 cars an hour are processed (see Fig. 5, point A). By adding 100 men the output is raised to 120 cars per hour (point B). Each individual job now has two men, who together can work it in much less time than one alone, and the line can be speeded up to handle more cars.

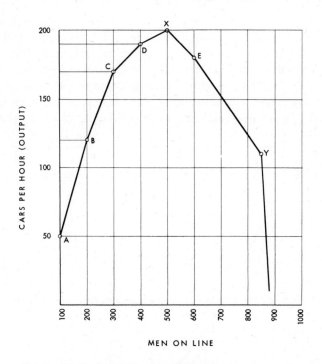

Fig. 5. Graph plotting the relationship between men on the assembly line and cars produced.

Adding another 100 men raises the output to 170 cars per hour (point C). Each job now has three men to work it, reducing the time two men consumed, and the line can be speeded up. Adding another 100 men will increase the output again, but now some jobs are being overly divided, men are getting in each other's way, efficiency begins to decrease, and the output increases to only 190 cars (point D).

Adding another 100 men gives an increase in output to only 200 cars per hour (point X), and adding still another 100 men results in a decreasing output of 180 cars per hour (point E). Point X then is the

point of diminishing returns. Adding men after that point results in a
steadily decreasing output until a point Y is reached. From this point
on there are so many men crowded along the line that production is
disrupted and output drops drastically.

A Corollary of Diminishing Returns

Fig. 6 shows a chart which plots a product's unit cost against
investment. This relationship illustrates an important corollary of
diminishing returns. For example, suppose the investment cost is spent
in redesigning one machine in an operation so that it will process the
product faster, which in turn will lower the product's unit cost.

Each new refinement to the machine results in a decreasing unit
cost until a point Z is reached. At this point other factors, which have

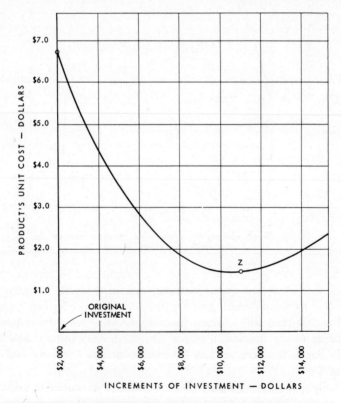

Fig. 6. Graph showing effect of equipment redesign (expressed as investment) on the product's unit cost. Costs shown are typical.

had an increasing deterrent effect, prevent any further decrease in the unit cost. These factors might be: (1) inability of other machines in the process to match the improved machine's efficiency, (2) inability of the material handling equipment to feed the machine fast enough, (3) excessive shutdown of the machine for servicing due to increased wear and tear. Since the deterring factors outweigh the factor of efficiency after point Z, increasing the investment to make the machine still more efficient will be unsuccessful. Perhaps by redesigning the other machines in the operation, or taking similar measures, the product's unit cost could be lowered, but this means a departure from the law of diminishing returns.

Although the law is concerned with physical output only, as we have seen it is the basis for cost computations. In any event, the tool engineer seeks the point of diminishing returns to arrive at the greatest economical output that can be expected per unit of input.

MANUFACTURING COSTS

Earlier it was mentioned that the tool engineer must often make a systematic, detailed analysis of costs before he can see where to economize. Although this type of analysis is sometimes called a *cost analysis,* the tool engineer need not be a cost accountant. He should possess a working knowledge of costs, however, and have the exacting approach of the cost accountant.

For our purposes, the finances of a business may be divided into four groups:

1. *Assets,* the tangible worth of a business.

2. *Liabilities,* a business' indebtedness as charged against its tangible worth.

3. *Income,* the financial return resulting in the operation of a business.

4. *Expense,* the cost of operating a business.

The tool engineer is only indirectly concerned with the first three groups. Since his responsibilities are so closely connected with these groups, he must know the effect his decisions will have on them. Of expense, the last group, he is only directly concerned with the portion that is incurred in production. The expenses incurred in administration, promotion, selling is the job of management to handle. The cost of production, the tool engineer's prime concern financially, is known

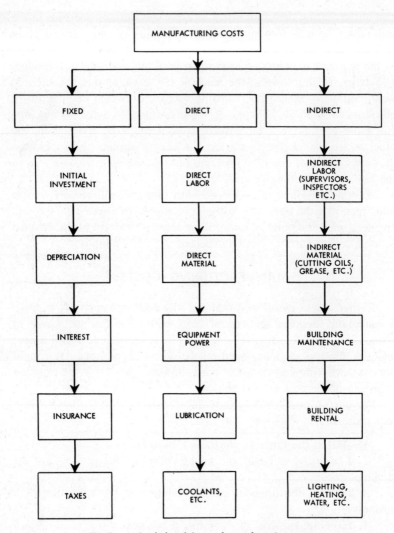

Fig. 7.   A simple breakdown of manufacturing costs.

as *manufacturing cost*, which is broken into three main groups: fixed, direct, and indirect costs. (See Fig. 7.)

Fixed Costs

These costs include the initial investment for production equipment and such charges as depreciation, interest, taxes, and insurance on the investment.

When a capital investment is made on production equipment, a satisfactory return is expected in a reasonable length of time. An obligation is incurred against a portion of the equipment's earnings to pay off and protect the original outlay of capital. This obligation continues until the equipment is completely paid off. The initial investment is composed of all costs incidental to procurement, which includes costs for transportation, handling, installation, and testing, plus any accessories required for operation.

Fixed costs can be expressed in equation form. Let I_a represent the cost for production equipment, transportation, handling, and accessories.

Let I_b represent the cost of setting up the equipment on the premises and testing it. Accountants generally charge this cost off to current expenses, but to ascertain true production costs it is a justifiable part of the initial investment.

Then the initial investment, $I_c = I_a + I_b$ in situations where the equipment being replaced has a negligible monetary value.

Where the replaced equipment is salvageable, let R represent its realizable value.

Then the net initial investment, $I_d = I_c - R$.

This investment is charged against production and distributed over prescribed periods of time. How it should be distributed is an economic problem and a number of variables must be considered. The actual decrease in value of the initial investment must be countered by an equal charge for equipment depreciation. Protection of the investment has to be made through tax and insurance payments, and by allowing for the current interest it would earn if invested in stocks or bonds.

Depreciation. Most mechanical and electrical equipment experiences a loss in value in a relatively short time, although the period of time is indefinite and difficult to define. Production equipment diminishes in value because of prolonged use, physical deterioration, and obsolescence. Where equipment loses its value due to deterioration and impairment from prolonged use, the depreciation is *physical*. Where equipment loses its value due to obsolescence the depreciation is *functional*. Deterioration is caused by corrosion, age, or exposure to weather. Prolonged use (excessive wear and tear) will cause equipment to lose its efficiency and accuracy.

Obsolescence is caused when comparatively new equipment has ceased to be economical because other designs have appeared that perform the same function more efficiently. It may also be caused by style changes in a product which is made by equipment that is largely unadaptable, or market saturation of a product made by unadaptable equipment. Functional depreciation is very difficult to foresee, another reason why the tool engineer must keep abreast of market development and the latest in production techniques.

The depreciation of production equipment is allocated over a period of years called the life of the equipment. Since it is hard to define this period beforehand, each unit of equipment must be treated independently. Individual estimates are figured and combined into one. The tool engineer bases his estimates on the equipment's intended use, its functional characteristics, comparisons with existing equipment of a similar nature, the manufacturer's test reports and similar data. Depreciation is closely controlled by tax authorities. To avoid a needless discussion of tax regulations, we are going to assume our depreciation rates meet the requirements of the authorities. This is a reasonable assumption.

The life of equipment may vary from a few months or less for highly specialized machines and tools, to ten years or more for durable equipment not markedly affected by changes in production techniques. The tool engineer's task is to develop the most realistic estimate on equipment life that he can. The method he uses to arrive at his estimate depends greatly on the equipment's construction and the accuracy required by management. Each unit of equipment presents its own problems.

Linear depreciation. Several methods are practiced in computing depreciation. For simplicity, the straight-line method is frequently used. Here the assumption is made that the decrease in value of production equipment is unvarying from year to year over the life of the equipment, which in most cases is a reasonably close approximation. This relationship can be readily formulated. Let:

I_N = initial investment for equipment in dollars,

N = number of years of useful life of the equipment,

I_n = value of equipment at the end of N years,

D = annual percentage allowance for depreciation,

D_c = annual cost of depreciation in dollars,

R_N = salvage value in dollars at the end of N years of useful life,

D_n = accrued depreciation in dollars to n years.

Since,

$$D = \frac{1}{N} \text{ and } D_c = \frac{(I_N - R_N)}{N}$$

we can combine these equations to eliminate N,

$$D_c = (I_N - R_N)D$$

(If the salvage value is negligible, then $D_c = I_N D$)
and,

$$D_n = nD_c = nD(I_N - R_N)$$

and finally,

$$I_n = I_N - nD(I_N - R_N)$$

Non-linear depreciation. The straight-line method gives a good approximation when the equipment involved is durable and not subject to continual modifications. With equipment that is relatively complex, specialized, and not durable, like subminiature electronic controls, non-linear methods are sometimes employed, although no method can be more than a well-informed guess. The purpose of some non-linear methods is to charge off heavier annual amounts for depreciation during the early years, thereby anticipating and accounting for the shorter life of intricate, less durable equipment. By the *reduced-balanced* method, a constant percentage is deducted each year from the value at the end of the previous year until the equipment is eventually reduced to its predetermined salvage value.

Other non-linear methods credit interest earnings to depreciation, reducing its charge to some extent. By one such method, interest on the remaining value of the equipment from year to year is added to the allowance for depreciation to provide equal amounts to pay off the investment. In recent years some companies have allocated depreciation according to the status of their business, charging off more when earnings are high and less when low. Following this policy, depreciation can be correlated with production output, volume of sales, manhours expended, or by whatever means a business measures its activity.

Some non-linear methods may prove accurate enough for certain types of equipment and not for others. Others may be accurate up to a point and not beyond. Still others may suit the cost accountant but not the tool engineer. Since estimating depreciation is a matter of predicting future value, inaccuracies are almost certain to appear with any method used. Therefore, the tool engineer must exercise discretion in his choice of non-linear methods. He may select one that is overly complex and yet does not provide an accuracy enough better than the simple straight-line method to warrant its use.

Interest, taxes, and insurance. Interest is money paid for the use of money, usually expressed as a percentage of the principal per unit of time. In our case the principal is the capital worth of the initial investment. A functional analysis of the production equipment is necessary to see whether or not the capital outlay is likely to be recovered. Since there is no guarantee of recovery, interest varies greatly in proportion to the soundness of the investment. Earnings of the investment are expected to recover the charge for interest as well as the principal.

Several alternatives are followed to establish a rate of interest. In some instances the rate is set at that of the market in which the capital outlay might be borrowed for the investment. In other instances the rate is set at that which could be realized if the capital outlay were invested in stocks and bonds instead of the equipment. More often, the rate will depend on the risk involved. The greater the risk the higher the rate of interest. The kind of business, the type of equipment, the status of the market affects the degree of risk.

The annual interest charge on depreciated production equipment is assessed on the undepreciated balance. Taxes and insurance are also assessed on the undepreciated balance, since they are proportional to the current value of the initial investment. Taxes are the normal deductions imposed by the government, which to a certain extent regulates their means of assessment. Insurance is the protection of equipment against fire, disastrous weather, negligence, accidents to operating personnel, etc.

Average annual interest rate. Assuming a linear depreciation and neglecting the equipment's salvage value, let:

I_N = the initial investment in dollars,

a = the annual interest rate in percent (estimated),

N = the years of useful equipment life (estimated).

Then,

$I_N a$ = the interest payment on the initial investment at the end of the first year. Note that the payment is charged at year's end, although calculated at the beginning of the year.

And,

$$\frac{I_N a}{N}$$ = the interest payment at the end of the year estimated to be the useful life of the equipment.

Therefore,

$$\frac{\left(I_N a + \dfrac{I_N a}{N}\right)}{2}$$ = the average interest *payment,*

which rearranged becomes,

$$\frac{I_N a}{2}\left(\frac{N + 1}{N}\right)$$

Since average rate is $\dfrac{\text{average payment}}{\text{initial investment}}$, dividing the ratio above by I_N gives,

$$\frac{a}{2}\left(\frac{N + 1}{N}\right) = A, \text{ the average annual interest } \textit{rate.}$$

Average annual tax and insurance rate. Taxes and insurance can be formulated in the same fashion as interest, since they have the same relationship to the investment as interest. The foregoing development for interest applies also to tax and insurance rates, which will always be considered together. If *b* represents the annual tax and insurance rate in percent, then:

$$\frac{I_N b + I_N b/N}{2}$$ = the average tax and insurance *payment,*

which rearranged becomes,

$$\frac{I_N b}{2}\left(\frac{N + 1}{N}\right)$$

Dividing by I_N gives,

$$\frac{b}{2}\left(\frac{N + 1}{N}\right) = B, \text{ the average annual tax and insurance } rate.$$

Direct Costs

These costs are incurred in the operation of production equipment. They include the costs of direct labor, direct material, power for the equipment, lubrication, coolants. Since direct costs are in proportion to the volume of production, it is a convenient way of grouping them, although the cost accountant may group them differently. They are also called *operating expenses*.

Direct labor costs are the wages paid workers for actual labor performed in the manufacture of the product. They are determined from job tickets or time cards turned in by the worker. Direct labor can be estimated fairly accurately from past experience with similar equipment and layouts. Job evaluation rates are established for each class of work on the basis of time cards and job tickets.

Direct material costs are the costs for those materials which are actually consumed in making the product. They are determined from the invoices of purchased material and, to avoid unnecessary accounting, usually include transportation and handling charges. Cost estimates can be developed from invoices for similar material and from blueprints showing bills of material of similar products. With materials, market conditions will sometimes affect the final purchase. Since adjustments can always be made to account for market conditions, they need not upset material estimates.

The tool engineer relies heavily on past records when he is making his analysis of direct costs. Because time brings changes, however, he must use his judgment before incorporating them into his final estimate. Here is another reason why the tool engineer must continually update himself or risk using obsolete information.

Indirect Costs

These are costs which do not have a direct relationship to volume of production. Certain labor and material costs are billed as indirect costs, often called *overhead*. Many costs are grouped with indirect costs because to group them with either fixed or direct costs would require an overly complex accounting procedure. For example, plant lighting is roughly proportional to production, since only equipment that is functioning needs light for its operators. Lights are not turned off, however, when equipment is temporarily shut down for servicing,

Fig. 8.   As an inspector, this man is charged to indirect labor.

the lunch hour, or other reasons, which means an adjustment would have to be made in the lighting cost if it were figured as a *direct* cost.

The components of indirect costs. Indirect labor costs are the wages paid workers who are not directly associated with the manufacturing process. Supervisors, inspectors, stockroom clerks, truckers are charged to indirect labor. Indirect material costs are those costs for materials and supplies which are not considered a part of the product or production equipment. Cutting oils, cotton waste, grease, washing compounds, simple lubricants are charged to indirect costs. Other indirect costs are for maintenance of buildings and grounds, building rental payments, lighting, heat, water.

There is no steadfast system for grouping costs. Some companies lump taxes, insurance, interest, and depreciation under indirect costs, although as we have seen, the usual practice is to group them under fixed costs. Some companies show equipment power as an indirect cost, but its inclusion with direct costs is justified. In any event indirect costs are charged by various methods to the several production departments and eventually, to each specific operation and its equipment.

Methods of distributing indirect costs. Since indirect costs do not vary in proportion to production, there can be no standard treatment of their distribution. Workable distributions are desired, however, and various methods—some more flexible than others—have been offered by specialists in the field. The tool engineer must select the method most suitable for his particular use.

Some tool engineers feel good distribution is obtained by the direct material method, where distribution is in proportion to the value of the direct material used in the product. An indirect rate is established in dollars for each dollar of direct material expended, either from previous practice or from a new estimate. Another method is to divide all indirect expenses by the units of the product manufactured, giving an overhead rate in dollars for each part produced.

Some tool engineers establish the indirect rate in dollars for each dollar expended in direct labor by dividing overall indirect costs into the overall cost of direct labor. Another practice is to divide the total hours of direct labor into the overall indirect cost, giving an indirect rate in dollars for each hour of direct labor expended. Another method establishes a machine hour rate, often called the *burden rate* of the machine. It is obtained by dividing the total indirect costs by the number of hours the machine is operated during the same period.

Space charges are sometimes considered by tool engineers. To determine these charges, the total overhead cost is divided by the square feet of space chargeable to the department. This establishes a space rate in dollars per square foot. The overhead charge to a machine may be computed by multiplying the square feet of area it occupies by the space rate.

ANNUAL AND UNIT PRODUCTION COSTS

The total cost of operation in dollars, R, and the unit cost, U, may be summed up in the following manner:

From previous statements,

I_d = net investment in equipment in dollars (initial investment minus salvage value),

D = annual percentage allowance for depreciation,

A = average annual interest rate,

B = average annual tax and insurance rates.

Then,

$Y = I_d (D + A + B)$, the average annual total fixed charges in dollars.

If,

$M =$ annual total cost of materials in dollars,

$L =$ annual total cost of direct labor in dollars,

$C =$ annual total cost of maintenance in dollars,

$E =$ annual total cost of power and supplies in dollars,

$F =$ annual total cost of space allotted per machine,

$T =$ annual total cost of indirect labor per machine,

then the total yearly cost,

$$R = Y + M + L + C + E + F + T$$

and the unit cost,

$$U = \frac{R}{P}$$

where,

$P =$ the total number of parts produced in the year.

The Importance of Cost Estimating

Breaking down manufacturing costs into many groups can never be completely systematized. New situations bring new problems which emphasize different costs. In one case, perhaps the depreciation rate on some piece of machinery will be critical, whereas in another case it may have no significance at all. The ability of the tool engineer to estimate costs quickly, accurately, and wisely is as vital as his grasp of technical matters. Since economy is the keynote in industry today, unsound estimates may ruin any chance for economical manufacture from the start.

CHAPTER THREE

Economic Selection of Machine Equipment

The purpose of Chapter One was to present an overall view of the field of tool engineering and at the same time stress economical production from the tool engineer's standpoint. Chapter Two analyzed manufacturing costs so that economical production could be recognized and achieved on a fairly systematic basis. The following chapters will continue to investigate economy in production, exploring more fully the means by which it can be realized.

An investigation of tool engineering divides logically into three main parts: a study of big equipment, small equipment, and manu-

Convair

Fig. 1. The drafting room of a modern engineering and design department. Here is where a tooling program begins.

facturing processes. Following this breakdown, with economical production as the goal, Chapter Three is devoted to *The Economic Selection of Machine Equipment,* Chapter Four to *Tool Economy,* and Chapter Five to *Economic Processing.*

Lathes, milling machines, drill presses, and larger machinery are called *machine equipment,* or machine tools (big equipment). Cutting tools; jigs, clamps and other fixtures; hand tools and inspection equipment are called *tools* (small equipment). To complete the basic terminology, *tooling* or *tooling up* means to design, buy and perhaps build all the necessary machine equipment and tools to manufacture a product by methods arrived at beforehand. A *tooling program* is a plan or procedure for tooling up. As stated earlier, *production equipment* is all equipment used in the manufacture of a product, including material-handling equipment. Chapter Five deals in part with the economic design and arrangement of material-handling equipment.

INITIAL CONSIDERATIONS

To best study the economics of machine equipment, tools, and manufacturing processes, we are assuming the tool engineer knows the quality and quantity of his product (including its raw materials) before he begins to plan and select equipment. Normally this is the case, although it is not absolutely necessary the tool engineer know all his product's specifications first. In special situations he might help design a product to utilize the equipment in his plant and process a quantity of it dependent on the raw materials on hand. Not knowing all the market possibilities, however, makes this sort of manufacture a gamble.

Market and Management Potential

In almost all cases a thorough survey of the market is made first to determine the demand for a product and the amount and degree of competition existing. When this is ascertained, detail plans are drawn up, which indicate the product's quality and quantity, and passed on to the tool engineer. Although it is likely he has been consulted earlier concerning production costs, methods, and other matters, only when he knows definitely what this quantity and quality will be can he proceed with his own planning.

In addition to knowing the quality and quantity of his product, the good tool engineer seeks assurance from management on the product's chances for a long term success. If management wants ten thousand special valves now and more later only if the valves sell, the tool engineer must plan differently than he would if ten thousand valves are desired now with assurances from management that more will be required later on. With smaller quantities probable, he will buy less expensive equipment and, in general, spend less. His decision depends mainly on his estimate of management. If they have accurately predicted the success of a number of products in the past, he can assume with a measure of confidence that the current product will sell too, and plan accordingly. The wise tool engineer will establish a sound rapport with management (the works manager, production chief, planning department head, chief designer, etc.) and, from past performance, size up its strengths and shortcomings.

Understanding Direct Labor Economy

To become oriented with respect to Chapters Three, Four, and Five, let us remember that a skilled craftsman can make almost any kind of product with a few simple tools, but in most cases the time he consumes would be so great as to make the cost of his efforts excessive. For him to produce a large quantity of the same article would not appreciably reduce the cost. Although the tools are inexpensive and only one man is involved, these factors are completely offset by the comparatively long time a skilled worker would spend in making a product. Because of the vast accumulation of manhours, the overall expense of a simple, one man operation is almost always prohibitive.

It follows that economical production can be achieved by reducing the charge for direct labor as much as possible without introducing offsetting costs. The direct labor charge is reduced by eliminating men from the manufacturing process altogether, reducing the time-per-part of those men necessary for production, and using less skilled manpower. In most manufacturing processes, reducing the direct labor charge (without causing offsetting costs) is the surest way to reduce overall costs. Other cost-cutting methods, such as improved interest, tax, and insurance plans, or a reduction in indirect charges, are not as effective.

The elimination of men from the manufacturing process is accomplished by replacing them with machine equipment and tools, and improving the operation of the process itself. In general, the more automated the equipment and the process, the fewer the men needed for operation. Complete automation is not feasible, however, since

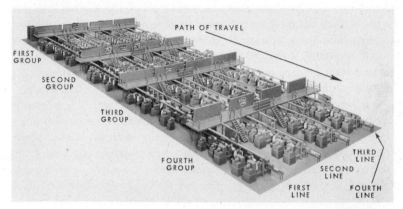

PATH OF TRAVEL

FIRST GROUP

SECOND GROUP

THIRD GROUP

FOURTH GROUP

FIRST LINE

SECOND LINE

THIRD LINE

FOURTH LINE

W. F. & John Barnes Co.

Fig. 2.   Scale model of a new installation requiring a unitized automation system of machine tools.

obviously a production line cannot be run with no men at all. In fact, a highly automated plant has greatly increased maintenance manhour costs, which are chargeable to direct labor. This is one of the offsetting costs mentioned in the previous paragraph. Another big offsetting cost, of course, is the high initial investment for production equipment.

Reducing the time-per-part of men on the line is accomplished by increased automation of machines and tools (so one man may, in effect, operate more equipment), efficient arrangement of operator controls, time and motion studies of operator movements, and by other means which are discussed in Chapter Five. Reducing the time men spend processing each part reduces the direct labor cost of the entire process. There are offsetting costs in time-per-part reduction too, such as increased downtime and maintenance costs. Increasing the use of automated machines and tools will also decrease the need for skilled manpower. The increased use of jigs and other fixtures also means less skilled manpower is needed, decreasing the wage rate, which in turn will reduce the overall direct labor cost.

Now that we have a grasp of the essential reasons why economical production is so heavily dependent on using the most suitable equipment and processes, we can proceed with a study of the economic selection of machine equipment.

Reasons for Equipment Selection

The most obvious reason for selecting machine equipment occurs

in the case of a new installation. In some respects this kind of selection
is easier than when equipment must be replaced or added to, because
limiting factors can usually be altered, if necessary, to suit the proposed equipment's design. Factors of floor space, equipment weight,
power, associated equipment, and other factors need not eliminate a
unit of equipment for a new installation if it has superior qualities.

Selecting machine equipment to replace that which is currently
operating can be more difficult. The present installation may be worn,
appear obsolete, or production requirements may have risen above
the installation's capacity. Replacement with different equipment will
likely be limited by the factors mentioned in the previous paragraph.
Occasionally more expensive equipment must be purchased only
because it meets the specifications, while similar equipment that is
less costly and will produce more economically can't be used. For our
discussion, however, we are assuming that the limiting factors never
narrow equipment choices automatically to just one.

Another reason for selecting machine equipment is to add to the
present installation. Normally the equipment currently operating is
adequate in all respects except capacity. To increase capacity is primarily a matter of adding units of the same type of equipment until
the desired total output is reached. Floor space and power requirements can be a problem in equipment supplement; also, there is a
danger of unbalancing the process. Highly automated plants today
often follow the "building block" principle, which stresses versatility
by using interchangeable parts, tools, and machines. In plants of this
nature, adding machine equipment is more or less routine.

In summary, the three basic situations requiring machine equipment are:

1. For a new installation.
2. For replacement of equipment currently operating.
3. For an addition to the present installation.

The technique of selecting. Although each situation has its own
problems, in all cases the technique of selection reduces to locating
eligible types of equipment, comparing each type against all others on
a basis of cost and function, and systematically arriving at the most
economical equipment.

Any discussion of machine selection is likely to become overly
complex if too many variables are considered at once. To avoid this,
equipment costs will be considered apart from equipment functions,

and wherever possible, each type of cost and function will be analyzed separately. An analysis will consist of comparing a feature of one unit of equipment with a similar feature of other units.

Cost Comparisons

Before investigating the types of costs, a glimpse now at how they are compared will make a cost investigation later more meaningful. Essentially a cost comparison is contrasting the total cost of a unit of machine equipment under consideration against other comparable units the market has to offer. Total cost may be on an annual or unit basis. Determining the total cost is accomplished by computing and summing up all the fixed, direct, and indirect costs studied in the previous chapter.

From Chapter Two, the total manufacturing cost,

$$R = Y + M + L + C + E + F + T$$

where,

$$Y = I_N (D + A + B).$$

These individual costs are determined for each unit of machine equipment under consideration and totaled. On a purely cost basis, the equipment that shows the lowest annual cost is selected.

Also from Chapter Two, the annual unit cost, $U = R/P$, where P is the number of units of the product that are processed annually. Knowing R, the unit cost of processing the product can be determined for each piece of equipment under consideration. The equipment that shows the lowest annual cost is selected.

Factors influencing comparisons. Several factors, like the material of the product, power, and space requirements, will not vary appreciably for a given installation or between comparable equipment. For comparison purposes, therefore, they can normally be disregarded. Where only one product is intended for manufacture by a unit of equipment, comparison and selection is relatively straightforward. Where a number of different products are involved, the process of comparing becomes complicated. Costs may differ from product to product, or one cost may be unimportant in the case of one product and critical in another. For these reasons and others, more detailed estimates must be drawn up for each cost and more exacting comparisons made. Although the procedure is complicated, the same principles as for single-product manufacture hold true.

It may appear that cost comparisons are nothing more than a series of computations with an end result of selecting equipment that has the lowest cost. This is not altogether true, since intangible as well as tangible elements are present. Obsolescence is a factor that cannot be accurately predicted. Maintenance, safety, the effect of operator comfort or discomfort at the machine, and other uncertainties are likely to exist which can't be assigned definite values. By drawing on his past experience, however, the tool engineer can develop realistic estimates for these intangibles. That certain factors are intangible should never be an excuse for guesswork or carelessness.

Survey and purchase comparisons. Two additional situations call for machine equipment comparisons: (1) where a survey is desired to check on the performance of the present installation against what the current market offers, and (2) to learn whether it is advisable to buy equipment for the manufacture of a part or parts of a product, or purchase the parts outright. The same principles for comparing costs apply to these situations as to the ones already covered. An efficiency survey often results in a combination of operations, or the addition of attachments, rather than an investment in new equipment. A decision to purchase a part or parts of a product generally depends on the quantity needed. It would not pay to manufacture a comparatively small quantity, since the cost would not offset the vendor's cost plus his profit. For a very large quantity, the reverse is usually true.

Illustrative example of cost comparing. The following example

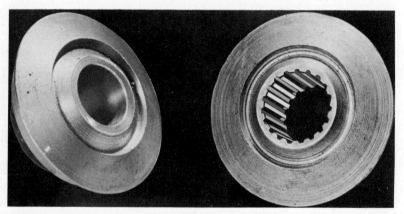

Sunstrand—American Broach Div.

Fig. 3.   Bevel side gears, before and after broaching the splines.

is purely hypothetical. A manufacturer of bevel side gears has a situation confronting him of economically broaching splines in his product. Upon a recent increase in gear production potential, due to a sizeable increase in demand, the broaching facilities of the plant were calculated to be inadequate. Until the increase in production potential three horizontal pull-type broaching machines had satisfactorily met the demand, but these machines have seen extensive service and are not useable in the new production schedule. The manufacturer has decided to replace the present machines with newer and more productive machines. Fig. 3 shows the bevel side gear, before and after broaching the splines.

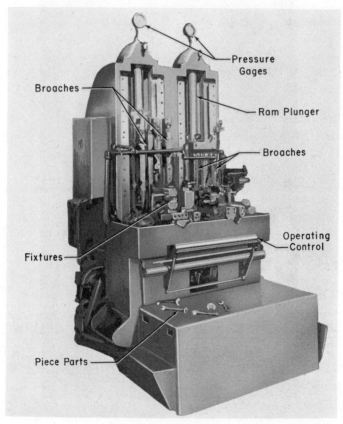

Colonial Broach Co.

Fig. 4.   A double-spindle, vertical, hydraulic broaching machine of the pull-type variety.

Broaching machine choices. The tool engineering department of the plant has conducted a thorough examination of the market, computed and compared costs, and has finally narrowed the search to two choices:

Choice A Broaching Machine. A double-spindle, vertical, hydraulic machine of the pull type shown in Fig. 4, a general class of machine in which the broaches are drawn or pulled through the work.

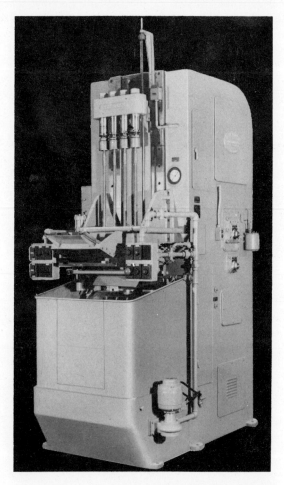

Sunstrand—American Broach Div.

Fig. 5. A four-station, vertical, hydraulic broaching machine of the pull-type variety.

This machine is equipped with fixtures for broaching automobile connecting rods and bearing caps, but with proper retooling it can be adapted for broaching gear splines.

The equipment can be tooled up for a broaching production rate of 550 parts an hour. The cost of one machine with tooling is $23,000. In order to meet the anticipated demand of 4,000,000 parts annually, it will be necessary to purchase five machines. Enough flexibility is built into this type machine so that with a minimum of retooling, different size gears can be broached and different broaching operations performed.

Choice B Broaching Machine. A four-station, vertical, pull-up type machine of the general class shown in Fig. 5. The close-up view in Fig. 6 shows four parts in the broaching position and four others ready for the next cycle. The machine is equipped with a gravity chute feed and loading slide so all the operator has to do is keep the

Sunstrand—American Broach Div.

Fig. 6. Close-up of the four-station broaching machine.

four stations in the chute filled with parts; the other operations are fully automatic. This type broaching equipment also provides adequate flexibility with a minimum of retooling.

The broaching production rate for this machine is 1000 parts an hour. Its cost with tooling is $35,000. In order to meet the annual demand of 4,000,000 parts, three machines will be needed, although together the three have a capacity well in excess of the four million quota.

Cost calculations. Three costs will not enter into our calculations: the salvage value of the old machines, which is assumed negligible, and the costs of direct material and indirect labor, which would be the same for both installations. The number of years of useful life for each type of equipment is estimated to be three years ($N = 3$). Other costs besides the initial investment are shown in Table I.

Conclusions. It is seen that a savings of $12,270 a year is realized if the four-station machines (choice B) are used. Perhaps if the two types of machines were estimated to pay for themselves in four or five years instead of three, the difference in savings would be less. With a longer equipment life, the yearly costs for the four-station

TABLE I

TYPE OF COST	SYMBOL	AMOUNT OF COST		COMMENT
		CHOICE A MACHINE	CHOICE B MACHINE	
INTEREST	a	10% PER ANNUM	10% PER ANNUM	THE ASSUMPTION HERE IS THAT EITHER TYPE OF MACHINE WILL BE EXPECTED TO PAY OUT ITS COST IN $N = 3$ YEARS.
TAXES AND INSURANCE	b	3% PER ANNUM	3% PER ANNUM	
DIRECT LABOR	L	$2.35 PER HR. PER MAN	$2.35 PER HR. PER MAN	ONLY ONE MAN IS REQUIRED TO OPERATE EITHER TYPE OF MACHINE
MAINTENANCE	C	$275 PER ANNUM	$480 PER ANNUM	FOR EACH MACHINE
POWER AND SUPPLIES	E	$310 PER ANNUM	$415 PER ANNUM	FOR EACH MACHINE
FLOOR SPACE	F	$60 PER ANNUM	$90 PER ANNUM	FOR EACH MACHINE

TABLE II

TYPE OF COST	SYMBOL	FORMULA FOR TOTAL INSTALLATION	COMPUTATIONS		RESULT (TOTAL)	
			CHOICE A MACHINE	CHOICE B MACHINE	CHOICE A	CHOICE B
TOTAL INITIAL INVESTMENT	I_N	I_N × NUMBER OF MACHINES	$23,000 × 5	$35,000 × 3	$115,000	$105,000
ANNUAL ALLOWANCE FOR DEPRECIATION	D	1/N (ASSUMING STRAIGHT–LINE DEPRECIATION	1/3	SAME AS A	0.333	0.333
AVERAGE ANNUAL INTEREST RATE	A	$\frac{1/2a(N+1)}{N}$	$\frac{1/2(0.10)(3+1)}{3}$	SAME AS A	0.066	0.066
AVERAGE ANNUAL TAX AND INSURANCE RATE	B	$\frac{1/2b(N+1)}{N}$	$\frac{1/2(0.03)(3+1)}{3}$	SAME AS A	0.020	0.020
ANNUAL TOTAL FIXED CHARGES	Y	$I_N(D+A+B)$	$115,000 (.333+ 0.066+ 0.020)	$105,000 (.333+ 0.066+ 0.020)	$48,300	$44,000
ANNUAL TOTAL DIRECT LABOR	L	$\frac{\text{TOTAL PARTS × HOURLY RATE}}{\text{PARTS PER HR. PER MACHINE}}$	$\frac{4,000,000 × 2.35}{550}$	$\frac{4,000,000 × 2.35}{1000}$	$17,100	$9,400
ANNUAL TOTAL MAINTENANCE	C	C × NUMBER OF MACHINES	$275 × 5	$480 × 3	$1,375	$1,440
ANNUAL TOTAL POWER & SUPPLIES	E	E × NUMBER OF MACHINES	$310 × 5	$415 × 3	$1,550	$1,245
ANNUAL TOTAL FLOOR SPACE	F	F × NUMBER OF MACHINES	$60 × 5	$90 × 3	$300	$270
TOTALS	R	Y + L + C + E + F	$48,300 17,100 1,375 1,550 300	$44,000 9,400 1,440 1,245 270	$68,625	$56,355

machine would be appreciably more, since it was designed more for high capacity than durability; maintenance and direct costs would rise, cutting into the comparative savings. The less productive double-spindle machine, being more durable, would not be subject to as great an increase in direct labor and maintenance costs.

The unit cost for broaching splines on each gear using the double-spindle machine is,

$$\frac{\$68,625}{4,000,000} = \$0.0171$$

Using the four-station machine the unit cost is,

$$\frac{\$56,355}{4,000,000} = \$0.0141$$

By using the four-station machine a savings-per-part of $0.003 (0.30 cents) is realized. Notice that the lesser charge for direct labor of this type machine accounts for most of the savings. Here is a typical case showing why the greatest opportunity for economy lies in holding direct labor costs at a minimum. Actually costs are not compared at each step as was done in this example. Instead, the costs of each type of machine being considered are computed (or estimated) and totaled, the total costs among machines are compared, then an individual cost by cost comparison is made, if necessary.

COST CONSIDERATIONS

Initial Investment

This investment is a fixed charge, as explained in Chapter Two. It is the only fixed charge we are going to consider here; others, like depreciation and interest, are covered adequately in the preceding chapter.

It is quite difficult to discuss an initial investment for machine equipment without considering the equipment's individual costs and functions. To avoid this, let's assume a unit of machine equipment has all the functional qualities desired by the tool engineer, and a total cost that proves to be the lowest among all comparable equipment. Let us also assume that transportation and installation costs are minor. The question remains: does the equipment have a productive capacity that is compatible with its cost? Knowing its cost is the lowest of all comparable equipment usually assures its approval by management.

On the other hand, management's approval is based on how long the equipment's earnings will take to pay off the initial outlay of money. If even the best equipment the field has to offer cannot repay the initial investment in what management considers a reasonable length of time, they will look on the transaction with disfavor. To buy the equipment despite its predicted shortcomings is a gamble that is usually not taken.

Factors influencing the investment. Determining how long a unit of machine equipment will take to pay for itself depends on a number of factors. The machine's mechanical performance is one factor, its durability another. The section on *equipment life* covers several factors involving purely routine calculations. The single biggest factor, however, lies outside the tool engineer's province: analyzing the market with a view toward accurately estimating the demand for a product. If an accurate estimate reveals the demand will be great, a large volume of the product can safely be manufactured, which will reduce the unit cost, increase the unit profit, and assure a total profit so the initial investment can be protected.

A good prediction as to product demand means a purchase of machine equipment based on this prediction becomes only a .calculated risk, and not a gamble. A *gamble* is not founded on enough reliable information; a *calculated risk* is founded on all the reliable information that is available. To determine demand, an efficient man-

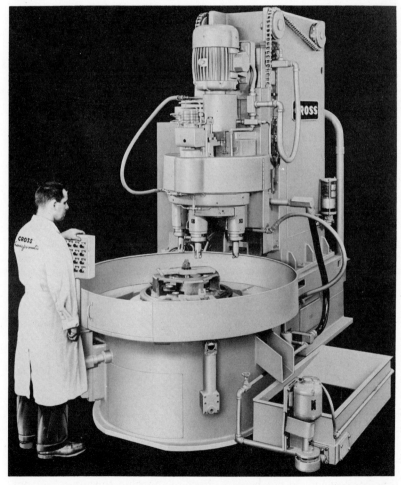

The Cross Co.

Fig. 7. A dial-type machine which precision bores different drive housings with a minimum amount of changeover.

agement organization exhausts all avenues of investigation in regard
to the buying market until it is satisfied the estimate it develops is
accurate. Here is another reason why the tool engineer should know
the capabilities of his management team. Providing the team is capable,
when it reports that his proposal for a certain unit of machine equipment would be a poor investment for the reasons just mentioned, he
should accept its judgment regardless of the equipment's high mechanical potential.

A typical machine with earning power. Fig. 7 shows a dial type
machine which precision bores nine different planetary drive housings.
The machine was selected for this operation because of a minimum
amount of changeover time from one type of housing to another.
Although the initial outlay of capital for this machine was relatively
high, in the final analysis it was decided that the savings from using
the machine would pay off the initial investment within an acceptable
time.

Direct Costs

The importance of economy of direct labor was established earlier
in this chapter. By comparison, other operating expenses directly proportional to output are small and not subject to change. For that
reason power, lubrication, and similar expenses will not be considered in machine equipment selection. Direct material costs we have
already assumed are dictated by management at the outset. In our
analysis, then, direct costs are substantially the charges for direct labor.

Since economy of direct labor is a matter of (1) eliminating men
from the manufacturing process altogether, (2) reducing the time-
per-part of men necessary to the process, and (3) using a minimum
of skilled manpower, any discussion will be concerned primarily with
production equipment and manufacturing processes, and not manpower as such. To avoid repetition, economy of direct labor will be
covered in a later chapter and in this chapter under *Direct Labor*
instead of here. The chapter on economic processing will deal with
the manufacturing process and operator motions, while the section in
this chapter will deal with machine equipment.

Indirect Costs

Costs which do not have a direct relationship to output will not
affect machine equipment selection to any degree. Wages for supervi-
sion will be less in highly automated plants; on the other hand, in-

spection wages will increase. Stockroom and toolroom wages remain about the same regardless of the type of machine equipment used. Since relatively few manhours are involved in indirect labor charges anyway, the tool engineer will not be influenced by them when selecting equipment. The costs of indirect materials, such as cutting oils, grease, and washing compounds are so minor and unavoidable that they seldom if ever influence a machine selection.

Equipment Life

The length of time in which a unit of machine equipment can repay its original costs is called the life of the equipment, or *equipment life*. There is a correlation between equipment life and depreciation. As we have learned, physical depreciation is due to deterioration and impairment from prolonged use. Corresponding to physical depreciation is *physical life,* the period during which equipment will

The Cross Co.

Fig. 8. The machinery installation using this electronic control unit has a comparatively short equipment life.

function satisfactorily before excessive maintenance costs make it unprofitable. Functional depreciation is due to obsolescence. Corresponding to functional depreciation is *serviceable life,* the length of time before obsolescence makes machine equipment unprofitable to operate. As with depreciation, physical life can be predicted fairly accurately from past experience. Serviceable life, on the contrary, is influenced by so many intangible elements that any prediction the tool engineer makes is likely to be a gamble.

A third expression of equipment life is called *critical life,* or minimum life. This life is the minimum length of time in which a unit of machine equipment can repay its original costs. There are no standard or definite periods of critical life among industrial concerns today. With the constantly increasing complexity of machinery, however, the shorter the critical life the better. As a rule most concerns today allow a period of from one to three years for automated, or partly automated, machinery, and from three to five years for nonautomated, or nearly nonautomated, machinery. For some concerns using single-purpose, extremely complex equipment, the period is often less than a year. In concerns utilizing general purpose, highly durable machinery the period may extend past five years.

Relationship to investment risk. Physical, serviceable, and critical life all have a relationship to the risk of an investment. The risk is considered good if critical life is short in comparison with the estimated serviceable life. Both serviceable and physical life must extend beyond critical life if the investment is not to be a loss. If serviceable life as estimated is short, it is unwise to demand a long physical life in machine equipment. Incidentally, the ideal life for overall *depreciation* falls just short of either serviceable or physical life, whichever is less.

Serviceable life becomes much less significant in places where general-purpose machine tools such as drill presses, lathes, or grinders are used. For this reason, if uncertainty exists in a special production venture, it is better to add the necessary attachments to standard machine tools, if possible, than purchase special equipment complete. If the venture fails, the only loss is in the attachments.

Computing Critical Life.

Let:

X = critical life of new machine equipment, in years,

P = total number of units of the products made per year,

V_1 = all costs, except the initial investment, per unit of product manufactured by the equipment to be replaced (old equipment), in dollars,

V_2 = all costs, except the initial investment, per unit of product the new equipment will manufacture, in dollars,

I_d = initial investment in new equipment, in dollars,

A = current annual interest rate,

B = current annual insurance and tax rate,

R_N = estimated salvage value of new equipment at the end of its equipment life, in dollars.

The basic equation is,

$$X \left[P(V_1 - V_2) - I_d(A + B) \right] = I_d - R_N$$

At this point, we are going to make a number of refinements. First, the total units of the product manufactured yearly will be the same for both old equipment and new. Second, *current* interest, tax, and insurance rates will be accurate enough, since computing the *average* values means estimating the length of equipment life, which is being solved for. Third, the expression $P(V_1 - V_2)$, since it represents a difference in costs, need not include any costs that are the same, or nearly the same, for both old equipment and new. Fourth, the types of costs included in V_1 and V_2 are equivalent.

Solving for critical life,

$$X = \frac{I_d - R_N}{P(V_1 - V_2) - I_d (A + B)}$$

This equation says, in effect: the ratio of the net investment to the savings realized by using the new equipment less its fixed charges, equals the critical life. In a cost analysis, the critical life for each unit of comparable equipment is computed using this equation, and the results compared. The same values for old equipment are used in each computation. Considering equipment life apart from other costs, that unit of machine equipment which has the shortest critical life is normally chosen. Again, if management feels even the shortest critical life of all comparable equipment in the field is not short enough, they will view any purchase as a gamble.

Illustrative example of critical life. Let's use the same machines from the previous example, adding data where necessary to create a new example, which will still be hypothetical because of unavoidable assumptions.

Let's assume the five double-spindle broaching machines have been in operation for several years and that due to their age and increasing inefficiency management feels a new installation is necessary. Let us assume further that the three four-station broaching machines have already been shown to be the best in the field, except for the matter of critical equipment life.

From the previous example,

The total investment of new equipment......... I_d = $105,000
The number of units of the product yearly...... P = 4,000,000
Current annual interest rate................. A = 10%
Current tax and insurance rate.............. B = 3%

Additional data,

Costs per part produced yearly by old equipment less
    the initial investment......................V_1 = $0.024
Costs per part produced yearly by new equipment less
    the initial investment......................V_2 = $0.012
Estimated value of new equipment at the end of its
    equipment life (per machine)..............R_N = $5,000

Solving for the critical life,

$$X = \frac{105,000 - 15,000}{4,000,000(0.024 - 0.012) - 105,000(0.10 + 0.03)}$$

$$= \frac{90,000}{4,000,000(0.012) - 105,000(0.13)}$$

$$= \frac{90,000}{48,000 - 13,650}$$

$$= \frac{90,000}{34,350}$$

$$= 2.62 \text{ years}$$

Since this length of life is reasonably short, management would be likely to purchase the new equipment. It is interesting to observe that a controlling factor in critical life computations is the spread between the costs-per-part of old and new equipment. The greater the difference, the less the critical life. As the original installation ages, its cost-per-part will rise due to increased maintenance, downtime, and other expenses; and in effect, cause the critical life of the new equipment to be shorter. For this reason a unit of new equipment might prove to have too long a critical life one year and an acceptable one the next. In no circumstances should the cost-per-part of new equipment be greater than that of the old equipment.

If more than 4,000,000 parts yearly are desired after the installation of the three four-station machines, whose combined capacity well exceeds 4,000,000 parts, production can be increased without regard to the critical life. In fact, an increased number of parts tends to offset the decreased cost-per-part, keeping the calculated critical life about the same.

Maintenance

Maintenance of machine equipment can be divided into three groups (notice the overlapping between groups, which cannot be avoided):

1. Maintenance which depends primarily on use rather than time. Lubricating, cleaning, minor adjustments, changing filters and electronic tubes are items in this group.

2. Maintenance which depends primarily on time rather than use. Replacing of gaskets, tension springs, certain electronic parts, and other replacements caused by deterioration with age comprise this group.

3. Maintenance which depends on both use and time. Realigning shafts, replacing damaged and rusted parts, rewiring motors fall in this group.

Maintenance has considerable effect upon physical equipment life but little upon serviceable life; whether maintenance can retard obsolescence at all is doubtful. Machines can be improved by redesigning them to function more efficiently, but such an improvement is not called maintenance. To prolong physical life is the primary purpose of maintenance programs, which achieves this through daily attention to items of upkeep and repair. A plan which arranges to cover the maintenance of minor items, such as lubrication and cleaning, according to a daily schedule, is sometimes called a *preventive maintenance program*.

Since using machine equipment requires time, all maintenance costs, whether functions of time or use, have a relationship to the passage of time. A close approximation of that relationship is depicted by a straight line. In other words, the cost of maintenance increases almost directly with time, which is usually expressed in years. If the annual cost of maintenance is M, then an equation expressing this straight line relationship is,

$$M = aP + bT + c,$$

where P is a function of the age of the equipment and *a, b,* and *c* are constants, or parameters, which are dependent on the type of equipment, its design, cost, time in service, etc. For each specific situation, these constants will have certain values. This equation only expresses the general relationship between total maintenance and its components. A working equation would necessarily be more involved.

WORK PROBLEMS

P—1.   Assume in the example relating to Figures 4, 5, and 6 the following changes are made:

a) Six double-spindle broaching machines and three four-station machines are being considered in order to meet the current demand of 3,200,000 gears per year.

b) The price of the double-spindle machine completely tooled is $20,000, and has an output of 500 parts per hour.

c) The price of the four-station machine completely tooled is $31,000, and has an output of 920 parts per hour.

d) It is expected that the double-spindle machines will pay out their cost in five years with a 12% return on the average investment, and the four-station machines in four years with a 15% return on the average investment.

e) Taxes and insurance are 2% per annum for both types of machines.

f) The cost of direct labor for either type of machine is $2.45 per hour. Each machine can be operated by one man.

All the other costs are the same as in the example. Find the total savings per year one type of machine can give over the other.

P—2. Find the savings-per-part that can be realized by using one type of machine instead of the other.

P—3. What is the critical life of the three four-station machines of **P—1**, assuming they are to replace the present overaged machines, if all costs in dollars per part produced on the current machines is $0.023, and those costs-per-part produced on the four-station machine is $0.008, capital charges not included? The four-station machines have an estimated salvage value of $1800 each. All other data remain the same as in **P—1**.

FUNCTIONAL CONSIDERATIONS

We will present a functional analysis of machine equipment in the same manner as was done for costs. Although it is extremely difficult to compare machines on individual features like productive capacity, accuracy, or flexibility, we shall attempt to do so to emphasize their importance in individual applications. Disregarding cost is also a liberty we will take that can't normally be taken. It must be recognized that in practice one machine is selected over another because it comes *closest* to providing what the tool engineer desires. Even when a machine is designed for a specific operation, it is often impractical to build one that follows the initial specifications exactly. To some extent then, the selection (or design) of machine equipment is a compromise between what is desired and what is available (or practical).

Productive Capacity

The parts a machine can process in a given period of time, usually an hour; or the time, expressed in fractions of an hour, required to process one part, is called a machine's *productive capacity*. Where the ratio of parts processed to an hour of time is great, as in the manufacture of screws or cams, the capacity is expressed in parts per hour. Where the opposite is true, as in the manufacture of crankshafts or bull gears, the capacity is expressed in time (usually minutes) per part.

When selecting machines, tool engineers do not compare maximum capacities, since ordinarily machines do not operate at full speed. Rather, each machine's normal capacity is projected to show a year's production. If this output does not reach a figure estimated as the machine's share of the total manufacturing venture, the machine is termed inadequate. To qualify for a specific installation, therefore, a machine must have a yearly output in excess of a predetermined minimum amount.

Remember, we are assuming the tool engineer knows the quantity and quality of his product before he begins to select equipment. It is wise to emphasize this point here because entirely different types of equipment are selected for low-production and high-production operations.

Computing production capacities of machine equipment is a subject in itself. A production rate based purely on mechanical performance is not likely to be realistic, although many industrial concerns will accept these rates from equipment manufacturers and adjust them to suit their own ends. For realistic rates, time and motion studies are necessary to determine the effects of the human element in an operation. Downtime and time lost for routine maintenance must also be accounted for. Since manufacturers of machine tools tend to overstate the capacities of their machines, industrial concerns will sometimes conduct their own investigations to find production rates that are realistic in their particular setup. Tool engineers analyze machine equipment operations with the same step-by-step thoroughness as in a cost analysis. The Economic Processing chapter deals briefly with the methods of time and motion studies.

Flexibility

Flexibility is desired in machine equipment for two reasons:

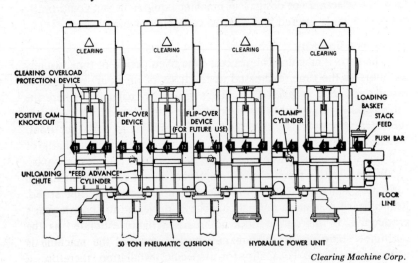

Clearing Machine Corp.

Fig. 9. Flow diagram of an automatic transfer press showing a typical sequence of operations. The flexibility of the press permits a number of different operational sequences.

(1) ability to perform a variety of necessary operations more economically than an installation of less flexible machines and (2) by performing many different operations, lessening the factor of equipment obsolescence. Machines that are highly flexible, however, normally are more expensive performing a single operation than a unipurpose machine performing the same operation; also, the capacity is usually less.

Selecting equipment with varying degrees of flexibility is a delicate procedure. A unit of equipment will perform certain operations that do not apply now but may later. Another unit of equipment may be ideal for short runs and inefficient for longer ones. A very difficult job, of course, is deciding whether to purchase one highly flexible machine or several less flexible machines. The highly flexible machine

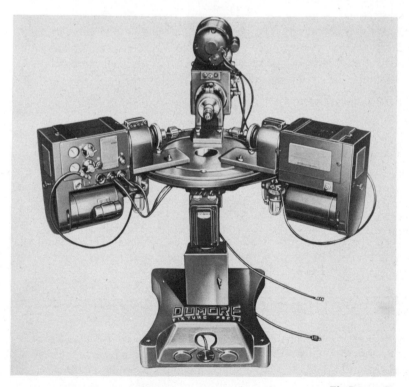

The Dumore Co.

Fig. 10. A circular production table unit, which permits a variety of machining operations.

will cost less initially than the total cost of several machines, but will process parts in a given setup at a lower rate. If a cost analysis shows the ultimate costs for each situation to be quite close, a functional analysis may be necessary to resolve the problem. Here a factor like obsolescence may favor one possibility over another.

Fig. 10 shows a circular production table assembly. The machine is a combination of frame and stand, with several different production units mounted atop the stand, which has mounting space for up to six tooling components. The assembly consists of a circular table which can be manually turned for positioning fixtures, a rigid column, a clamp for holding the table, and a solid base. This arrangement permits a variety of machining operations, like single and multiple drilling, tapping, facing, chamfering, to be performed on long or short runs.

The arrangement in the figure is a typical setup of three tooling components, with simple brackets, in position for drilling, tapping, and facing operations. The components are fully automatic with built in electrical and pneumatic controls, and a reversing motor for withdrawal after tapping. Assemblies such as this are ideal for small-parts machining in an automated manufacturing process.

Adaptability

Adaptability is not the same as flexibility. A machine that is adaptable can perform one or more operations, then if necessary be modified with minimum difficulty to perform another or other operations in place of the original operation. A uni-purpose machine can be adaptable.

A good example of an adaptable machine is a rotary-table milling machine (see Fig. 11). To adapt it only the subplate affixed to the table that carries the fixtures is replaced with a different plate of fixtures. As we have seen, flexible equipment is able to perform many types of operations without modification.

Adaptability is desired in machine equipment for two reasons: (1) to avoid the inherent risk of buying new equipment for a special operation, and (2) where new equipment to perform a particular operation is not available. The first reason is caused by management's decision that under the circumstances the capital outlay for new equipment would be a poor investment. By adapting equipment on hand, the possible loss is reduced to attachments and fixtures necessary to the adaptation. The second reason is caused by the proposed

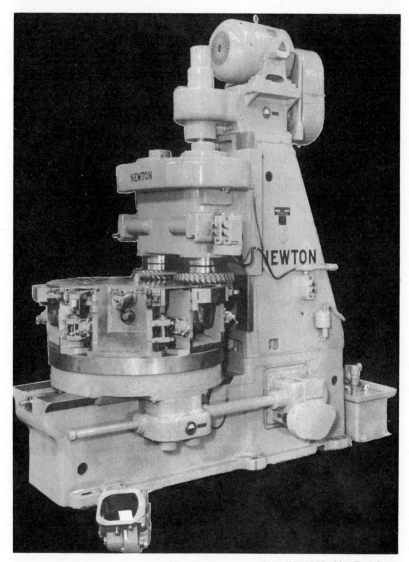

Consolidated Machine Tool Corp.

Fig. 11. A rotary vertical milling machine set up for continuous milling.

equipment being so special nothing like it is on the market or, another cause, no machine manufacturer has a particular unit of equipment on hand, although the equipment is only temporarily unavailable.

In machine equipment selection, the matter of adaptability is more a recognition of the reasons mentioned than actually seeking equipment for those reasons. The tool engineer correlates the nature, volume, and quality of his product to future conditions. If his current product is relatively short-termed, subject to change, and of low quality, it would be wise for him to consider buying equipment that is fairly adaptable.

Accuracy

Not many general statements can be offered on equipment's ability to machine parts with precision. Each situation calls for different tolerances which must be treated individually when selecting machine equipment. Since equipment costs vary roughly as the degree of accuracy required, the tool engineer must avoid purchasing machines that provide a precision over and above the requirements. The plans provided by the product designer specify allowable tolerances for all machine surfaces. To go beyond what is required means incurring unnecessary expense unless, of course, the tool engineer is certain later products will require closer tolerances.

Tolerance is defined as the acceptable variation from an ideal size. Tolerances in many machining operations today are in the order of $\pm$ 0.0001$''$ and some are even closer. Most equipment that has many automatic features does not provide this kind of precision. Although separate operations may be capable of high precision, without some human guidance there is apt to be accumulative error, which prevents high overall precision. Those who work daily with automated equipment know that it is in need of continual minor adjustment to assure best operation. Since requirements of large volume and high precision do not normally occur together for one product, however, there is no real problem here.

When selecting equipment, the tool engineer must also account for human error by giving preference to those types of machines that are as nearly foolproof as possible. From the standpoint of precision the most desirable machine frees the operator from making motions and decisions that are liable to affect the accuracy of the part. Machines with special feed tables, jigs, gages and other attachments fall into this category. Up to a point, then, human control may cause inaccuracies; after this point, a certain amount of human control is needed to prevent inaccuracies. For best results in his own processes, the tool engineer must know where this point lies.

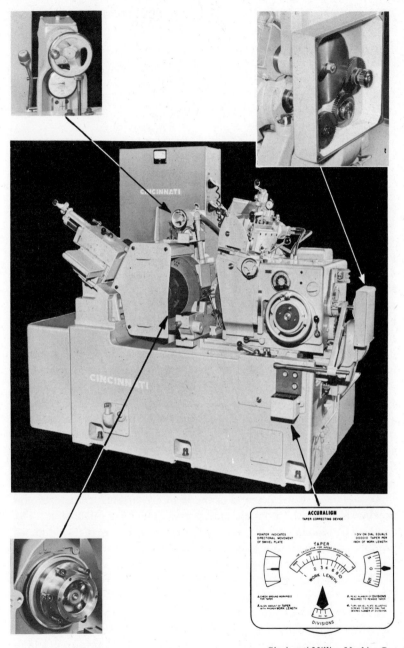

ACCURALIGN
TAPER CORRECTING DEVICE

Cincinnati Milling Machine Co.

Fig. 12. A centerless grinding machine with attachments to increase automation and precision.

Automatic Features

Principle reasons for employing automated machinery are to:

1. Reduce the time-per-part factor.
2. Reduce the cost-per-part factor.
3. Reduce the amount of direct labor.
4. Reduce the amount of skilled labor.
5. Increase the productive capacity.

These reasons are not distinct — there are inter-relationships among them all—but they are the obvious reasons for which the tool engineer seeks machine equipment that is wholly or partly automated.

Reasons 3 and 4 are in the vital area of direct labor costs. Reducing the amount of direct labor is mainly a transferring of repetitive and unskilled operations from man to machine. Loading and unloading, feeding, and other routine work-handling operations can be done more efficiently by machines. To reduce the amount of skilled labor means increasing the amount of automatic control and instrumentation. The elimination of human judgment in such operations as measuring the depth of a cut, the smoothness of a surface, the diameter of a hole reduces the need of skilled labor for operation. Many inspection operations as well as work operations are now accomplished by automatic machines and computers.

Advantages to automating. An increased productive capacity at reasonable cost is probably the greatest single advantage to automating machinery. "At reasonable cost" are crucial words in this context because there are several methods of increasing production without automating, the simplest being a mere addition of machines to a process. Today, if the demand of the market warrants it, the common practice is to select automatic machinery rather than other types. The degree of automation advisable will vary roughly as the amount of product demand. Here is another reason why the tool engineer should know the capabilities of management.

Reducing the time-per-part figure is important if imminent deadlines must be met; in other words, where a quantity of parts is desired within a very limited time, as in the automobile industry. In this situation capacity is not so important as time. Also, the time-per-part figure can be projected to show a year's production for a machine and this amount compared with other comparable machines, as was done earlier in this chapter. Here, capacity is more vital than time.

Reducing the cost-per-part figure becomes important when establishing competitive prices is paramount. The figure is commonly used by management, accountant, and tool engineer alike, especially in comparatively high volume and low cost applications, as in the manufacture of screws, automobile parts, tin cans, etc. Because they are rates rather than totals, time-per-part and cost-per-part data are especially valuable when comparing equipment.

The five reasons for selecting automated equipment do not mean distinct types of equipment exist for each reason. It is possible that one machine, such as that shown in Fig. 13, has all the features necessary to suit all five reasons. However, automated equipment sought mainly for a reduction in labor will have more work-handling attachments on it than one where high capacity is desired. Equipment to reduce the degree of skilled labor will have more gages on it than one where a low time-per-part figure is sought. In general, other minor differences will exist between comparable units of automated equipment, depending on the reason each is intended to fulfill.

Buhr Machine Tool Co.

Fig. 13.   A modern, highly flexible transfer machine. Many of the operations offer high precision.

An automated transfer machine. Fig. 13 shows a modern transfer machine that qualifies in every way as a unit of automatic equipment. Furthermore, the user has been able to obtain high-precision machining on those of the 115 operations that require it. Some part dimensions are held to tolerances specified in tenths of a thousandth inch.

This machine has sixteen work stations and space for ten more in the future. A conveyor system moves the parts automatically from station to station, throughout the process. Many inspection devices check the parts during the machine cycle. A number of probing points are built into the process so that any improper machining will result in closing the machine down and activating lights on the control panel and also at the probe station to pinpoint the trouble.

The machine will perform drilling, chamfering, reaming, spot facing, boring, tapping and other operations. Within its range of operations, it has great flexibility, output potential and processing speed, while offering good precision and a minimum of human control. Its biggest disadvantage is that it is designed for one part. Production of this part must be high to justify the initial investment. However, since the machine is built of standard components and has idle stations, it can be converted for making a different part.

Direct Labor

In machine equipment selection, the consideration of direct labor is closely related to a consideration of a machine's automatic features. As a general rule, the amount of manpower needed for operation varies *indirectly* as the degree of automation. Other factors, like flexibility and adaptability, may or may not affect the direct labor factor, so no definite statement can be offered about their relationship.

Manpower utilization. The importance of effective utilization of manpower in the operation and maintenance of machine equipment cannot be over-emphasized. With many industrial concerns it is the first consideration they make when selecting equipment. In recent years the great advance of business and office machines is due partly to the obvious savings in manpower users of this equipment can realize despite a high initial cost. For example, say a $10,000 machine requiring one operator will do the work of two persons. The vendor of this machine has this selling point: "If you buy my machine you'll save the equivalent of a person's yearly salary over a three year period, so that in effect you can pay off the machine in three years with the savings." Since most office machines are expected to be in service longer than three years, the vendor's selling point is a good one.

Cost and function have the same relationship to direct labor for different reasons. On a cost basis, the less the direct manpower involved the better so long as the initial outlay of capital can be repaid, through savings in direct labor, in a reasonable length of time. On a functional basis, the less the direct manpower the better so long as the product's quality is not lowered below minimum standards. As discussed under *accuracy,* eliminating human influence is desirable up to a point, beyond which inaccuracies are likely to occur. Also, since maintenance manpower increases with increased automation, a point may be reached where *overall* direct manpower begins to increase. (Remember, maintenance manpower is considered as a part of direct labor.)

Means of reducing direct labor. As a review, the three principal means by which direct labor can be reduced in machine equipment operations are:

1. Combining and increasing the efficiency of operations requiring human control. This involves time and motion studies, which

American Automatic Typewriter Co.

Fig. 14. A modern business machine.

is a distinct field often conducted by separate agencies. The purpose of the studies is to eliminate unnecessary operator motions, rearrange controls and other devices so the operator can manipulate them efficiently, and evolve an efficient step-by-step process of operation. If a study of a particular unit of equipment is effective, a number of men may be eliminated from the overall installation.

2. Increasing the degree of automatic control. This means reducing the attention an operator must give a unit of equipment so he can handle the control of additional equipment.

3. Taking steps to decrease situations requiring maintenance. This includes making equipment maneuverable enough so that a simple failure in one part of the equipment can be bypassed without closing down the machine altogether. A simple example of this is putting duplex strainers in lubricating oil systems, so that if the strainer in use becomes clogged the reserve can be switched in without closing down. It is also important to build sufficient checks and inspection stations into the equipment so failures can be noticed and located quickly.

When selecting machine equipment, the recognition of the methods of reducing manpower becomes essential. With experience the tool engineer learns to see which equipment has been submitted to rigid time and motion studies, which equipment has undergone thorough testing with the purpose of lessening breakdowns, which equipment has the most effective automatic features. Recognizing *how* direct labor can be reduced, the tool engineer selects the equipment which best employs these labor reducing methods.

There is another aspect to direct labor considerations, already touched upon, which should be included here to complete the discussion. The skill requirements for machine equipment operators may be downgraded by transferring judgment and adroitness from man to machine. This is accomplished by increasing the use of jigs, fixtures, and other tools, and increasing the degree of automatic control in precision machining operations. Processes that require less human skill mean a savings in direct labor cost because of a lesser wage rate.

Standardization

Standardization, or making parts interchangeable, is an accepted procedure in modern mass production. Although interchangeable parts may have close tolerances, it is a fact that tolerances as great as functionally possible exist in manufactured products today. The secret of mass producing items with many moving parts, such as automobile engines, is based on determining and using the most liberal functional tolerances which are still commensurate with good product performance. The greater the variation permissible from the ideal size—but still within acceptable limits—the greater the ease of manufacture. The universal recognition of tolerance in machining operations is an acknowledgment that variations are inevitable in the physical dimensions of a product. No practical machining method has yet been perfected by which ideal dimensions can be obtained.

Advantages of standardization. The advantages of standardization are obvious. Perhaps its greatest advantage is that parts can be stocked, so when like parts become worn or damaged in operation, repair is simply a matter of replacement. In this respect standardization often will cover a field, so that spark plugs, for instance, will fit many makes of cars, or light bulbs of various ratings will fit the same socket. Production advantages: parts can be processed and assembled

Buhr Machine Tool Co.

Fig. 15. These fixtures, used on a transfer machine, were made with interchangeable components by mass-production methods to insure part accuracy.

more quickly, inspection costs are reduced, the amount of skilled labor necessary for operation is reduced, the manufacturing equipment itself does not require a high accuracy of performance, making the equipment less expensive. (To a certain degree the manufacturing equipment itself can also be made of standard parts.) The overall result, of course, is that a greater volume of a product can be processed at a lower unit cost.

Standardization by equipment selection. The tool engineer influences standardization through his selection of machine equipment. He determines what degree of accuracy is obtainable in equipment to be purchased, and correlates this information with the product designer's estimation of the functional accuracy necessary. His chief desire is to see that no tolerances are unnecessarily close. His familiarity with machine equipment qualifies him to select equipment with the best tolerances compatible with product quantity and quality, costs, and machine performance. Not only can the tool engineer recommend what equipment should be purchased but also what dimensions and tolerances in the product should be altered, if possible, to give the most economical production.

Effective standardization of parts is extremely important in industry today. Greater speeds of moving parts means higher precision is necessary without introducing costs that would make volume production prohibitive. The tool engineer's job is to see that high precision and quantity manufacturing remain economically feasible.

CHAPTER FOUR

Tool Economy

This chapter is divided into three main sections: (1) tool formulas, (2) economy of cutting tools, and (3) economy of all other tools except machine tools, which was covered in the chapter on machine equipment selection. The third section will deal with the economy of hand, work holding, and inspection tools. The second section will cover the economic selection of cutting tools and also the economic operation of some types of cutting tools.

The chapters on tool design and cost estimating will include in much more detail certain points brought out in this chapter. Again we are going to assume the tool engineer knows the quantity and quality of his product before a tooling program is begun, and again we will attempt to keep discussions of tool costs and tool functions separate, although it is not done in practice.

TOOL FORMULAS

Selecting tools is approached in much the same way as machine equipment selection. In many cases a cost by cost comparison between tools is conducted to determine the most economical tool, although in considering tools other than machine tools, the critical nature of costs is greatly reduced. Since the analysis of costs presented previously covers all types of manufacturing equipment, we will not adopt that general information to apply here.

Basic Questions Requiring Formulas

In this section we will present a number of simple formulas which are used by tool engineers in solving problems concerning tools other than machine tools. These formulas were developed by Professor J. W. Roe for jigs and fixtures,[1] but they can be applied in solving other tooling problems as well. Professor Roe's formulas are intended to supply answers to one or more of four basic questions the tool engineer is likely to ask about tooling requirements. These questions are:

1. What minimum quantity of parts must be processed to pay off a tool, based on the savings in direct labor the tool will give over the present one? The cost of the tool and the estimated savings-per-part are known. For example, how many parts must be processed to justify buying a $600 tool to save $0.02 on the direct labor charge of each part?

2. What maximum sum can be spent on a tool, based on the savings in direct labor the tool will give over the present one for a stipulated quantity of parts? The estimated savings-per-part and quantity of parts are known. For example, how much can be spent on a tool for a specified 50,000 parts, if the tool can save $0.04 on the direct labor charge of each part?

3. What minimum length of time will a tool take to pay for itself, based on the savings in direct labor the tool will give over the present one, for a stipulated production rate and carrying charges? The tool's cost, estimated savings-per-part, rate of production, and fixed charges are known. For example, how long will a tool costing $400 take to pay for itself if there are savings of $0.03 per part on direct labor, 200 parts an hour, and annual fixed charges of $5,000?

4. What maximum profit can be earned by a tool, based on the savings the tool will give over the present one, for a stipulated quantity of parts? The tool's cost, estimated savings-per-part, and quantity of parts are known. For example, what profit will a $300 tool earn if it will save in direct labor cost $0.04 a part on 25,000 parts?

Notation Used in Formulas

Let us establish formulas which will answer these questions. First it is necessary to specify symbols for the various factors which are to be formulated. They are:

N = number of parts processed annually, or per single run of less than a year's duration,

[1] *Principles of Jig and Fixture Practice*, J. W. Roe, MECHANICAL ENGINEERING, Feb. 1941.

A = annual percentage allowance for interest on the initial investment,

B = annual percentage allowance for insurance and taxes,

C = annual percentage allowance for maintenance,

H = number of years required to pay off the investment with the tool's savings,

$1/H$ = annual percentage allowance for depreciation, figured on a straight-line basis,

I = estimated cost of the tool ready to run, including costs incurred in its design, material and toolroom costs, in dollars,

Y = annual cost of setups, in dollars. The expense of putting the machine into normal running condition is included here.

$Z = I(A + B + C + 1/H) + Y$, the fixed charges plus setup costs.

Except for N, these symbols represent the annual fixed charges and the setup costs. The annual savings a proposed tool will give over the present one are represented by these symbols:

S = annual total savings in direct labor costs, in dollars. These savings are equal to the number of parts processed annually (N), multiplied by the estimated savings-per-part in direct labor the proposed tool will give over the present one (s).

T = annual total savings in labor overhead, in dollars. These savings are equal to the annual total savings in direct labor costs (S), multiplied by the rate of overhead on the labor saved (t).

P = annual gross operating profit in excess of fixed charges, in dollars.

Developing the Formulas

To break even, the annual total savings in direct labor costs plus labor overhead must equal the annual total fixed charges and setup costs for a comparable period:

$$S + T = Z + Y$$

or,

$$Ns + Nst = I(A + B + C + 1/H) + Y$$

which becomes,

$$Ns(1 + t) = I(A + B + C + 1/H) + Y$$

Solving for N,

$$N = \frac{I(A + B + C + 1/H) + Y}{s(1 + t)}$$

Solving for I,

$$I = \frac{Ns(1 + t) - Y}{(A + B + C + 1/H)}$$

Solving for H,

$$H = \frac{I}{Ns(1 + t) - I(A + B + C) - Y}$$

P, the gross annual profit, is equal to the difference between (S + T) and (Z + Y). Solving for P,

$$P = Ns(1 + t) - I(A + B + C + 1/H) - Y$$

Factors such as interest, insurance, taxes, maintenance, and depreciation do not vary appreciably for normal periods of time in any one industrial organization, assuming a fairly stable management policy exists, and tool engineers often combine these near constants into a single factor for convenience. In many industrial concerns costs for tools are estimated as a percentage of machine equipment costs based on past knowledge and experience. Thirty-five percent is a common percentage assigned in high production plants. For relatively low production, however, a tool cost analysis as is conducted in machine equipment selections should be made. Dimensional and finish tolerance also affect how tool costs should be determined.

Notice that solving for symbols *N, I, H,* and *P* supplies answers to basic questions 1, 2, 3, and 4 respectively.

Illustrative Examples

(1) *Solving for number of parts.* The production department of

Snow Mfg. Co.

Fig. 1.   A horizontal indexing fixture.

a manufacturing concern is planning to purchase a fixture (shown in Fig. 1) for tapping an aluminum die casting. The fixture is a horizontal indexing device designed for tapping twelve equally spaced ¼"—20 through holes in the die casting. A Microswitch arrangement integral with the fixture automatically controls the complete cycle of tapping the twelve holes. The hourly production rate is estimated to be 100 parts, or 1200 holes, an appreciable improvement over the present arrangement, in which a simple manually-operated fixture without automatic control is used. The present fixture has reached a point where either it must be completely overhauled or replaced. Management has decided to replace it, possibly with the fixture of Fig. 2.

Snow Mfg. Co.

Fig. 2.   A vertical clamping fixture.

The final selection of the fixture under consideration is based on the answer to this question: How many parts must be processed using this fixture in one run or lot each year to return its cost in two years out of the savings gained over the present fixture? The following data is known:

The estimated cost of the fixture together with its Microswitch control ready for operation is $375 (I),

The estimated savings in direct labor cost-per-part is $0.005 (s),

The percentage overhead on direct labor savings is 30% (t),

The estimated cost of each setup is $6 (Y),

The annual percentage allowance for interest on the invested capital is 6% (A),

The annual percentage allowance for insurance and taxes is 3% (B),

The annual estimated allowance for maintenance is 8% (C),

The estimated equipment life is 2 years (H),

The annual percentage allowance for depreciation on a straight-line basis is ½ or 50% (1/H).

Solving for N, the number of parts per year,

$$N = \frac{I(A + B + C + 1/H) + Y}{S(1 + t)}$$

$$= \frac{375(0.06 + 0.03 + 0.08 + 0.50) + 6}{0.005(1 + 0.3)}$$

$$= \frac{375(0.67) + 6}{0.005 \times 1.3}$$

$$= \frac{251.25 + 6}{0.0065}$$

$$= 39,577 \text{ parts per year.}$$

In order for the fixture to pay for itself out of savings in two years carrying its fixed charges and overhead, with a single run per year, a minimum of 39,577 parts must be processed each year. If this amount falls within the tool engineer's estimation of an economic lot size, the fixture will probably be purchased. Remember, however, that factors of initial costs and functional requirements must also be considered in the final analysis.

(2) *Solving for number of parts.* If the parts of example 1 are put through in 8 runs or lots per year, how many parts must be processed annually to return the cost of the fixture out of savings in two years?

The only factor that will change from the previous example is the setup cost. Since there are now 8 runs instead of one, the setup cost becomes 8 × 6, or $48. Substituting this amount into the equation and solving for N,

$$N = \frac{251.25 + 48}{0.0065}$$

$$= 46,038 \text{ parts per year.}$$

Notice that increasing the number of setups per year increases the value of the numerator in our equation, which increases the number of parts that must be processed annually. However, as will be seen when investigating economic lot sizes in Chapter Five, it is sometimes more economical to have multiple lots despite a higher manufacturing cost-per-part because of storage, unautomated equipment, the long-term production schedule, and other limiting factors.

(3) *Solving for lot size.* Let us assume that the fixture of the foregoing example is to pay for itself in a single lot in a year. How large should that lot be?

The only factor that will change from example 1 is H, the equipment life. The depreciation allowance becomes 1/1, or 100%. Substituting this value into our equation and solving for N,

$$N = \frac{375(0.06 + 0.03 + 0.08 + 1) + 6}{0.0065}$$

$$= \frac{375(1.17) + 6}{0.0065}$$

$$= 68,423 \text{ parts per year.}$$

The values A, B, and C are assumed as full year values, although the actual run may be completed in less than a year. If the run is very short, the fixed charges and maintenance values may be reduced in proportion to the fraction of a year the lot takes to be processed. Notice that demanding a shorter equipment life means more parts must be processed annually.

(4) *Solving for investment.* The fixture shown in Fig. 2 is of the vertical clamping type, used in a driller machine that drills a $^{23}\!/_{64}''$ hole in a stainless steel casting. The estimated drilling time is 12 seconds, giving a production rate of 240 parts per hour. A spring-loaded locator in the fixture positions the parts; the same fixture can also be used for a $^3\!/_8''$ reaming operation.

How large a capital investment is justified in a fixture like this for a single run of 35,000 castings at an estimated savings in direct labor cost of $0.01 per part?

Let us assume that all values are the same as in example 3 except $s = \$0.01$ and Y, the setup cost $= \$10$. Solving for I, the estimated cost of the tool ready to run,

$$
\begin{aligned}
I &= \frac{Ns(1 + t) - Y}{A + B + C + 1/H} \\
&= \frac{35,000(0.01)(1 + 0.3) - 10}{0.06 + 0.03 + 0.08 + 1.00} \\
&= \frac{350(1.3) - 10}{1.17} \\
&= \$380.
\end{aligned}
$$

This money is the amount needed as a capital investment to cover the fixture's complete cost.

(5) *Solving for investment.* How much of an initial investment is justified in a fixture similar to that in Fig. 2, only one of more rugged design so that it will process 50,000 castings per year in eight runs? A savings in direct labor of $0.007 per casting is estimated. The fixture's cost is to be paid off in two years. Assume all other values are the same as those in example 4:

$$
\begin{aligned}
I &= \frac{50,000 \times 0.007(1 + 0.3) - 8 \times 10}{1.17} \\
&= \frac{350(1.3) - 80}{1.17} \\
&= \$320.
\end{aligned}
$$

(6) *Solving for production time.* How long will a fixture similar to the one in example 4 take to pay for itself, estimating its cost at $430, with a single setup cost of $80? Assume all other values are the same as those in example 5.

$$H = \frac{I}{Ns(1 + t) - I(A + B + C) - Y}$$

$$= \frac{430}{(50,000 \times 0.007)(1.3) - 430(0.17) - 80}$$

$$= \frac{430}{(455 - 73 - 80)}$$

$$= 1.42 \text{ years.}$$

This length of time is assuming continuous production; in other words, a single run is processed that takes 1.42 years.

(7) *Solving for profit.* Assume the fixture in example 6 costs $300 instead of $430. What will be the gross annual profit if the fixture meets all other conditions of example 6, including the depreciation allowance percentage of 1/1.42, or 70.5%?

$$
\begin{aligned}
P &= Ns(1 + t) - I(A + B + C + 1/H) - Y \\
&= 50,000(0.007)(1 + 0.3) - 300(0.17 + 0.705) - 80 \\
&= 455 - 300(0.875) - 80 \\
&= \$112 \text{ per year.}
\end{aligned}
$$

ECONOMY OF CUTTING TOOLS

A detailed discussion of cutting tools is not possible here because of the many different kinds in use and the variety of machines in which they can be used. Cutting tools include milling cutters, drills, taps and dies, reamers, borers, saws, broaches, abrasives, and a wide range of single-point cutting tools. Drills, reamers, taps, offset boring heads, counterbores may be attached either to a drill press or a milling machine. Single-point tools may be used on lathes, shapers, planers, boring mills, and turret lathes.

In a broad sense, what holds true for a drill in a milling machine will also hold true for a bit in a lathe. In either case, the greater the speed of the tool or the work, the shorter will be the tool's life, the deeper the cut it can make with each pass, the harder must be the material of the tool, the more frequent the necessity to resharpen, etc. We can say, therefore, that the relationship among different cutting

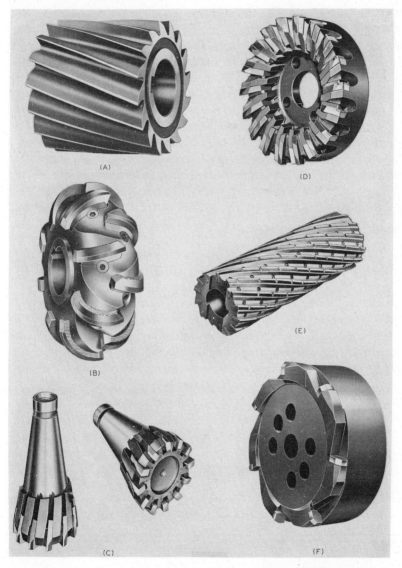

Cincinnati Milling Machine Co.

Fig. 3. Types of milling cutters. (A) Plain helical milling cutter, (B) form milling cutter with inserted teeth, (C) inserted tooth end mills, (D) inserted tooth face mill with sintered carbide blades, (E) slab milling cutter with inserted blades, (F) solid milling cutter with brazed-on tips of sintered carbide cutting material.

tools in machining operations is similar, although the degree of change may differ greatly with changes in similar variables, such as speed, material of the tool, or its design. Based on this statement, what is said in this section applies to all kinds of tools in a general way, while specific situations are covered in the examples and illustrations.

A selection of tools is called for when new machine equipment is purchased, when retooling programs are undertaken, or when the present fixtures prove unsatisfactory in operation. The last reason most often applies to cutting tools, which will wear out too soon, overheat, lack tensile strength, fail to provide the necessary accuracy, and other reasons. The tool engineer learns to look for these possible failings when selecting cutting tools, matching the tool's characteristics to the particular operation it must perform on a given product.

Tool Life and Cutting Speed

For cutting tools, tool life is specified as that period between resharpenings (commonly called regrinding). Since a cutting tool's life is so closely related to its speed, they will be considered together. These two factors far outweigh any others in the treatment of cutting tools. Over the years tool engineers have come to consider tool life a basic criterion by which cutting tools may be economically selected. Extensive experiments have been conducted to arrive at practical means for rating and tabulating tool life values. Having accurate values at his disposal, the tool engineer can estimate the amount of influence other variables, such as hardness, tensile strength, and chemical composition have on his selection.

The Taylor equation. Early in this century F. W. Taylor expressed the relationship between tool life and cutting speed with this empirical equation,[2] still recognized today as a valuable formula in the field of metal cutting:

$$VT^n = K$$

where,

V = cutting speed in feet per minute (fpm),

T = tool life or actual cutting time between resharpenings, in minutes,

K = a constant whose value depends on the variables of a par-

---

[2] *On The Art of Cutting Metals*, F. W. Taylor, Trans. ASME Vol. 28, 1907.

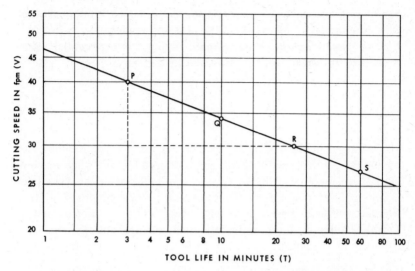

Tool Engineer's Handbook

Fig. 4. A typical tool life—cutting speed relationship. A single-point tool was used. Cuts in annealed SAE 2340 steel were made dry at 0.200 inch depth and 0.050 inch feed with high-speed steel tools. The log-log graph has a vertical scale 2.67 times the horizontal. To plot the line, tests were made at P, Q, R, and S.

ticular machine and also the material of the product being worked. It is numerically equal to that theoretical cutting speed which gives a tool life of one minute,

n = exponent whose value varies with the machine and product material variables.

Obviously a presentation of just a few tool life—cutting speed relationships with a given machine and product would soon grow into a complex array of tool, machine, and material variables. There are reliable technical handbooks in the field that tabulate these relationships. The "Tool Engineer's Handbook," published by the McGraw-Hill Book Co., Inc., is recommended.

Plotting the Taylor equation on log-log paper will result in a straight line as shown in Fig. 4.[3]

In this equation, the value of the exponent, n, has been found to vary from $\frac{1}{4}$ to $\frac{1}{10}$, depending on the variables of machine and product. Carbide tools will give a value close to $\frac{1}{4}$; high speed steel or

---

[3] *Metal Processing*, O. W. Boston, JOHN WILEY & SONS, INC., N. Y., 1941.

cast alloy tools, values close to $\frac{1}{10}$. For convenience, a nominal value of $\frac{1}{6}$ is assigned to the exponent by most tool engineers.

The Taylor equation rearranged. Using this exponential value, we can rearrange the Taylor equation in this way:

$$V = \frac{K}{T^{1/6}} \qquad (1)$$

Arranged in this form, the equation is useable for roughly estimating the cutting speed that will give a desired tool life when machining a given material with any type of tool material. Mean values for *K* are required and these can be arrived at through practical tests, which are usually based on a cut having a cross-sectional area of 1/1000 square inch as representing an average cutting condition. Knowing *K*, the cutting speed can be determined for any desired tool life.

Although the Taylor equation is valuable in determining cutting speeds for a known or desired tool life, it does not provide the most economical cutting speed. Normally, however, it will furnish speeds that can be used in practice, depending on the accuracy with which the constant *K* was determined.

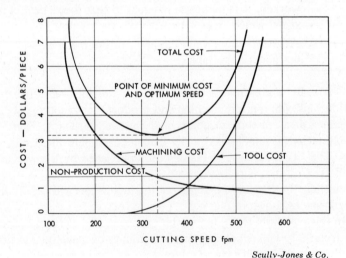

Scully-Jones & Co.

Fig. 5. Graph showing the relationship between total machining cost and cutting speed.

Optimum cutting speed. Tool engineers call the cutting speed that will give the lowest total machining cost the *optimum cutting speed*. The Taylor equation shows that if a tool is run very fast, although removing metal quickly while it is cutting, the tool's usefulness will be short-lived. On the other hand, a tool will last a long time if it is run slowly but will be inefficient. The optimum cutting speed falls somewhere between these extremes.

Fig. 5 plots cutting speed against cost of machining. The tool, machining, and non-production costs are plotted separately and totaled to give the uppermost curve. The lowest point on this curve is the point of minimum cost and optimum speed. Notice that non-productive costs, such as indirect labor charges, do not influence the cutting speed.

Using the tool life formula. The simplest manner in which to determine the optimum cutting speed is to find the tool life for minimum machining costs, and then to adjust the known cutting speed to give this minimum cost tool life. This relationship can be expressed as:

$$T = \frac{(1/n - 1)R}{L + O} \qquad (2)[4]$$

where,

T and n are the same symbols as those in the Taylor equation.

R is the tool replacement cost, in dollars per cutting edge. This cost is made up of the tool changing, grinding, and depreciation costs. The tool changing cost is the tool changing time × (the operator's rate + the overhead rate). The tool grinding cost is the grinding time

TABLE I

TOOL MATERIAL	MATERIAL MACHINED	n	$\frac{1}{n} - 1$
High Speed Steel	Steel Cast Iron	.125 .14	7 6
Carbide	Steel Cast Iron	.2 .25	4 3

Scully-Jones & Co.

Typical values of $(1/n - 1)$.

___

[4] *Optimation*, SCULLY-JONES AND CO., 1957, Chicago, Ill.

$\times$ (grinder's rate + the overhead rate)/number of cutting edges. The tool depreciation cost is the cost of the tool/(number of resharpenings $\times$ number of cutting edges).

L is the direct labor rate, in dollars per minute.

O is the overhead rate, in dollars per minute. L and O represent the cost of running the machine.

Typical values of n and $(1/n - 1)$ for high-speed steel and carbide cutting tools are found in Table I.

Using the cutting speed formula. Optimum cutting speed is calculated with this equation:

$$V_{op} = V_{in} \times M \tag{3}$$

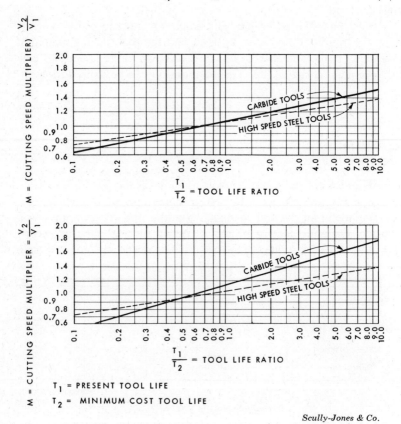

Scully-Jones & Co.

Fig. 6. Graphs plotting the relationship between the tool life ratio and cutting speed multiplier for steel (top) and cast iron (bottom) materials.

where V_{in} is the initial cutting speed,

M is a multiplication factor which is determined from the experimental graphs in Figs. 5 and 6.

Using the graphs. To use these graphs the ratio of the present tool life (T_1) to the minimum cost tool life (T_2) must be known. T_2 is computed from equation 2; T_1 is the present tool life of the cutting tool for which the optimum speed is desired. Using the graphs the following steps are taken:

1. Compute the ratio T_1/T_2 and locate it on the X-axis of the graph of Fig. 6, top or bottom, depending on whether steel or cast iron is being machined.

2. From this point project a line up to either the solid or dotted line, depending on whether the material of the tool is carbide or high-speed steel.

3. From this point of intersection, project a line across to the X-axis and read M, the cutting speed multiplier.

Using the initial speed, which is known, the optimum cutting speed can be computed from equation 3.

Illustrative Example

(1) ***Solving for optimum speed.*** Let us compare the two tools shown in Fig. 7. The tool on the left is a brazed carbide tool of style *BR*; the tool on the right is a solid carbide tool of style *SBR*.

We shall compute and compare the minimum cost tool life and optimum cutting speed for the tools. The *BR* tool at present has a

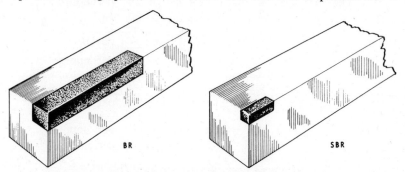

Fig. 7. Styles BR and SBR Tools. The style BR tool is a brazed carbide insert (carboloy 78B) with a 1" x 1" x 7" shank; cost, $2.65. The style SBR tool is a solid carbide insert (style SQ, carboloy 78B) ½" x ½" x 1½"; insert cost, $5.23.

TABLE II

COST	STYLE BR	STYLE SBR
1. TOOL CHANGING COST: Tool changing time x (Machine labor + overhead), $ per tool	2 min. x $0.121 per min. = $0.242 per tool change	Solid insert rotated to new cutting edge 1/2 min. x $0.121 per min. = $0.061 per tool change.
2. TOOL GRINDING COST: Grinding time x (grinding labor + overhead), $ per cutting edge	5-1/2 min. x $0.133 per min. = $0.74 per tool grind	15 min. x $0.133 per min. 8 cutting edges per grind) = 0.25 per cutting edge.
3. TOOL DEPRECIATION COST: Total Cost Divided by (Number of grinds x number of cutting edges per grind) $ per cutting edge	`$2.65 / 6 grinds = $0.44 per tool grind	$5.23 / (8 grinds x 8 cutting edges per grind) = $0.08 per cutting edge.
TOTAL REPLACEMENT COST	$1.42 per cutting edge	$0.39 per cutting edge.

TOOL REPLACEMENT COSTS (CHANGING, DEPRECIATION, GRINDING*)

*Grinding is a common expression for resharpening. In this instance, since grinding is actually done, the expression is more meaningful.

Scully-Jones & Co.

Tool replacement costs.

cutting speed of 180 feet per minute in steel and a tool life of 240 minutes. The optimum conditions of the *BR* style tool will be used as the initial conditions for the *SBR* style tool. The tools are fully described in the figures.

The following data is known (the values are hypothetical):

The machine operator's rate is	$2.25	per hour
The machine overhead rate is	$5.00	per hour
Labor plus overhead is	$7.25	per hour
or	$0.121	per minute
The tool grinder's rate is	$2.00	per hour
The grinder overhead rate is	$6.00	per hour
Labor plus overhead is	$8.00	per hour
or	$0.133	per minute

The tool replacement costs are shown in Table II.

For the *BR* style tool the replacement cost is computed as $1.42 per cutting edge; for the *SBR* style tool, $0.39 per cutting edge.

From Table I the value of $(1/n - 1)$ for both tools is seen to be 4. We now have all the data necessary to compute the minimum cost tool life:

For the *BR* style tool,

$$T = \frac{(1/n - 1)\ R}{L + O}$$

$$= \frac{4(\$1.42)}{(\$0.121)}$$

$$= 47 \text{ minutes.}$$

The tool life ratio is $T_1/T_2 = 240/47 = 5.1$.

For the *SBR* style tool,

$$T = 4\ (0.39/0.121) = 13$$
The tool life ratio is $47/13 = 3.6$.

From the graph of Fig. 6, *M* is found to be 1.4 for the *BR* style tool, and 1.3 for the other.

For the *BR* style tool,

$$V_{op} = V_{in} \times M = 180 \times 1.4 = 252 \text{ fpm}$$

For the *SBR* style tool,

$$V_{op} = 252 \times 1.3 = 328 \text{ fpm.}$$

(2) *Solving for cost reduction.* This example shows how costs can be reduced and production increased when the optimum cutting speed is used. The tool styles and operating conditions are the same as in Example 1. The following data is known (again all values are hypothetical):

Tool Styles: *SBR* compared to *BR*

Tool Material: Carboloy 78B

Material to be Machined: SAE #4340, Forged, 221 BHN, 36″ Cylinder, 6″ Dia.

Machine Tool: 25 HP Engine Lathe, which has a feed of 0.015 ipr.

Cutting Fluid: 20:1 Soluble Oil

Depth: 1/8 inch.

TABLE III

Tool Style Cutting Speed Tool Life	Initial Speed BR 180 fpm – 110 rpm 240 Min.	Optimum Speed BR 255 fpm – 150 rpm 48 Min.	Initial Speed SBR 255 fpm – 150 rpm 48 Min.	Optimum Speed SBR 325 fpm – 190 rpm 13 Min.
(1) MACHINING COST				
$= \dfrac{\text{Machining Time* } \times}{\text{(Labor + Overhead)}}$ $= \text{(min.)} \times \text{(\$ per min.)}$	$= \dfrac{36 \times (\$0.121)}{0.015 \times 110}$ $= \$2.64$ per part	$= \dfrac{36 \times (\$0.121)}{0.015 \times 150}$ $= \$1.93$ per part	$= \dfrac{36 \times (\$0.121)}{0.015 \times 150}$ $= \$1.93$ per part	$= \dfrac{36 \times (\$0.121)}{0.015 \times 190}$ $= \$1.53$ per part
(2) TOOL COST				
$= \dfrac{\text{Tool Replacement Cost}}{\text{(Tool Life} \div \text{Machining Time)}}$ $= \dfrac{\$ \text{ per cutting edge}}{\text{parts per grind}}$	$= \dfrac{\$1.42}{(240/21.8)}$ $= \$0.13$ per part	$= \dfrac{\$1.42}{(48/16)}$ $= \$0.47$ per part	$= \dfrac{\$0.39}{(48/16)}$ $= \$0.13$ per part	$= \dfrac{\$0.39}{(13/12.6)}$ $= \$0.39$ per part
(3) NONPRODUCTIVE COST				
$= \text{Load Time} \times \text{(Labor + Overhead)}$ $= \text{(min.)} \times \text{(\$ per min.)}$	$= 2 \times \$0.121$ $= \$0.24$ per part	$= 2 \times \$0.121$ $= \$0.24$ per part	$= 2 \times \$0.121$ $= \$0.24$ per part	$= 2 \times \$0.121$ $= \$0.24$ per part
TOTAL MACHINING COST $= (1) + (2) + (3)$	$\$3.01$ per part	$\$2.64$ per part	$\$2.30$ per part	$\$2.16$ per part
PRODUCTION RATE $= \dfrac{\text{min. per hour}}{\text{min. per part**}}$	$\dfrac{60}{21.8 + 0.2 + 2}$ $= 2.5$ parts/hr.	$\dfrac{60}{16 + 0.6 + 2}$ $= 3.23$ parts/hr.	$\dfrac{60}{16 + 0.2 + 2}$ $= 3.28$ parts/hr.	$\dfrac{60}{12.6 + 0.5 + 2}$ $= 3.97$ parts/hr.

*Machining Time $= \dfrac{\text{Length of part}}{\text{Feed} \times \text{rpm}}$

**Min. per part = machining time + tool changing per part + nonproductive time

Scully-Jones & Co.

Machining costs and production rates of styles BR and SBR tools.

The calculations for this comparison are shown in Table III. Fig. 8 shows a graphical representation of the various relationships.

Table III shows that when the optimum cutting speeds are used, production rates are increased and costs reduced. From the graph of Fig. 8 we see that production rates can be increased further by increasing the cutting speed but with increased costs as a result. When using the original tool life of four hours in the style *BR* tool, the total machining costs are \$3.01. When using the minimum cost tool life of 48 minutes, the total machining costs are reduced to \$2.64, a savings of 0.37 per part; and the production rate has been increased 30%.

By changing to an insert tool, style *SBR*, with a tool life of 48 minutes, costs were further reduced to \$2.30 per part. When the cutting speed has been increased until the tool life is 13 minutes for the

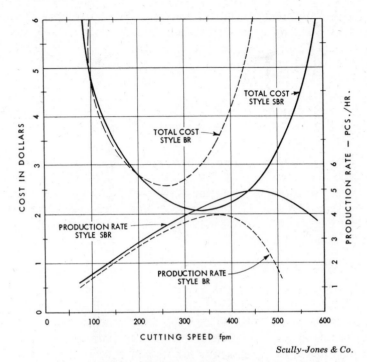

Fig. 8. Effect of cutting speed on total cost and production rate for styles BR and SBR tools.

style *BR* tool, the total machining costs are further reduced to $2.16 per part with a 21% increase in the production rate (see Fig. 8).

The overall cost reduction, using minimum cost cutting speeds and less costly tools, is shown to be $0.85 per part or a 28% savings, while the production rate has been increased 59%.

WORK PROBLEMS

P—1. An SAE 1045 carbon steel is to be machined under average cutting conditions, using a high-speed-steel tool and a cutting fluid (rather than dry). A tool life of six hours is desired. From the Tool Engineer's Handbook a value of 364 *(K)* is obtained for the SAE 1045 Carbon steel and a value of 2.67 $(T^{1/6})$ for a six hour tool life. What is the approximate cutting speed?

P—2. The data for this problem is the same as for Illustrative Example (1) except that cast iron instead of high-speed steel is being cut. What is the optimum cutting speed using *BR* and *SBR* style tools?

P—3. The data for this problem is the same as for Illustrative Example (1) except that the total replacement cost for the style *BR* tool is $1.90 per cutting edge and $0.57 per cutting edge for the style *SBR* tool. Find the optimum cutting speeds for both tools.

P—4. The data for this problem is the same as for problem No. 3 except that cast iron instead of high-speed steel is being machined. Find the optimum cutting speed for both *BR* and *SBR* style tools.

P—5. The data for this problem is the same as for Illustrative Example (2) except that the machining cost for the style *BR* tool is $2.95 per part for initial speed and $2.10 per part for optimum speed; for the style *SBR* tool $2.10 per part for initial speed and $1.62 per part for optimum speed. What is the total machining cost for both style tools and both speeds?

Other Cutting Tool Factors

Tool life and cutting speed are the chief factors that influence the tool engineer in his selection of cutting tools. Also, in determining the shortest tool life and the optimum speed, he becomes familiar with other factors that are inter-related with tool life and speed, and usually subordinate to them. These factors will be considered now in brief. The chapter on tool design contains a section on cutting tools from the designer's standpoint.

Matching the tool to the operation. The plans provided by the product designer specify quite definitely the dimensions and tolerances of the product. Assuming these values are realistic, the tool engineer must provide cutting tools that will give at least minimum-standard dimensions and tolerances for all machine surfaces. The point here is to avoid selecting tools that are far superior to the requirements of the operation. Since cutting tools that are designed for high precision cost more, using high-precision tools on a product that requires only average accuracy of its machined surfaces is an unnecessary expense. Not only is the initial expense more than usual, but the resharpening cost is more, and more frequent shutdowns are required for resharpening.

A careful matching of a cutting tool with a particular application extends to selecting the best tool material and design. Tool materials and designs far superior to those the operation demands will mean added initial expense, although any further expense is unlikely. It must be emphasized that a cutting tool whose precision, material, and design factors are in excess of requirements is not to be avoided; only tools which give a *wasteful* excess should be avoided.

If the tool engineer can see that in the near future he will need cutting tools which furnish a precision greater than his current requirements, he may consider investing in the more accurate, and therefore more expensive, tools. To decide the issue, the tool engineer may resort to a cost analysis of both the long and short range programs. Since he can't normally account for the future, however, the practice of matching the cutting tool to the current operation is wise.

Material of the tool. Selecting the best cutting tool material for a machining operation requires years of experience. The metallurgy of cutting materials alone is a wide field which is constantly growing and uncovering new and better cutting materials. Depending on the operation being performed and the material machined, tool variables like the following must be considered in any selection: hardness, tensile strength, machinability, chemical composition, cold working history, temperature, temperature of the chip. These and other variables are treated more fully in the Tool Design Chapter.

The important point to remember here is that a cutting tool must have durability and be able to impart adequate precision to the surface it must machine. Since a number of tools will meet these general stipulations for a particular machining operation and material, the selection of the most economical tool depends on a cost by cost comparison combined with fulfilling specific functional requirements.

Design of the tool. A tool's design is as important as its material composition. In mass production today the majority of cutting tools are standardized in design, with refinements made when necessary to suit special situations. The tool engineer has a vast market at his disposal from which to select the tool he wants. If by chance he needs a tool that is not offered by the market, he can always design his own, using reference data and handbooks to help him in determining proper angles, thread sizes, dimensions, tolerances, etc.

Again, adequate durability and precision must be designed into a cutting tool. The range of tools which meet these stipulations are narrowed down by cost and functional analyses. Recognizing the most economical tool design functionally is another case where the tool engineer must weigh all factors, passing on only those which suit his current requirements. He and the tool designer must work as a team in this regard.

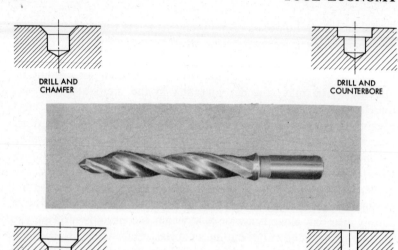

DRILL AND
CHAMFER

DRILL AND
COUNTERBORE

DRILL TWO DIFFERENT
DIAMETER SIZES

DRILL AND
REAM

Mohawk Tools, Inc.

Fig. 9.   A twist drill that combines different machining operations, as shown in the surrounding drawings.

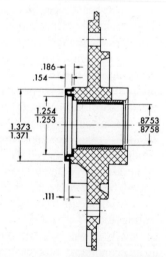

DeVlieg Machine Co.

Fig. 10.   The left view shows a turret lathe attachment that allows precision cluster tooling. Using this attachment in the machining of the magneto housing in the right view means nine surfaces can be machined at one pass, with tolerances as shown.

Miscellaneous factors. Other factors, not related to tool life and speed, which the tool engineer may consider are:

1. Automation of the tool's motions.
2. Combining tools.
3. Combining tool operations.
4. Providing for faster setups and feeds.

One way cutting tool manufacturers design tools that produce more finished work per hour is by combining operations or tools. Cutting tools that are capable of performing multiple operations with each pass, such as drilling and counterboring or drilling and reaming, also reduce the time-per-part factor. Turret and cluster tools also contribute to increasing capacity and reducing the time-per-part.

Compared to tool life and speed, these miscellaneous factors are not likely to play an important part in the tool engineer's selection of a cutting tool, although in a special situation they might. For instance, fast feeding a tool, if possible, to shorten the time-per-part factor.

ECONOMY OF WORK-HOLDING, HAND, AND INSPECTION TOOLS

Work-holding, hand, and inspection tools must also be selected, designed, and used economically. In general, the same practice applies in gaining economy with these tools as with machine and cutting tools. For example, a manufacturer intends to drill a casting in several locations. If he has a small number of castings, say on the order of twenty, no special drilling jig would be used. The operator would lay out the holes on each casting by hand and drill them. Two hundred castings would allow a simple device, primarily one that would transfer the laying-out routine from man to jig. Two thousand castings would permit a drilling jig of sizeable cost, one that would transfer from man to jig all the repetition of laying-out, work-holding, and guiding the drill. For any number of castings, therefore, economical production is indicated by principles similar to those we have already stressed.

Work-holding Tools

Work-holding tools are jigs and fixtures. A jig is a device for holding a part while an operation is being performed and at the same time guiding the cutting tool that performs the operation. A fixture is simply a device for holding a part while an operation is being performed. Many types of clamps, mandrels, vises and vise jaws, chucks, V-blocks, holders, jacks are classed as fixtures.

Jigs and fixtures fulfill a function caused initially by the advent of mass production techniques. As explained earlier, modern manufacturing of standardized parts is based on the theory that every part in a production process will be made within tolerances of reasonable limits. Jigs and fixtures offer a means of producing parts with standardized design, since their function is to establish a constant relationship between the part and cutting tool.

Just as the tool engineer conducts a systematic analysis in selecting machine equipment, so does he in jig and fixture selection. He analyzes every operation necessary to process a part, from raw material to finished product. With jigs and fixtures, of course, his analysis is geared toward work-holding requirements, including the desired work-cycle time, machining time, passes necessary, total quantity of parts to be produced, time and motion reports, number of holes to be drilled or cuts to be made, sequence of machine operations, etc.

Although certain principles exist in jig and fixture design, the tool engineer and designer should not feel obliged to obey them without question. In specific cases good judgment acquired through knowledge and experience will usually lead to good designs. The field of jig and fixture design absorbs the skills and energies of the highest level engineers.

Jigs. The chief means by which economy can be realized with jigs is in their design. The factors of material and proper usage are minor in comparison. The basic principles of jig design are few and comparatively simple. Since the range of jig designs is vast, the tool engineer's ability to apply the basic principles with ingenuity and originality is essential. He works closely in this regard with the tool designer.

The degree of accuracy which must be imparted to a product and the amount of money that can be spent on it will determine the type of jig that can be designed. In most cases the tool engineer does not set these values; they come from management and are based on its appraisal of the market with respect to demand and a product design that will be saleable. Knowing these values, the tool engineer can apply the following basic principles to create an economical jig design.

Locating the part. The part must be able to be located in the jig quickly and accurately. The operator must be able to handle each part

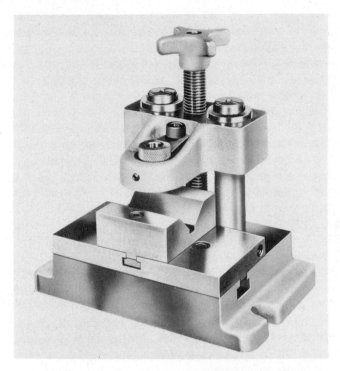

Rockford Engineered Products Co.

Fig. 11. An adjustable V-block drill jig.

and insert it in the jig in the same way. Since unskilled labor will normally be used, the jig must have a simple, foolproof design, so parts can be located with a minimum of wastage, which results with erroneous handling. To insure proper handling, the locating points should be visible to the operator so he can see that the part is seated correctly before it is clamped in place. Because the locating points in the jig will wear with repeated use, they should be hardened and made easily replaceable.

If the part has not been machined previously, so that locating must be performed on a rough or unfinished surface, not more than three fixed points of support can be used. Geometrically, using three or less *fixed* points assures proper contact of part to jig. Other supporting points may be used, but they should be adjustable to compensate for the irregularities of a rough surface.

Clamping the part. Each part must be secured firmly in the jig without causing distortion or springing. Each part must be secured in the same position. To assure this, the holding devices should be positioned as nearly above or across from the locating points as possible; with unfinished parts, as near the fixed locating points as possible.

Work-holding tools must be positive and quick-acting, yet simple in construction and operation. Threaded devices are positive in action but are usually not fast enough for mass production operations. Since wrenches are often misplaced or lost, handwheels or knobs should be used with threaded devices. Cams and wedge-actuated clamps are fast and positive in action, but are not recommended where heavy and rapid vibrations might be experienced.

In regard to strength and size, work-holding tools, and jigs in particular, should be designed to match the job. A clamp suitable for holding a drill-jig leaf may not have the strength for prolonged use on a milling fixture. On the other hand, a vise is not recommended in applications where a simple clamp would suffice. The size of the part, the holding force necessary, and the frequency of setups heavily influence the design of the jig clamp.

More ingenuity and originality can be brought into play by the tool engineer and designer in devising effective clamping means than in any other phase of jig design. If the time required to place and clamp down the part in the jig is longer than the time necessary to machine the part, the jig is not efficient. The machine is idled a period of time while the jig is being loaded and unloaded, which leads to uneconomical production. A load-unload time less than a corresponding machining time is therefore essential, and the means used to assure the lesser time, without sacrificing other functional requirements, must be carefully and ingeniously thought out.

In recent years some industrial concerns have utilized jigs and other work-holding tools which are made of plastics. The advantages of plastics over steel in many applications are: economy of fabrication, savings in weight, ease of modification (if necessary), ease of duplication, high durability. Drill jigs 42 inches in diameter have been fabricated of plastics and used successfully in practice. The big disadvantage to plastic tools, which may soon be overcome, is that they do not lend themselves to products which require very close tolerances.

Chip removal and safety. In jig design, means must be provided to remove accumulated chips quickly and conveniently. Chips on locating surfaces might cause the part to seat improperly, or chips wedged around the part might force it out of place. Good jig designs account for chips by eliminating flat surfaces and corner pockets where chips can lodge. Surfaces should be sloping and ample clearance allowed around the part so chips can be brushed or washed out. Where structurally possible, many jigs have openings in their sides for easy disposal of chips.

In the design of tools, and especially jigs, the tool engineer must always keep the operator's safety in mind. In jig design sharp corners and projections should be avoided and the jig loading and unloading point kept a safe distance from the cutting tool. All controls involving the jig should be placed so the operator's hands will not come in contact with moving machinery while operating them. The use of foot controls is recommended for this reason. All operations of placing and clamping the part should be carried out from the working side of the jig, making it unnecessary for the operator to move his hands between the jig and the cutting tool.

Good jig design practice:

1. Always design tool guides of jigs to have enough rigidity so there is no danger of losing the correct relationship between the cutting tool and the part.

2. Design jigs as strong and rigid as required without introducing excess weight. Since most jigs are portable, excess weight will cause operator fatigue, especially if many setups are necessary.

3. Keep jigs as simple in design as possible. The simpler the jig the fewer the components to wear or become damaged.

4. Utilize standard jig components, many of which are available commercially, whenever possible. Just like any other mass-produced item, standard jig components are almost always less expensive than ones made special. Such items as drill bushings, handwheels, thumbscrews, certain clamps and jig legs, and many other items, are available in a variety of styles and sizes.

Fixtures. As with jigs, the greatest opportunity for saving with fixtures is in their design. The same principles apply in fixture design as in jig design. Fixtures do not guide the tool, however, and are used primarily in milling, broaching, lathe, and planing operations. Other fixtures not used with machine tools are identified by the function they fulfill, such as assembly fixtures or welding fixtures.

Design considerations. In fixture design, the tool engineer must take

Snow Mfg. Co.

Fig. 12. An automatic indexing and clamping fixture.

into account a heavy thrust due to feeding the part into the cutting tool, which is seldom encountered in jig design. Because of this heavy thrust, fixtures must be sturdily built and as low as possible. If fixtures are too high in relation to the work table or other reference support surfaces, they are subject to distortion or springing when in contact with the cutting tool. For this reason clamping devices in fixtures are stronger and more massive than in jigs and the locating points more positive.

Excessive clamping forces may cause deflection of the part being machined. To a certain extent the amount of deflection can be anticipated, but variations in materials, speeds, and other factors make consistently accurate predictions impossible. Deflection of parts can never be eliminated, but it can be reduced and controlled.

Necessary precautions. Certain precautions must be taken with work-holding tools, especially if the part is of a delicate nature and deflects easily under required cutting and work-holding forces. These precautions are:

1. If possible, clamps should bear directly over fixed locating points.

2. Clamping forces should be opposed by adjustable supports where the clamping arrangement of precaution 1 is not possible.

3. Work-holding devices should be arranged, wherever possible, to transmit deflection-inducing forces through its rigid members so that these forces are not further transmitted to the part or work table of the machine.

4. The arrangement of work-holding fixtures, cutting tool, and part should be such that the cutting zone is as close as feasible to the machine's table. A good way to establish this relationship is in the design of the work-holding fixture.

5. Steps should be taken to prevent the operator from exerting excessive force in applying clamps or additional supports. Care must be used to see that these supports do not themselves introduce additional reflection.

6. The fixture should be matched to the job, using inexpensive fixtures for short runs, especially if an unusual design is called for.

As with jigs, the type of fixture to be used for a given set of conditions depends not only on economical manufacture, but also on the machine the fixture will be mounted on. Since the machine is governed by conditions that will yield economical manufacture, a fixture governed by like conditions will assure overall economical conditions.

Hand Tools

The primary methods of achieving economy with hand, or small, tools is by: (1) Control of distribution, and (2) prepositioning.

Control of distribution. Control of distribution begins with the location of the tool crib. A typical crib should be as centrally located as possible without interfering with efficient flow of production, and be close to the repair-resharpening shop and foremen's offices. The layout of a tool crib depends on its size, the type of production it must service, number of operations being serviced, most frequently-used tools, and the budget allowed hand tool storage. A liberal budget allows extensive shelving, use of trays, racks, and other storage arrangements.

A tool crib is no better than the efficiency of its classification methods. Hand tools vary so widely in function, material from which made, and means for applying them in operation, that classification is often difficult. Since a tool crib will contain cutting, hand, work-holding, and inspection tools, classification is commonly divided into tools for measuring and testing, removing material, adding material, changing shape without removing material, changing appearance, positioning, protecting, and assembling. Most hand tools would be placed in positioning and assembling classifications.

A typical system. There are many practical systems of distributing hand tools from the tool crib. A typical system used in large tool rooms will provide means to indicate where the tool is located in the crib, the kind of tool, its size or some other identifying term, to whom it has been checked out, his badge number, the job number for which the tool is intended, date of removal, date of return, condition of tool at time of removal and return, department charged, quantity of issue, and other factors dependent on specific toolroom, plant, and production policies. Small toolrooms will have less extensive systems.

Proper control of distribution also includes an accurate inventory of stock, records of damaged and lost tools, and means of accounting for hand-tool usage over a prescribed period of time, usually the length of a run. This last-named record—valuable in the case of special tools—can yield economical usage by noting those tools which are inadequate for a particular operation because of an excessively high wear-per-time factor.

Matching to production. Obviously economical control of hand tools can best be achieved if the tool crib size, location and layout, and the classification and distribution of tools is designed to match the over-all production situation as closely as possible. The *overall* situation means different types of operations, different sizes and lengths of runs, and the anticipated, long-term production schedule of the plant. In plants where many different types of operations are performed or in unautomated plants, efficient control of hand tools results in sizeable savings.

Prepositioning. The practice of prepositioning is for production-line hand tools only. Prepositioning a hand tool involves time and motion studies to arrive at the best standby location for the tool. In any work cycle involving a hand tool, an operator, a part, and/or a machine, there is one best position where a tool should be placed when it is not in use. In a time and motion study many actual work cycles are conducted, each one different only in respect to the hand tool's location. Each cycle is timed and each position noted. The cycle that gives the shortest elapsed time is the most economical choice. If the tool's location in this position is functionally safe and otherwise presents no problems, a holder can be devised to mount the tool in that, the standby, position.

Hand drills, screwdrivers, wrenches, and other small tools that are mounted at about the level of their intended use, positioned in

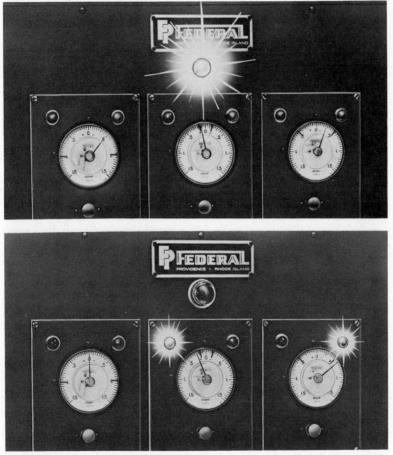

Federal Products Corp.

Fig. 13. Views of a control switchboard. When the master light is "ON" the part is acceptable (top view). When the master light is "OFF" the part is not acceptable (bottom view). In the bottom view the left light indicates "SCRAP", the right light, "SALVAGE".

the best manner for natural removal and replacement by the operator, and held in place firmly but are easily removable, constitutes prepositioning. In operations that employ many production-line hand tools, time and motion studies with a view toward prepositioning can give worthwhile savings over an extended period of time.

Inspection Tools

Inspection tools are commonly called *inspection gages,* as distinct from reference gages, which are used to determine sizes of other gages or to calibrate instruments, and working gages, which are used by the operator for any gaging necessary to the operation he is performing. In addition to standard gages, in recent years the use of X-ray machines, "Magnaflux" instruments, sonic and ultrasonic devices, and other highly special instruments are playing an increasingly valuable role in mass-production inspection.

Standard gages are of six general types: plug, ring, snap, thread, pin, and form. Inspection tools like vernier calipers, micrometers, gage blocks, and gear testers are one or more of these general types. The gage that is used for a particular inspection operation depends on many factors, among them tolerances desired, shape of the surface inspected, the material inspected, the budget allotted to inspection and inspection tools.

Economy with inspection tools. Without entering into a discussion of gaging systems, an extremely broad and often complex subject, the principal means by which economy is gained with inspection tools are:

1. Designing tools that conform to good gaging practice; that is, designing gages which are long-lasting, especially the contact surfaces, can be manipulated quickly and easily, and which measure tolerances of a part adequately without providing needless precision.

2. Requiring gages to conform with the principles of motion economy, such as prevention of undue operator strain and conservation of time and skill.

3. Matching the tool to the job. For example, in low rate production simple gages can be used because the time element is not crucial. As the production rate increases, gages must be operable in correspondingly shorter times. Although fast-responding gages cost more initially, their overall cost is justified because the production process is not disturbed.

4. Using gages in a process only where they are absolutely essential. In a typical production process there are many different operations that require little or no inspection in which gages are necessary.

5. Checking gages in use regularly to make certain they have not lost their accuracy.

6. Wherever possible functionally, designing gages with a view toward future requirements. Not only are special gages expensive but only rarely can they be utilized later. Avoiding this with the purchase of standardized gages and gage parts will prove the most economical over a period of years.

Although economy of inspection tools is relatively minor when compared with economy of direct labor or machine equipment, it is important nevertheless. Often in mass production operations gage economy must give way to the absolute necessity of designing gages to measure within specified tolerances and operating times; however, always striving for economy may influence the functional element in gaging, either in suggesting better methods or in adapting methods to suit the gages on hand. Constantly striving for economical inspection in high production operations probably led to the development of automatic gaging.

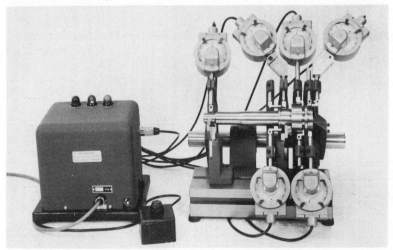

C. E. Johnson Gage Co.

Fig. 14. An electronic inspection device that performs six measuring operations simultaneously.

Automatic gages. Automatic gages are making an important contribution to precision-controlled production in the metal-working industries. Some of these automatic inspection units are complete gaging circuits consisting of standard inspection components. A typical unit has built-in memory and comparator devices that match air pressure signals, representing inspection measurements, with other air pressure signals, representing reference measuremnts. A paired set of signals that do not match produce a third signal, an electric correction pulse that progresses through memory circuits, which control the machine tools at various stations along the line. This electric feedback signal will correct the machine tool settings accordingly.

Although automatic gages have high initial costs, they are usually justified in large-volume production by the accuracy, reduction in indirect labor, and rapidity of operation they afford. On some units as many as thirty separate dimensions can be checked simultaneously in a few seconds, inspecting parts ranging from crankshafts and cylinder blocks to ball bearing assemblies and turbine blades.

CHAPTER FIVE

Economic Processing

For our purposes we will define *processing* as the one or more operations necessary to handle, convey, and machine a part after its forming stage through to its assembling stage. With metals, a forming operation means molding, forging, casting, extruding, pressing, rolling, etc., a material into a desired shape. Products of these operations constitute the rough stock for processing operations. Forming operations are highly specialized processes in themselves. Since most manufacturing concerns do not have the facilities to perform them, they purchase their rough stock from steel mills, foundries, forging shops, and other places specializing in forming operations.

When a part reaches the assembling stage it normally does not require further machining or finishing. It is ready to be assembled with different parts, the assembly forming a complete product. Between the forming and assembling stages is the middle stage we call processing. In Chapter Five we will be concerned chiefly with the methods of economical processing not covered in Chapters Three and Four.

ELEMENTS OF A PROCESS

To understand how economical processing is achieved, it is first necessary to define the elements of a process. A manufacturing process consists of four primary and four secondary elements. The primary elements are:

1. Bringing the part to the equipment that will machine it.
2. Positioning the part for machining.

Link-Belt Co.

Fig. 1. Tru-Trac car-type conveyor for 1100 lb. coils of hot strip.

3. Machining the part.
4. Removing the part to a storage point.

The secondary elements are:

1. Planning the process.
2. Receiving the raw material for the part.
3. Inspecting the part.
4. Shipping the finished part.

This ranking is arbitrary. The latter group is considered secondary because its elements do not contribute directly to the processing operations, which agrees with what has already been said. We will discuss the primary elements first.

Primary Elements

Element 1 consists of obtaining a part from stock and transporting it either directly to the machine or to a transfer station. The transfer station will complete the moving, most often over a conveyor system (see Fig. 1). Fork lifts, tractor trailers, and hand trucks provide the most ordinary means of part handling.

Element 2 consists of positioning the part in a jig or fixture, securing it, and positioning the work table and work-holding tool until the part is next to the cutting tool.

Element 3 consists of machining the part—drilling a hole, milling, planing, etc.

Element 4 consists of retracting the cutting tool and/or the work table, unclamping the part and removing it to a stocking point. Fork lifts, trailers, hand trucks, conveyor systems aid in part removal.

Economic processing in 1 and 4 is attained in several ways. Various factors influence the choice of the best material-handling systems. (The term "material handling" is used interchangeably with

Snyder Tool & Engineering Co.

Fig. 2. 110-foot long multi-unit transfer machine on which parts move from one operation to the next in a linear path. Here material handling equipment is integral with the machine.

"part handling.") These factors include the sequence of operations, machining time, the kind of parts (size, shape, weight) to be handled, the nature of handling indicated, and the budget allotted for handling.

Material handling equipment must transport parts with a speed compatible with the machining time of the process. If compatibility does not exist, the overall increased cost due to an increased time-per-part factor will almost certainly be excessive over a period of months. In general, the earlier a stockpile of parts can be built up in the work cycle and the longer the pile can be kept intact over a cycle's duration, the greater will be the savings in time, manpower expended, and costs involved in the handling.

Material handling. The best sequence of operations, as far as material handling is concerned, is a matter of individual plants since no two plants have the same size and shape spaces available. In most plant layouts, the shorter the overall handling distance the better. Conveyors are excellent for steady straight-line flow of cer-

Mechanical Handling Systems, Inc.

Fig. 3. An overhead monorail conveyor system in a warehouse. A fork lift removes material from trucks. Notice that boxed material is stored on pallets.

tain parts (see Fig. 3 which shows a monorail conveyor), while fork lifts are valuable for moving a large quantity of parts in one load. Although a sequence of operations depends mainly on the most economical procedure for machining the part, the tool engineer and the process engineer do not overlook the substantial savings that can be realized with a skillful arrangement of handling equipment. If possible, they may alter some portion of the process to suit a superior handling arrangement.

The size, shape, and weight of a part are big factors in handling systems. Over the years handling equipment has been classified primarily according to weight of pay load, speed of movement, types of movement, and recommended usage. Equipment types are usually divided into four main groups: manual equipment, wide area; power equipment, wide area; gravity equipment (unpowered), fixed path; power equipment, fixed path. The tool engineer also has access to the design specifications issued by the handling equipment manufacturer. If nothing fits his requirements he can design, and have built, equipment to suit his particular process, although special designs may be economical for that process only.

Operating within a budget. The maximum costs which can be expended on handling equipment, as specified by management's budget, requires careful investigation. Selecting material handling equipment is undertaken in the same fashion as selecting machine equipment, which was explained in Chapter Three. Normally the purchase of relatively expensive equipment is justified if the overall, long-term cost of production is the most economical using that equipment; however, the purchase of less expensive equipment is justified in short runs, where using expensive equipment would mean a layout of capital that might not be paid off. If possible, a budget should not prevent the purchase of handling equipment which will yield overall, long-term economy.

Matching handling equipment to the operation it must perform is important functionally as well as costwise. Fork lifts must be flexible enough to perform all their different operations efficiently. Conveyor systems must move fast enough and not be subject to frequent jammings or breakdowns. Cranes must be able to swing a load of parts at desired angles without becoming sluggish in operation. All handling equipment must be able to move parts without damaging them in any way. Correctly matching handling equipment to the job it must perform requires familiarity with material handling processes, which the well-rounded tool engineer will have and will be able, therefore, to select handling equipment best suited for a particular process.

A typical drilling operation. For a typical drilling operation, which incorporates the four primary elements, the procedure can be outlined as follows:

1. Obtain the part to be drilled from stock.
2. Load it on the drill machine's work table or in a jig or fixture.
3. Position the part.
4. Clamp it.
5. Position the drill over the part.
6. Drill the part.
7. Retract the drill from the part.
8. Unclamp the part.
9. Remove it from the work table, or jig or fixture.
10. Transport the part to a stocking point.

Secondary Elements

Of the secondary elements in a process, by far the most important is the planning necessary to devise the process. In some respects it is the most important step of all, because here is where economical production can be permanently built into the process. If the "building in" is good enough, the process will give economical production for its duration.

Planning the process. Essentially, planning the process has four aims:

1. To reduce the process into a series of operations, each of which is suitable functionally.
2. To study each operation separately to find the most economical performance for the process intended.
3. To organize the operations and arrange them in sequence to give overall economical performance.
4. To provide the means to carry out the process as planned.

The receiving and shipping operations are largely dependent on the materiél policies of individual plants. Since they are rarely critical and undesirable conditions relatively simply to rectify, receiving and shipping operations will not be included here.

Inspecting the part. Inspection procedures are also dependent for the most part on plant policy. Whether inspection is accomplished by machine or by human guidance certain pre-determined standards must be met. If they are not, steps must be taken to correct the fault. For instance, if defective parts are reported from various sources in the field, the tool engineer must increase the frequency of his spot-checking operations, examine his inspection tools and instruments to see that they still give design precision, investigate the methods of inspection, or whatever else he finds necessary to correct inadequate inspection. Of course, he must also investigate the causes behind the processing of defective parts. All this must be carried out without altering or interfering with the basic process.

TIME AND MOTION STUDIES

As mentioned earlier, this is a field in itself. Time and Motion Study engineers conduct analyses with the purpose of finding the most economical form of a particular operation; standardizing the methods, materials, tools, and equipment; accurately determining the time required by the average operator to perform his tasks; and training the operator in new methods as determined by the study.

F. W. Taylor is generally acknowledged as the originator of time and motion studies as we know it today. His work began in 1881, was continued and expanded admirably by the Gilbreths in the early

Syntron Co.

Fig. 4. The duties of this operator have been subjected to rigid time and motion studies. The operator's position, the height of the vibration feeder bowls, the arrangement of the chutes all conform to time and motion principles.

years of this century, until today most large industrial concerns have departments devoted exclusively to time and motion research; in addition, many private agencies exist which provide this service to industry.

When applied to the manufacturing process, time and motion studies may be conducted either in the planning stage or after the process is in operation, although the latter is more often the case. If effective, time and motion studies can result in:

1. Conservation of operator and mechanical motions.
2. Alleviation of undue operator strain and heavy manual labor.
3. Conservation of human skill.
4. Combination or elimination of operations.

These improvements can lead to more economical production if properly carried out. Extensive time and motion studies may serve to indicate management's healthy attitude toward the value of minute economies in relation to long-term economy.

Conservation of Motion

Conservation of motion is accomplished most simply by repeating a series of operations identical in every respect except one, and clocking the time each operation takes. The varying factor may be the position of the machine's controls, the location of the loading or unloading stations, work-holding designs, handling methods, arrangement of the handling and machining units, etc. The operation which takes the shortest time to perform is the most economical if it does not result in undue operator strain or heavy manual labor, threaten the product's quality and quantity, or introduce costs that might never be paid off. These stipulations can be avoided if they are accounted for in the beginning and made limiting factors for all different operations that are tested. As a result of motion conservation, time is also conserved, which contributes to overall economy.

Principles of motion economy. Over the years a number of principles have been evolved which hold true in a vast majority of processing situations. The most important ones are:

1. Replace operator movements by using automated machinery, especially in the case of routine movements.
2. Combine operations by combining tools or using controls with multiple functions.
3. Transfer hand motions to motions of the feet or knees.

4. Aid locating and clamping motions with jigs, fixtures, special tools, and quick-acting devices such as hydraulic clamps.

5. Reduce the size of the machining and handling areas to a minimum by using compact machine tools and well-designed, compact handling equipment and operations.

6. Minimize the use of the operator's eyes by keeping the area of necessary eye travel small, eliminating controls that are difficult to see, and aiding positioning operations that tend to strain the eye.

Alleviation of Operator Strain and Fatigue

Alleviation of undue operator strain and fatigue is accomplished

The Bodine Corp.

Fig. 5. With many operations requiring skill performed automatically, this machine conserves on human skill.

by providing comfortable working conditions which conform to physiological norms. If the operator's position is sitting, his tasks should be arranged so that they can be done without his having to assume uncomfortable positions. Most of his tasks should be at "elbow level" with ample clearance for his feet so that pedals may be depressed without twisting or straining the foot. All controls should be within easy reach and physically easy to operate. The positioning of controls, the height of the work table, the operator's relation to the table, should conform to time-tested standards based on average-sized men.

Alleviation of heavy manual labor is accomplished by transferring those operator motions which require undue strength to equipment with suitable mechanical advantage. In high-volume production this is almost always power-driven machinery. Small plants may use block and tackle arrangements or hand jacks. Transferring heavy labor from man to machine will decrease the fatigue factor of the operator and therefore increase his efficiency.

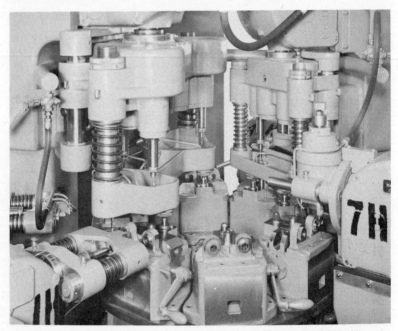

Hartford Special Machinery Co.

Fig. 6.   Close-up of an automatic power indexing machine with eight work-position stations and a multi-tooling arrangement.

Conservation of Skill

Human skill may be conserved by reducing the amount of it required to process a part, which is a problem of the product designer, or transferring the skills required from operator to tools. Using machinery that automatically performs certain measuring operations, and using jigs and fixtures can effectively conserve on human skills. Making tools foolproof is another way to conserve on skill. Most jigs and fixtures are good examples of this type of tool because parts can be located and clamped in one and only one position in them. Using gages and other precision instruments to aid the operator is a major way of conserving on skills.

Combining and Eliminating Operations

Combining operations is accomplished by simultaneously doing two or more operations, or arranging several cuts successively in an operation. Fig. 6 shows an automatic power indexing machine that performs simultaneous drilling, reaming, and milling operations. The indexing mechanism is designed to actuate or move the rotary table upon which the parts are mounted (see Fig. 7). This indexing brings the parts successively in line with each tool spindle as required by the

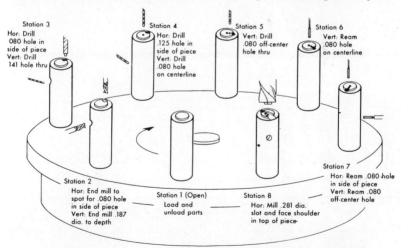

Hartford Special Machinery Co.

Fig. 7. Schematic diagram of the worktable of the automatic indexing machine shown in Fig. 6. This diagram shows the eight stations on which parts are mounted, and describes the types of operations and the sequence in which they are carried out in this production cycle.

production sequence. The part being fabricated, which is shown in its finished form at station 8, is for a gun.

When this machine is in operation there are eleven tool spindles working simultaneously, and each of the eight stations is performing one or more operations on a part. Fig. 7 illustrates both the types of operations and the sequence in which they are carried out in this

Commander Mfg. Co.

Fig. 8. This multi-drill performs seven drilling operations simultaneously.

production cycle. After each operation is completed, the rotary table automatically moves clockwise one station (see arrow in Fig. 7) and positions the parts for the next operation. The parts remain mounted on the rotary table throughout the cycle and are fed from tool to tool as the table completes a revolution.

In this machine then each part is indexed, or passes through the eight stations and undergoes eleven different machining operations. Notice that at stations 2, 3, 4, and 7, two operations are performed simultaneously. The operations to be performed at each station are described in Fig. 7.

Notice also station 1 is an open station and does not have a machining tool. The parts are merely loaded and unloaded here. When a finished part returns to station 1 from station 8, it is removed, and a raw piece is loaded at station 1. The only manual operations are the loading and unloading of the parts, and with additional mechanization, they could also be made automatic. The machining operations are carried out continuously except for the

The Dumore Co.

Fig. 9. A machine with combined drill and tap operations.

brief periods between operations when the tools are retracted and the table indexes from station to station.

Simultaneous drilling, tapping, and boring operations are common methods of combining operations. Drill and countersink, drill and tap (see Fig. 9), drill and bore are common methods where cuts are successively integrated.

Eliminating operations through time and motion studies by first observing those motions that serve no functional purpose, then re-performing the operations without them, will usually result in eliminating at least one operation in a complicated process. Eliminating operations is most often achieved in the material handling phase of a process.

ECONOMIC LOT SIZE

In processing, lot size is a basic consideration in the tool engineer's calculations, although in most cases the actual setting up of production schedules and lot sizes is outside his province. But lot sizes and lot numbers influence the entire manufacturing process. Small lots and frequent setups indicate the use of general-purpose machine tools, simple jigs and fixtures, a minimum of different operations, and manual handling. Large lots and infrequent setups allow greater expenditures for automated equipment and machines that are uni-purpose, highly productive, and have complicated setups. Since the size of a lot affects the tool engineer's plans so heavily, a discussion of lot sizes is necessary.

Conditions Influencing Lot Sizes

Two methods of determining economic lot sizes will be presented. The first method is by trial and error, the second by the Lehocsky formula. Either method is influenced by the following conditions:

1. The type of production. A plant that manufactures crank-shafts will have much different problems than one that makes ball bearings.

2. The demands of the market. In regard to lot sizes, it is important that management have a good understanding of the market. Often too large a lot causes purchase of equipment that cannot be paid off in a short time. Calling for a large lot, the product demand for which does not materialize, endangers the investment.

3. The time and cost to set up the process for production.

4. The amount of working capital invested in the parts, which includes the processing investment as well as the initial investment.

5. The cost and amount of storage for both unfinished and finished parts. Storage of finished parts is more critical, since unfinished parts can be purchased and brought in as they are needed, whereas finished parts, depending of course on their demand, must be stored until disposition can be arranged.

Economic Lot Size by Trial-and-Error

The trial-and-error method of calculating economic lot sizes is very practical and used by many industrial concerns. It is based on a compromise between producing all the parts in one lot or in many lots. One lot production means, among other factors, that the cost of storage may be excessive if production time is much less than the time anticipated for disposal of finished parts. Providing for many lots means, among other factors, that the cost of setups may become excessive. Somewhere between these extremes a compromise must be reached. A practical example will best show this.

A practical trial-and-error example. Let us assume that the annual demand for a product amounts to 5,000 items, and that under normal conditions of production it will take four weeks or 160 working hours to manufacture that amount. If the total number of parts is produced in one lot, they must be carried in inventory and stored until completely exhausted 48 weeks later. Rental must be charged for floor space which might better be used for faster-moving items. Since the finished parts represent an investment in fixed, direct, and indirect charges, capital is frozen (and the interest it could earn lost) until the parts are disposed of. Also, certain units of equipment may not be utilized efficiently, or at all, during the non-productive period.

An axiom of economics is that working capital should be paid off through earnings as soon as possible. These earnings, in turn, become working capital for succeeding items of manufacture. The continual using of earnings as working capital is called *turnover*. The average time that elapses between investments is the *turnover rate*. The more turnovers in any given period, the smaller the working capital required for operation. Single lot production may reduce the turnover rate below an economical minimum.

Eliminating extremes. Assuming the setup time for the process of our example is eight hours, a single lot production would absorb the

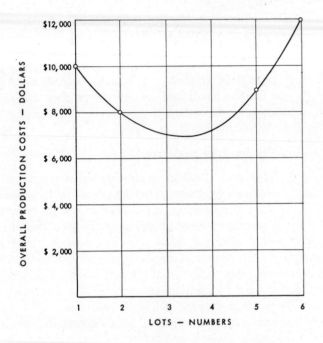

Fig. 10. Plotting lots against estimated overall production costs.
The least production cost determines the most economic lot size.

setup cost in a ratio of 8/5000, which is relatively small. At the other extreme, making runs every other month means the setup cost would be absorbed in the ratio of 6 × 8/5000, a cost-per-part figure that is six times greater and relatively large.

To find the most economical lot size is a matter of selecting a lot number which lies somewhere between one and six (see Fig. 10). Two lots, each taking four weeks to run off every six months, would reduce the storage problem but capital would still be tied up for too long a period. Five lots, each taking four weeks to run off about every ten weeks, would still mean an excessively high cost-per-part factor because of setup costs.

In choosing between three and four lots yearly, conditions peculiar to individual plants can make the difference. Plants with a variety of steady-selling products would probably prefer four lots, while plants with relatively fast-moving products of large volumes would probably choose three lots. Many other factors, including type of machine equipment, the time of the year, and the long-term produc-

tion schedule, will affect the final choice. In any case there is one
lot number that will give the most economical overall production.
Dividing this number into the number of parts gives the most economical lot size. For quarterly lots in our example, each lot consists
of 1,250 parts.

Plotting trial and error values. Fig. 11 shows a graph which
depicts the relationship between lot size and the total cost-per-part.
At one extreme, a small lot size gives a high cost-per-part, or unit
cost, value. This is caused by the costs of setup, and other factors
independent of lot size, being divided by relatively few parts. At the
other extreme, a very large lot size also gives an increasing unit cost.
This is caused by the increasing costs of direct and indirect materials

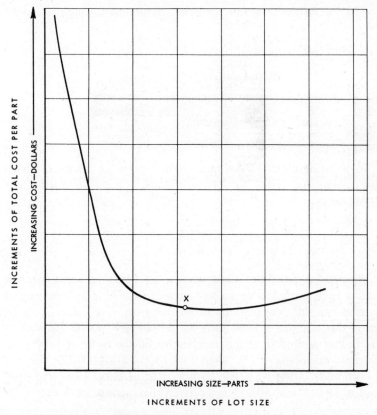

Fig. 11. This graph shows the relationship between lot size and total costs-per-
part for any normal manufacturing operation. Point X is the economic lot size.

and labor, including storage and maintenance charges, all of which vary directly as the lot size varies. On this basis, point X in Fig. 11 is the economic lot size.

Economic Lot Size with the Lehoczky Formula

A number of mathematical formulas exist which will give the most economical lot either by size or number. Most of these formulas are too complex and difficult to handle in practice. When more exact results are desired than the approximate method already presented, the Lehoczky formula[1] is often used. This simple formula gives sufficiently accurate results for most applications and is easy to use. Let:

X = number of lots to be produced per year,

M = interest on raw material, assuming a single purchase yearly,

L = setup charge,

$$J = \frac{\text{output desired}}{\text{rated capacity of equipment}},$$

$$S = \frac{\text{cost of finished product}}{\text{cost of raw material}}.$$

Without developing the formula, which employs the use of higher mathematics and is not significant in itself, solving for X, the final expression is:

$$X = \sqrt{\frac{M}{L}\left(\frac{S + J - SJ}{2}\right)}$$

Illustrative example. Let's assume an order of screw-machine parts is to be produced on a single-spindle automatic machine, which by itself has sufficient capacity to fill the order. The rate of production of this machine is 1800 parts per 8-hour day (denominator of J). The output desired from this machine to fill the order is 1400 parts per day (numerator of J). Then $J = 1400/1800 = 0.77$. The cost of each setup is \$45 (L). The cost-per-part of direct labor and overhead is \$0.015 and \$0.012 respectively (numerator of S except for

---

[1] Adapted from, *Production Planning and Control,* by L. P. Alford and J. R. Bangs, THE RONALD PRESS CO., 1950.

material cost). The cost of raw material per part is $0.008 (denominator of S).

The interest rate on the raw material if purchased once a year is 6% for 260 working days (5 days per week, 52 weeks per year). The interest for 260 working days is $0.06 \times 1400 \times 260 \times 0.008$ (M).

$$M/L = (0.06 \times 1400 \times 260 \times 0.008)/45 = 3.88$$

The cost-per-part of the finished product is the sum of costs of material, direct labor, and overhead—all on a per-part basis.

$$S = \frac{0.008 + 0.015 + 0.012}{0.008} = 4.37$$

Substituting these values into the Lehoczky formula,

$$X = \sqrt{3.88 \left[\frac{4.37 + 0.77 - (4.37 \times 0.77)}{2} \right]}$$

which resolves to,

$$X = 3.4 \text{ lots per year.}$$

Dividing this value into the annual number of working days $\left(\frac{260}{3.4} \right)$ gives a span of 76.5 working days for each lot. Since the daily output from this machine is 1400 parts, the economic lot size is $1400 \times 76.5 = 107,100$ parts.

SAFETY IN THE PLANT

The promotion of safety is important to economical production; also, it builds good public relations and good employer-employee relations. Besides the tangible effect of work stoppage and damage caused by accidents, there is the intangible effect of shock and loss of morale to men involved in the process, especially if a man has been badly hurt. For days and perhaps weeks after the accident production may be reduced due to this tension.

In modern mass production operations a man tending a machine may perform over ten thousand identical or nearly identical operations in a day. The human mind cannot be expected to remain sharp

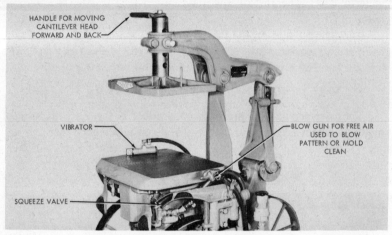

HANDLE FOR MOVING
CANTILEVER HEAD
FORWARD AND BACK

VIBRATOR

BLOW GUN FOR FREE AIR
USED TO BLOW
PATTERN OR MOLD
CLEAN

SQUEEZE VALVE

Osborn Mfg. Co.

Fig. 12.   Two-handed operation of a jolt-squeezer safeguards the operator's fingers.

and attentive for that many operations. Management should accept
this situation as inevitable and take steps to lessen the chance for
accidents, and especially those caused by an operator's momentary
laxity. Safety should include protection for:

1. The working zone.
2. Controls.
3. Moving parts.
4. Plant air.
5. Overloads.

Working Zone Protection

Each class of machine tool and cutting operation presents its own
problems of safeguarding. Safety devices usually consist of screens
and barriers to prevent accidental entry into the working zone while
the tool is cutting. In manual feeding, similar protection must be
provided to keep the operator's hands out of danger. Most screens
and barriers can be swung out of the way or removed while the
operator changes or adjusts the cutting tool. For added protection,
when the safety device is not in place the machine should not be
operable.

There are many kinds of safety devices. One not strictly protective, is an arrangement whereby the operator can feed the parts at

a point outside the working zone altogether. There are also electrical-mechanical interlocking devices, which prevent certain operations from being performed until others have been completed; electronic "watchdog" devices, and various tripping devices.

A sweep guard is used on punch and stamping presses, machines that have caused an alarming proportion of industrial accidents. The guard is a sweeping arm, padded to prevent injury to personnel, that is attached to the ram of a press through a cam and toggle assembly. When the ram descends, the arm is mechanically thrust across the danger zone, clearing the operator's hands and arms if they are still within the zone. Screens are placed behind the sweep arm to prevent the operator from reaching around it. Some plants now use electronic devices to accomplish the same results as sweep guards.

Controls Protection

Controls that are subject to accidental operation should be protected. Usually simple mesh bands placed across the control panel will guard against accidental bumping and still let the operator

National Safety Council, Inc.

Fig. 13. Tumbling barrel used for finishing small castings. Danger from dust has been eliminated by the exhaust system.

manipulate the controls. Pedal controls require guards so they are not actuated by falling objects or inadvertently depressed. Interlocks are also used in control devices as a safety precaution, assuring a correct sequence of operations. Electrical and electronics switchboards and panels should be properly grounded and rubber floor mats placed around them. Safety instructions and resuscitation signs should be posted in prominent places around switchboards, control panels, and machinery.

Hammond Machinery Builders

Fig. 14. A device that collects dust, including metallic particles, from light and medium dust sources, such as around mills, lathes, etc.

Plant Air Protection

Keeping the air in industrial plants free from dust (including minute particles of metal) and other harmful elements is essential. Various dust collectors and air filters are available on the market. Fig. 14 shows a unit which provides a low-cost means of collecting dust from air not heavily polluted. It is equipped with a blower wheel of the self-cleaning paddle type, dynamically balanced and mounted on the exhaust of the plant's ventilation system.

Moving Part Protection

Protecting against moving parts in machine equipment can easily be provided by enclosing shafts, gears, flywheels, and other rotating assemblies with screens or metal shields. With high-speed moving parts this is very important.

Overload Protection

Overload protection is provided by trip devices that are actuated when the speed, pressure, temperature, or power reaches dangerous limits. The trip will automatically shut down the machine or bring it under control. In diesel-powered machinery, for instance, the overspeed trips will either cut off the air supply to the superchargers or reset the fuel rack to a safe limit. All machinery should have remote-control shutoffs so that in case of fire or other emergencies where the machinery can't be reached, the power to it can be turned off. Some plants have master remote switches that can cut off banks of machinery in an emergency.

Safety rightly begins in the planning and design stage. It should be as much a part of the designer's aims as functional and cost considerations. Safety is also a prime concern of the tool engineer. In his calculations to develop the most economical manufacturing process, safety of machinery and personnel is vital. The wise tool engineer recognizes that stressing safety can lead to economical production if the overall picture is kept in mind. In general, we can say: "A safe process is an economical process."

HOW TO ECONOMIZE IN A PROCESS

Here is a brief summary of the chapters on machine equipment, tools, and the process approached in a slightly different manner.

Economy in the manufacturing process, which includes machine equipment and tool economy, divides into two distinct sections: (1) planning the economical process, and (2) maintaining the economical process. If an economical process is planned and maintained, the actual processing will be economical. Since the methods in these sections have already been explained, a listing of them is sufficient.

Planning the Economical Process

A. Planning the economical process is achieved with the most economical results from:

1. Establishing the product's demand based on the market and the product's design.

2. Establishing the product's quantity and quality based on demand, including material to be used.

3. Establishing the processing methods based on the product's design and demand, including lot size.

4. Developing the machining and handling operations and their sequence.

5. Developing the arrangement of machine tools and material handling equipment.

6. Developing plant layout as to space, power, lighting, etc.

7. Selecting machine tools and material handling equipment by cost and function analyses.

8. Selecting cutting tools, jigs and fixtures, and gages by cost and function analyses.

9. Preparing operator instruction sheets, route sheets, progress charts, job tickets, etc.

10. Scheduling of material, tooling, stock items, shipments of completed parts, etc.

11. Arranging for tool storage, control, and maintenance.

12. Arranging for overall maintenance and repair.

13. Arranging for adequate inspection.

Maintaining the Economical Process

B. Maintaining the economical process is achieved (after examining the process in actual operation) by:

1. Introducing time and motion studies to eliminate unnecessary operator motions.

2. Eliminating or combining operations, if possible. This includes material handling, cutting tool, jig and fixture, and machine tool operations.

3. Introducing automated equipment or automated attachments to eliminate operations poorly controlled by human performance, and vice versa, depending on costs. This includes routine handling operations and inspection operations.

4. Conducting cost analyses to see that costs are close to those estimated in the planning stage.

5. Checking auxiliary operations, such as maintenance, inspection, and tool storage, to see that they are performing efficiently.

6. Standardizing where possible. This includes both the product and production equipment, especially that equipment which is subject to rapid wear.

7. Meeting all safety requirements.

In addition, reports from sources in the field (such as salesmen and distributors) should be studied to assure that the product's demand, its quality and quantity, and inspection methods are adequate. The tool engineer plays a leading role in most of the steps listed. Even in those operations which are not a part of his duties he still has interest because they overlap into his area of responsibility.

CHAPTER SIX

Processing Details

Previous chapters have explored the components of a manufacturing process on a relatively broad scale. This chapter will enter into a more detailed discussion, covering the fundamentals of a tool layout, quality control, and the forms used to convey information.

TOOL LAYOUT

Before a tool layout can be developed a number of problems must be resolved. In fact, the layout is greatly dependent on the solutions to these problems. First of all, the product must be studied closely to determine the best process to manufacture it. Next the tooling program must be established. The quality and quantity of the product, the lot size, the time allowed for manufacture, the process' relationship to the overall scheme of plant production—these problems and others of a similar nature must be resolved before the tool engineer can develop his tool layout.

When the machine equipment and other tools have been selected and the process is definitely identified, the tool engineer is ready to begin specifying the number and kinds of operations to be performed, and the additional tooling necessary for complete machining of the product.

A Turret Lathe Layout

Fig. 1 shows a detailed drawing of a steering clutch hub for a tractor. The part is an iron casting that must be machined to the tolerances indicated on the drawing. Figs. 2 and 3 present a typical tool layout for the casting. The machine is a turret lathe.

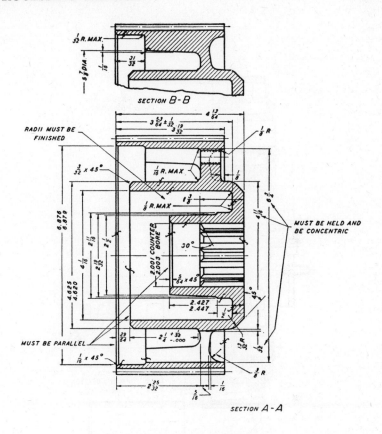

Fig. 1. Detail of a steering-clutch hub.

The first problem is designing a toolholder to hold and position the part for machining. Since the casting's shape is unusual, the tool engineer or tool designer decides to design special jaws that will mount on the master jaws of the lathe's chuck. Tools for the various positions and operations shown in Figs. 2 and 3 are designed in accordance with the machining to be done, as specified by the following steps:

First position. The tooling consists of a single-point boring bar which roughs and counterbores the center hole and rough-faces surfaces *C* and *D* in Fig. 2 on the inner surface of the casting. A specially-designed tool (shown in the figure) rough-turns surface *A*, and another special tool rough-turns surface *B*. The bar supporting this

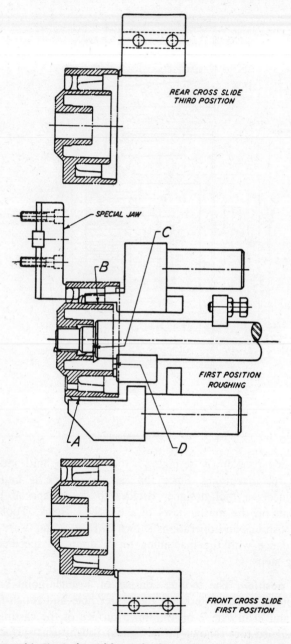

REAR CROSS SLIDE
THIRD POSITION

SPECIAL JAW

C

B

FIRST POSITION
ROUGHING

A

D

FRONT CROSS SLIDE
FIRST POSITION

Fig. 2. Here and in Fig. 3, the tool layout for five positions on a turret lathe is shown.

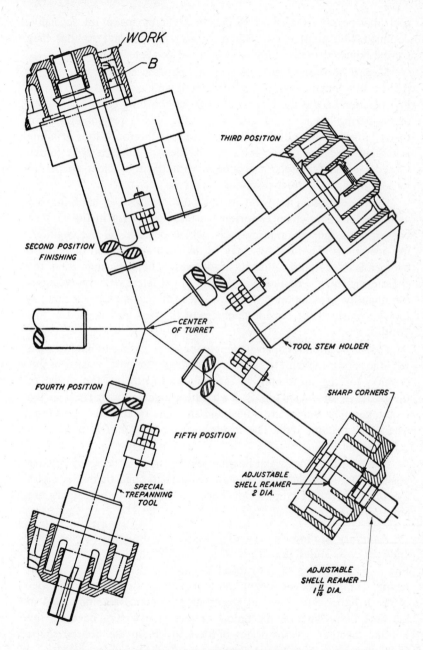

WORK

B

THIRD POSITION

SECOND POSITION
FINISHING

CENTER
OF TURRET

TOOL STEM HOLDER

FOURTH POSITION

SHARP CORNERS

FIFTH POSITION

SPECIAL
TREPANNING
TOOL

ADJUSTABLE
SHELL REAMER
2 DIA.

ADJUSTABLE
SHELL REAMER
$1\frac{11}{16}$ DIA.

Fig. 3. This complete setup is for machining the part shown in Fig. 1.

tool may be set to the correct depth of cut by means of specially-designed adjustable stops. The tool bits are designed so that they can be adjusted individually to obtain the correct dimensions.

Second position. The tooling in this position consists of a single-point boring bar (shown in Fig. 3), a tool similar to that used in the first position except the bits are set for the finishing cuts. The design of the boring bar is simple and inexpensive and is recommended for turret lathe tooling, although the resetting of the tools after grinding is difficult because of the bar's special design. Surface *B* is finish-turned. Adjustable stops are integral with the toolholder to permit its setting in the correct position.

Third position. The turret in this position employs a boring bar with tool bits that chamfer various surfaces as shown in Fig. 3. The bar supports four chamfering tools, which perform all the chamfering operations. The tool bits may be adjusted and locked in position by means of suitable adjustment devices. The bar supporting the chamfering tools is designed according to the latest recommendations for quantity production on turret lathes, and is highly efficient. A tool for finishing the outside diameter of the part also is used in this position.

Fourth position. A special trepanning or recessing toolholder that will not permit the cutter blade to cut through the part, is used in this position for the machining of the bottom section on the inside of the parts, as shown in Fig. 3. Two cutter blades are inserted in the toolholder. The blades are adjustable and may be reground and reset when they become dull. The inside recess of the part is finished in this position.

Fifth position. A special floating reamer arbor is designed for this position to permit the multiple flute reamers to align themselves with the previously bored holes, as shown in Fig. 3. Both reamers are adjustable and of the shell type.

Auxiliary tooling. Special tool blocks are designed for the front and rear cross slides, which are seen in the first and third positions in Fig. 2. These blocks support tool bits used for the rough- and finish-facing. Tool blocks supporting the tool bits, as used in various types of turret lathes, are designed according to practice recommended in the field of production machining. These blocks may be made by welding together several pieces of steel to obtain the desired shape and form.

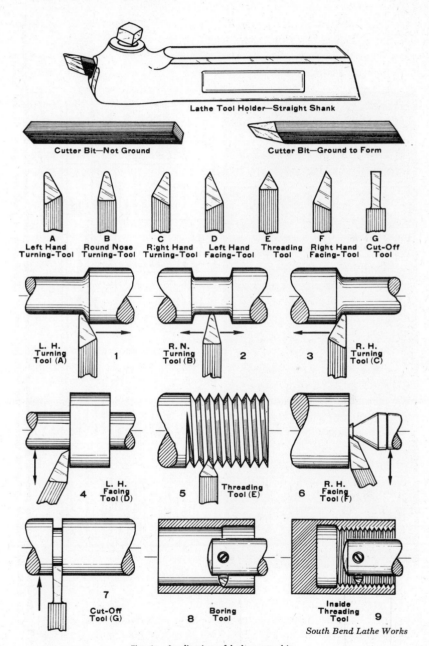

Lathe Tool Holder—Straight Shank

Cutter Bit—Not Ground

Cutter Bit—Ground to Form

A
Left Hand
Turning-Tool

B
Round Nose
Turning-Tool

C
Right Hand
Turning-Tool

D
Left Hand
Facing-Tool

E
Threading
Tool

F
Right Hand
Facing-Tool

G
Cut-Off
Tool

L. H.
Turning
Tool (A)   1

R. N.
Turning
Tool (B)   2

R. H.
Turning
Tool (C)   3

L. H.
Facing
Tool (D)   4

Threading
Tool (E)   5

R. H.
Facing
Tool (F)   6

Cut-Off
Tool (G)   7

Boring
Tool   8

Inside
Threading
Tool   9

South Bend Lathe Works

Fig. 4.   Application of lathe cutter bits.

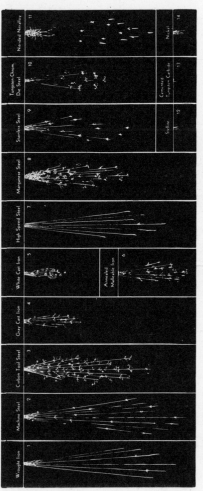

Metal	Volume of Stream	Relative Length of Stream, Inches†	Color of Stream Close to Wheel	Color of Streaks Near End of Stream	Quantity of Sparks	Nature of Sparks
1. Wrought iron	Large	65	Straw	White	Very few	Forked
2. Machine steel	Large	70	White	White	Few	Forked
3. Carbon tool steel	Moderately large	55	White	White	Very many	Fine, repeating
4. Gray cast iron	Small	25	Red	Straw	Many	Fine, repeating
5. White cast iron	Very small	20	Red	Straw	Few	Fine, repeating
6. Annealed mall. iron	Moderate	30	Red	Straw	Many	Fine, repeating
7. High speed steel	Small	60	Red	Straw	Extremely few	Forked
8. Manganese steel	Moderately large	45	White	White	Many	Fine, repeating
9. Stainless steel	Moderate	50	Straw	White	Moderate	Forked
10. Tungsten-chromium die steel	Small	35	Red	Straw*	Many	Fine, repeating*
11. Nitrided Nitralloy	Large (curved)	55	White	White	Moderate	Forked
12. Stellite	Very small	10	Orange	Orange	None	
13. Cemented tungsten carbide	Extremely small	2	Light Orange	Light Orange	None	
14. Nickel	Very small**	10	Orange	Orange	None	
15. Copper, brass, aluminum	None				None	

†Figures obtained with 12" wheel on bench stand and are relative only. Actual length in each instance will vary with grinding wheel, pressure, etc. *Blue-white sparks. **Some wavy streaks.

Norton Co.

Fig. 5.   Characteristics of sparks generated by the grinding of metals. Identification by this means is called "spark testing." It is a convenient test when the chemistry of steel is unknown; however, for complete identification, it does not replace chemical analysis..

The cutter bits are held in the correct position by means of back-up screw blocks which make it possible to adjust the cutter whenever necessary. Suitable means are provided to lock the blocks securely when the proper position is determined.

The toolholder and bars are made of several steel sections welded together, with means provided to adjust and lock the cutter bits in the desired position. The cutting tools used on turret lathes include single-point cutters, drills, reamers, taps, boring tools, and others, each of which must be carefully specified when desired for applicable operations. (See Fig. 4 for various types of lathe cutter bits and their applications.)

Cutters must be ground and set for correct machining. These materials are commonly used in the construction of cutters: carbon tool steel, high-speed tool steel, ceramics, carbides, cemented carbides, and diamonds. The tool engineer must know the qualities of each material and correctly match it to the operation to be performed. (See Fig. 5 for a quick means of identification of fifteen metals used in industry for part components, cutting tools, etc.)

Layout drawings. Figs. 2 and 3 show the positions that the tool engineer, working with the tool designer, develops and details in drawings. These drawings are used by lathe operators in establishing their setup. The figures show the complete setup for machining the casting, although for ease of reading here, tool bit dimensions and surface tolerances are not included.

The positions shown, together with appropriate explanation, constitutes a tool layout drawing. In our case it is a simple layout. Highly flexible transfer machines require a more complex set of plans, although the overall process breaks down into a series of individual operations which can be treated in the same fashion as we did in our example. No matter how complicated the process, the important point to remember is that the tool engineer should prepare layout drawings that are readily understood by the operator, with layouts he can apply in the simplest and most economical manner.

A Vertical Turret Lathe Layout

Another tool layout is shown in Fig. 6. This layout is for the efficient machining of a gear blank on a vertical turret lathe. By combining operations, simple gear blanks may be produced singly or in large lots to good advantage. Combining operations whenever possible economizes in time and tools and produces work of high quality.

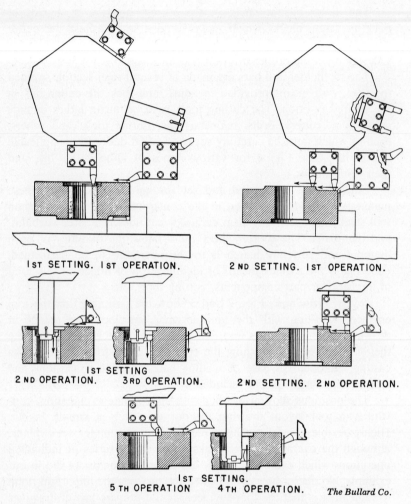

1ST SETTING. 1ST OPERATION.

2ND SETTING. 1ST OPERATION.

2ND OPERATION.

1ST SETTING
3RD OPERATION.

2ND SETTING. 2ND OPERATION.

5TH OPERATION

1ST SETTING.
4TH OPERATION.

The Bullard Co.

Fig. 6. Typical tool layout for machining a gear blank on a vertical turret lathe.

After all operations of the first setting are completed, the machining of the second setting can be begun. Soft jaws, machined in position under chucking tension, hold the part true to center while the outside diameter is finished and the cuts lapped.

QUALITY CONTROL

Inspection, as we have already discussed, employs various methods to compare or "check" a product against accepted specifications or other recognized standards. Since the act of inspecting is usually conducted after the part is complete, inspection in itself does not improve quality. Essentially, inspection is a screening operation that separates acceptable parts from unacceptable parts. To call this quality control is erroneous because, although product quality is maintained, overall economical manufacture may not be the result.

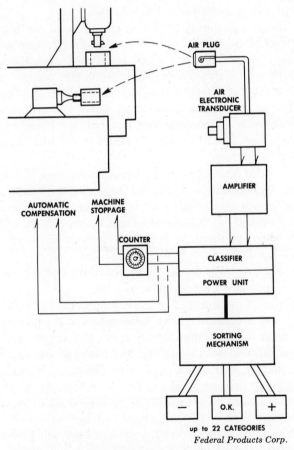

up to 22 CATEGORIES
Federal Products Corp.

Fig. 7. An air-electronic gaging system for control of internal dimensions. The system is arranged to perform sorting, machine-stopping, and tool-compensating functions. The system automatically classifies parts according to their internal diameter, which is taken by an electronically-controlled air plug.

The Purpose of Quality Control

Quality control attempts to assure parts of high quality without a high percentage of rejections due to inspection, and without introducing needless expense in a production installation. The first step is establishing the level of quality. The tool engineer has only an indirect influence here; management, after studying the market, sets the quality level. For the quantity of parts desired and level of quality, the air-electronic system shown in Fig. 7 is warranted. Although an expensive system, it is economical in the long run.

After the manufacturing process is planned and put into operation, the level of quality is maintained by making proper use of the methods for controlling quality which, if accomplished, allow predictions about the product's future quality using that process. In other words, the number of defective parts may be anticipated and corrective action taken to avoid such manufacture later. The accuracy of the prediction depends on the inspection methods, the layout of the frequency chart, and the ability and experience of the tool engineer and quality control engineer.

Predictions of future quality are based on the laws of chance and probability. By carefully inspecting and recording the quality of parts today, the quality that is likely to exist at any future time can be predicted. Although no manufactured article can ever be exactly reproduced, when measured by statistical methods limits are seen to exist which can be controlled. Within these limits reliable predictions can be made, assuming the limits are practical and the measuring instruments themselves are reliable.

Good predictions can lead to improvement in the quality of the product as well as indicating what adjustments in the process are required to maintain the desired quality level. Any actual improvement depends on the skill with which the tool engineer and designer can convert statistical information into better designs. This information may or may not indicate known causes for unacceptable parts. Unknown causes usually do not remain so for long. A recurring condition of unacceptable parts means a significant change has occurred in the existing production process, which sooner or later will be discovered and corrected.

Quality control, regularly and skilfully practiced, can result in maximum production, economy, and quality under given conditions of production.

Methods for Controlling Quality

Although a number of methods exist for controlling quality, they divide into three common categories:

1. Initial part and rechecking method.
2. Frequency-chart method.
3. Sampling method.

Each of these methods is best suited for particular applications. The first-named is useful where production runs are short and products differ from run to run; also, control features must be positive and unvarying. The second method is better for very long runs, or where equipment is used that controls the quality desired, such as an automatic screw machine or various types of transfer machines. The sampling method is valuable where assembly line personnel exercise a relatively large influence on the product, since successive samplings tend to place the responsibility for quality on line personnel.

Initial part and rechecking method. This method calls for the inspection of one or more parts at the beginning of a run to find out if the overall process and individual machine setups have been properly made. An inspector—and occasionally the tool engineer—closely examines these initial parts. From his examination the inspector can decide whether or not the line personnel possess the proper tools and gages, understand their duties, and have other necessary information to assure the processing of parts that meet specifications.

The inspector examines enough parts to satisfy himself of a representative sampling. All parts are inspected 100% and parts not meeting the specifications are rejected. A thorough examination will include checking the working area and duties of each member of the assembly line, the small tools and gages each member uses, his knowledge of the operations he must perform. Inspecting the part means seeing that its material meets specifications as to hardness, composition, and finish; that its dimensions are correct; that its appearance conforms to good workmanship.

Checking dimensions will determine how close to the desired dimension the parts are being produced. Excessive deviation indicates the setup should be adjusted until an average number of parts will be satisfactorily near the desired dimension. Acceptable variations from the desired dimension must fall within established tolerance figures.

Inspection procedures. If the initial inspection shows the parts are being processed with adequate quality, the inspector will prepare tags which identify the part, operation, and nature of the inspection, and attach them to the machines comprising the process.

Rechecking after the initial part inspection is necessary if the tools, especially the cutting tools, are subject to rapid wear and if the part's tolerances are very close. The inspector should begin his inspection by examining the work areas, the machines, and the operators' motions and general alertness while the process is in actual operation. He should note if the tools performing the operation are functioning smoothly and according to specifications. He

Mechanical Handling Systems, Inc.

Fig. 8. Conveyorized water testing of compressor and coils for leaks.

should inspect the process to see that the parts are being handled correctly so there is no chance of damaging them.

Next the inspector should examine enough parts to assure a representative sample. All the parts he inspects should be freshly processed and not from a stockpile. Sometimes merely comparing parts just processed with parts from the initial inspection is adequate; sometimes, especially if the part has close tolerances, a detailed inspection must be made. The water method depicted in Fig. 8 is a sure, positive means of testing compressors and coils.

Satisfactory, unsatisfactory operations. A satisfactory operation means the inspector can indicate on the inspection tag the number of parts processed since the initial part inspection or the last recheck; he initials the tag to show his approval. Approved parts should be removed from the general working area to avoid being mixed in with subsequent rejects.

An unsatisfactory operation means the inspector will show "rejected" on the inspection tag and notify the foreman that the process is producing defective parts. Cutting tools must be resharpened, operators given further instruction, the process adjusted, or whatever is necessary to correct the condition which is producing an excessive number of defective parts. During this reconditioning time, the tag is kept at the inspector's station and when satisfactory parts are again produced, the inspector marks up the tag as he would for the initial part inspection.

With the completion of a run, an inspection of the last part is made, which is conducted in the same way as the initial inspection. Here the purpose is to determine the extent of wear and tear of the equipment and tools. The inspector notes the general condition on the tag and also whether the last part was approved or rejected, and why.

Frequency-chart method. This method, also called the control-chart method, utilizes statistics to predict future product quality and to pinpoint excessive dispersion of current data.

In the laying out of a chart, the first step is the gathering of well-planned data. The chart is developed on the theory that parts are inspected according to variations from the desired dimension, so that the characteristic to be controlled is evaluated through measurable means and on a continuous scale.

The desired measurements of parts produced in a process under study are arranged in groups. Each group consists of measurements

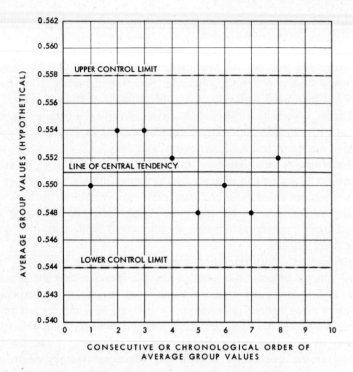

Fig. 9. A graph for average. The order of values may be expressed on a time base. The bottom numbers, for example, could be time in minutes counted from a beginning reference time.

of a few parts that have been processed either in consecutive or chronological order. Two values are calculated for each group: (1) the group average, and (2) the group range, or the difference between the largest and smallest measurements in each group. These values are plotted on the *graph for average* and the *graph for range,* as shown in Figs. 9 and 10.

On the graph for average, the mean average for all groups is plotted. Using applicable tables, control limits are placed at a specified distance on both sides of this near average. Any average value of any group falling outside these limits is said to be "out of control." Whenever "out of control" values occur, an investigation is made to learn why and, if feasible, corrective action is taken.

Quality predictions. Predictions can be made as to future quality if the plotted values remain almost wholly within the upper and lower specification limits. In general, however, we can say that the higher

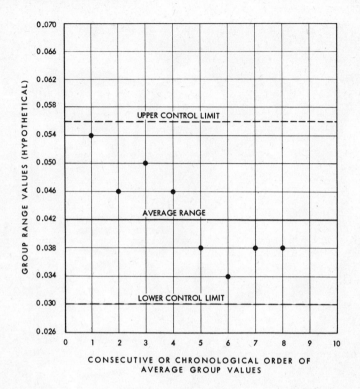

Fig. 10. A graph for range.

the quality desired, the less likely will frequency charts give accurate predictions. The main reason is that in plotting data, more values will fall outside the chart's limits because the limits are narrower.

The statistical approach to quality control is a wide and complex field requiring a firm grasp of the principles of statistics. The tool engineer should understand these principles, although he is not expected to be a mathematician. He works closely with the quality engineer to establish and maintain a desired level of quality.

Sampling method. The third method of quality control is a combination of the initial inspection and frequency-chart method. It is not comparable to a 100% detail inspection, which merely identifies and separates parts according to whether or not they meet the specifications.

A sampling inspection is really a judging operation. It is conducted by run or lot and is used to evaluate part quality so that a

Magnaflux Corp.

Fig. 11. An inspection unit set up for inspecting connecting rods by the magnaflux method. Each rod shown represents a portion of a sample taken from one lot.

decision may be reached—either acceptance or rejection of the lot.

A sampling plan must be efficient and accurate. Very small samples are economical but inaccurate. Very large samples are accurate but uneconomical. Between these extremes lies the best sampling plan.

Sample size, types. In judging lot quality, the size of a sample determines almost conclusively the accuracy of the sampling. To this extent, samplings expressed as a percentage of a lot are misleading. A fifteen percent sampling is accurate for a large lot but is inaccurate for a small lot. A sample of 100 parts reveals almost as much to the experienced tool engineer in a lot of 10,000 parts as in one of 1,000.

There are several different types of sampling plans. Basically, a sample of a predetermined number is taken from a lot of adequate size. The entire lot is either accepted or rejected depending upon the number of rejected parts in the sample. If no decision can be reached in one sample, two or more samples are taken until a definite decision can be made. Theoretically, samples can be taken until every part has been inspected. Fig. 11 shows a sampling of connecting rods being inspected.

Graph of sampling plan. For any normal operation a graph as shown in Fig. 12 can be developed on which total samples can be plotted. The graph's limits are calculated on the basis of acceptable and unacceptable quality, the risk of rejecting a good lot or accepting a bad lot, and other conditions that apply to a particular process.

Any total sampling of S defective parts that lies above the upper line means the lot is rejected. Any total sampling of S defective parts

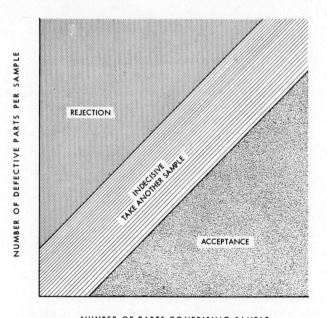

NUMBER OF PARTS COMPRISING SAMPLE

Fig. 12. A sampling plan of inspection.

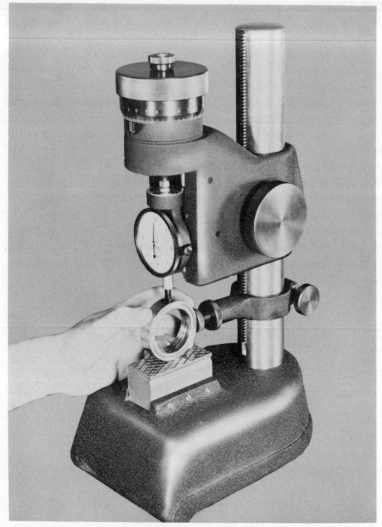

Federal Products Corp.

Fig. 13.   A dial indicator gage for checking diameters.

that falls below the lower line means the lot is accepted. Any sampling of S defective parts that falls between the lines means another sample must be taken, or the lot accepted or rejected depending on past experience with that process. Each sample is relatively small and is taken in succession. After inspection a total sample is calculated, which indicates the total number of rejected parts in the sample. The number of rejected or defective parts is plotted on the graph.

Quality Control Instruments

The dial indicator gage shown in Fig. 13 is a typical quality control instrument. The indicator is a complete unit and can be mounted singly, or several instruments may be located so as to contact the part at the points to be gaged, permitting inspection of all dimensions at the same time, as shown in Fig. 14.

Other types of gaging devices for checking a multitude of measurements are comparators, air gages, electric gages, and combination gages. The electric gage assembled in a head may be mounted on a production machine, and arranged to stop the machine automatically when the work has been brought to size. The light unit of the gage or indicator may be located directly on the machine, such as a production grinder, or when desired, remotely. When grinding has

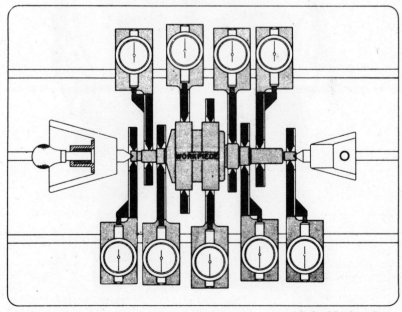

Federal Products Corp.

Fig. 14. Nine dial indicators like the one in Fig. 13 set up for simultaneous checking of rotor shaft diameters.

proceeded far enough to bring the work within tolerance, the grinding machine is stopped automatically. More complex cycles may also be accomplished with this machine.

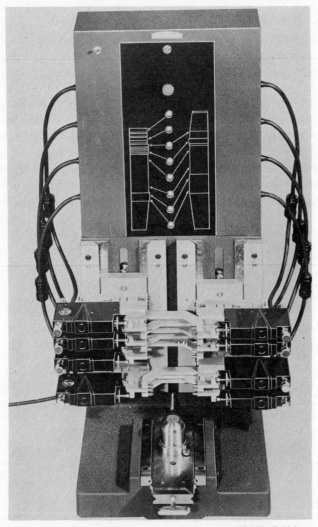

The Sheffield Corp.

Fig. 15. Combination gage for simultaneously checking different dimensions on a part. It consists of electric gage heads which actuate the panel lights if any of the dimensions are out of size.

A multiple or combination gage, shown in Fig. 15, measures a number of critical dimensions simultaneously. It is a combination gage using several electric gage heads to check dimensions. A master signal light may be used to integrate all the individual lights so that the inspector need watch only it to determine if all dimensions are within tolerance. At the master light's warning, the individual signals are examined in order that the incorrect dimensions may be located. In the figure, eight dimensions of a shell body may be inspected simultaneously.

FORMS USED TO CONVEY INFORMATION

Besides the actual production plans, the methods used in a manufacturing process to communicate and record information are through operation sheets, bills of material, instruction sheets, and route sheets. The production plans, which we will not investigate here, are the detail plans that specify the design of the product, the process, and in some cases the production equipment. To insure clarity and ease of understanding, methods of communication must conform to certain specifications and styles. With this in mind, we will investigate the layout and organization of the forms mentioned in sentence one.

Operation Sheets

Operation sheets serve as a visual record of all phases of a manufacturing process. No operation, no matter how minor, should go unrecorded, even if the operation requires no scheduling or integrating into the body of the process. Operation sheets are sometimes called *process sheets, planning operation sheets,* or *work sheets.* (See Fig. 16.)

Sheets of this nature have the main purpose of adequately describing what is to be done in the process. Some will be more complicated than others, some will contain spaces for comparatively trivial information, but a majority will require certain similar information. For a typical process a general layout will include spaces for these headings:

1. Part name and number, including component parts and subassemblies.
2. Lot and operation number.
3. Production equipment, its class, type, and serial number.

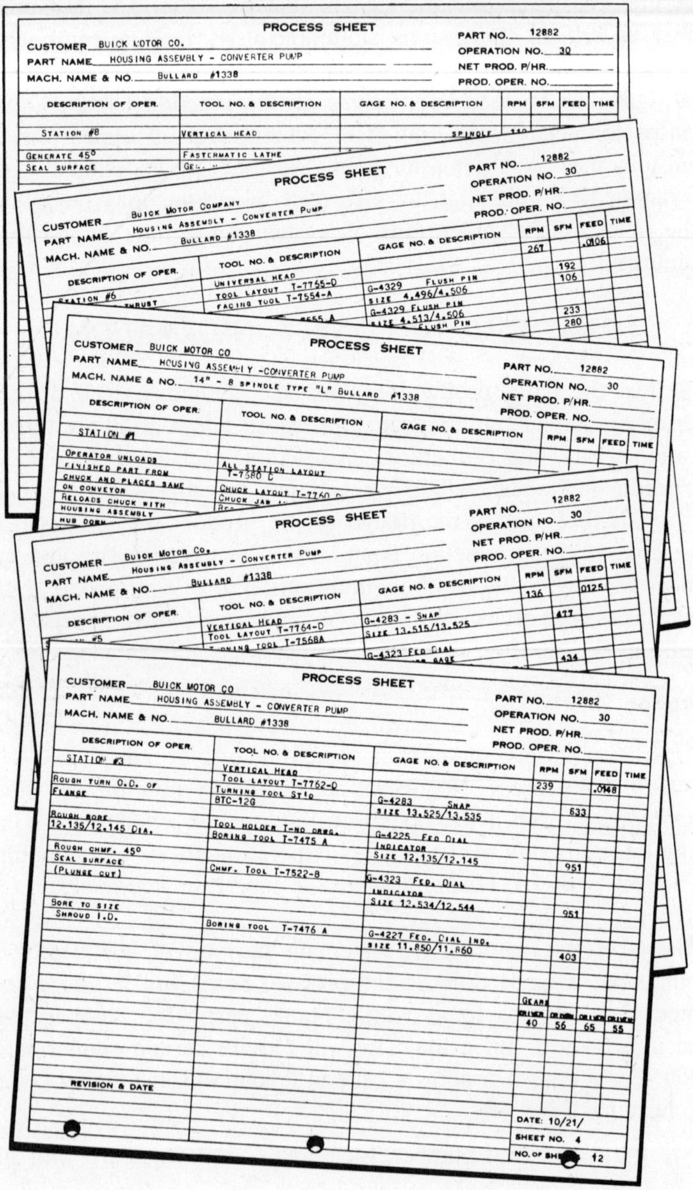

PROCESS SHEET

CUSTOMER __BUICK MOTOR CO.__
PART NAME __HOUSING ASSEMBLY - CONVERTER PUMP__
MACH. NAME & NO. __BULLARD #1338__

PART NO. __12882__
OPERATION NO. __30__
NET PROD. P/HR. __-__
PROD. OPER. NO. __

DESCRIPTION OF OPER.	TOOL NO. & DESCRIPTION	GAGE NO. & DESCRIPTION	RPM	SFM	FEED	TIME
STATION #8	VERTICAL HEAD	SPINDLE				
GENERATE 45°	FASTERMATIC LATHE					
SEAL SURFACE	GE					

PROCESS SHEET

CUSTOMER __BUICK MOTOR COMPANY__
PART NAME __HOUSING ASSEMBLY - CONVERTER PUMP__
MACH. NAME & NO. __BULLARD #1338__

PART NO. __12882__
OPERATION NO. __30__
NET PROD. P/HR. __
PROD. OPER. NO. __

DESCRIPTION OF OPER.	TOOL NO. & DESCRIPTION	GAGE NO. & DESCRIPTION	RPM	SFM	FEED	TIME
	UNIVERSAL HEAD		267		.0106	
	TOOL LAYOUT T-7755-D	G-4329 FLUSH PIN		192		
	FACING TOOL T-7554-A	SIZE 4.496/4.506		106		
STATION #6 THRUST	7555 A	G-4329 FLUSH PIN		233		
		SIZE 4.513/4.506		280		
		FLUSH PIN				

PROCESS SHEET

CUSTOMER __BUICK MOTOR CO__
PART NAME __HOUSING ASSEMBLY -CONVERTER PUMP__
MACH. NAME & NO. __14" - 8 SPINDLE TYPE "L" BULLARD #1338__

PART NO. __12882__
OPERATION NO. __30__
NET PROD. P/HR. __
PROD. OPER. NO. __

DESCRIPTION OF OPER.	TOOL NO. & DESCRIPTION	GAGE NO. & DESCRIPTION	RPM	SFM	FEED	TIME
STATION #7						
OPERATOR UNLOADS FINISHED PART FROM	ALL STATION LAYOUT T-7586 C					
CHUCK AND PLACES SAME ON CONVEYOR	CHUCK LAYOUT T-7740 D					
RELOADS CHUCK WITH	CHUCK JAW					
HOUSING ASSEMBLY HUB DOWN	Re					

PROCESS SHEET

CUSTOMER __BUICK MOTOR CO.__
PART NAME __HOUSING ASSEMBLY - CONVERTER PUMP__
MACH. NAME & NO. __BULLARD #1338__

PART NO. __12882__
OPERATION NO. __30__
NET PROD. P/HR. __
PROD. OPER. NO. __

DESCRIPTION OF OPER.	TOOL NO. & DESCRIPTION	GAGE NO. & DESCRIPTION	RPM	SFM	FEED	TIME
STATION #5	VERTICAL HEAD	G-4283 - SNAP	136		.0125	
	TOOL LAYOUT T-7764-D	SIZE 13.515/13.525		477		
	BONING TOOL T-7568A	G-4323 FED DIAL				
		GAGE		434		

PROCESS SHEET

CUSTOMER __BUICK MOTOR CO__
PART NAME __HOUSING ASSEMBLY - CONVERTER PUMP__
MACH. NAME & NO. __BULLARD #1338__

PART NO. __12882__
OPERATION NO. __30__
NET PROD. P/HR. __
PROD. OPER. NO. __

DESCRIPTION OF OPER.	TOOL NO. & DESCRIPTION	GAGE NO. & DESCRIPTION	RPM	SFM	FEED	TIME
STATION #3	VERTICAL HEAD		239		.0148	
ROUGH TURN O.D. OF FLANGE	TOOL LAYOUT T-7762-D	G-4283 SNAP		633		
	TURNING TOOL STYD BTC-12G	SIZE 13.525/13.535				
ROUGH BORE 12.135/12.145 DIA.	TOOL HOLDER T-NO DRWG.	G-4225 FED DIAL INDICATOR				
	BORING TOOL T-7475 A	SIZE 12.135/12.145		951		
ROUGH CHMF. 45° SEAL SURFACE	CHMF. TOOL T-7522-B	G-4323 FED. DIAL INDICATOR				
(PLUNGE CUT)		SIZE 12.534/12.544		951		
BORE TO SIZE SHROUD I.D.	BORING TOOL T-7476 A	G-4227 FED. DIAL IND. SIZE 11.850/11.860		403		

GEAR			
DRIVER	DRIVEN	DRIVEN	DRIVER
40	56	65	55

REVISION & DATE

DATE: 10/21/
SHEET NO. 4
NO. OF SHEET 12

Fig. 16. Typical operation sheets. Shown are sheets 3, 4, 6, 7, and 9 of twelve sheets necessary for operation 30 on part number 12882.

4. Time expended, including setup and machine time.
5. Material specifications, including stock size.
6. Brief description of operation, including references to detail plans.
7. Dates, including beginning and completion dates.
8. Process and part prices.

The headings. The part name and number links the part with the operation sheet; many companies file their sheets by part number. Recording the lot number is important when reference must be made to past quality. The operation numbers serve to arrange the operations according to the actual order in the process. Production equipment identification is valuable in developing quality, economy, maintenance, and other controllable data for specific equipment. Time-per-part entries are especially valuable in cost computations.

The material specifications furnish a convenient record of the raw material—its grade, type, and quantity—of the part, and knowing the stock size allows the purchase of stock material in proper quantities. A description of the operation is merely naming the machining operation, including sizes, number of cuts, dimensions and tolerances.

The beginning and completion dates provide useful historical and reference data. When a revision is made in a product, in the process, or in production equipment, a new operation sheet is written up and the old one marked "obsolete" and filed. At any future time these obsolete sheets offer a satisfactory record of the operation. Process and part prices are usually expressed as rates applied to the part, machine, or process and are vital to the cost accountant.

The body. The arrangement of the body of the operation sheet, as distinct from its headings, is fairly standard. The body consists of space for the following items:

1. Operation number and description.
2. Department or shop in which the operation is performed.
3. Name and type of equipment used, its setup time, production rate, and identifying number.
4. Auxiliary tools and gages, their sizes, serial numbers, and functions.

Methods for numbering operations are many. Some plants use a sequence of numbers beginning with 1; others begin with 10, following with 20, 30, 40, etc., so that operations may be added later without upsetting the sequence. Some plants use codes to identify their operations. For example, the first digit in operation 347 may stand for a drilling operation, the second digit for the drill number, the third for the particular type of drilling operation. Coded systems permit operations to be readily identified by numbers only.

Although concise, the operation description must be clearly and accurately stated so that misunderstandings are avoided. The descriptions shown in Fig. 16 illustrate how clarity is achieved without wasting space. The three main facts that must be shown in any description are: (1) the name of the machine operation, (2) the dimensions applying to the operation, and (3) the number of cuts in each operation.

The department or shop where the operation is to be performed is always indicated for each operation. In the preparation of route sheets, the applicable machine serial number for the operation is used. Some departments may have their own numbering system for their machines, so the department itself must be indicated to insure that the correct machine is specified. Since overhead rates vary between departments, the cost accountant must know the applicable department or shop for each operation.

Value of operation sheets. A good operation sheet lists the workholding, hand, and inspection tools, describing them and indicating the quantities needed. Both standard and specially-designed tools should be adequately described. A complete and accurate listing of auxiliary tools provides valuable information to the cost estimator, the department supervisor, and tool crib attendant as well as the tool engineer.

The value of complete, well-planned operation sheets cannot be over-estimated. They are extremely useful for reference, for on-the-job applications, for computing costs, for scheduling, for future planning, and for the drawing up of bills of material, instruction sheets, and route sheets. Operation sheets are an integral part of the tool engineer's communications equipment.

Bills of Material

A bill of material is simply an organized listing of all the components that comprise an assembled product and is usually prepared by the product designer. Duplicate bills are supplied those departments which make effective use of them in their routine. The cost department uses a bill of material as a check list in computing costs; the purchasing department uses it to order parts; the stock room to

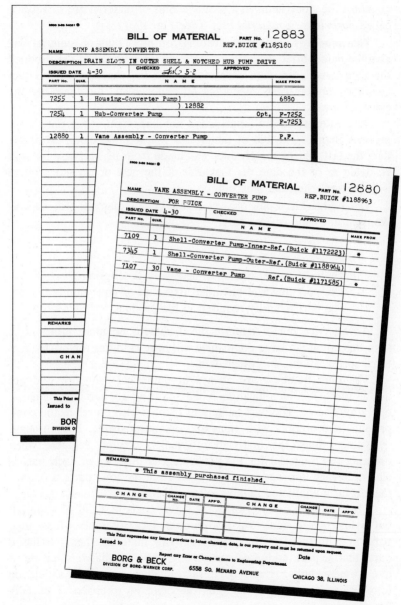

Fig. 17. Typical bills of material. Since these bills are abbreviated, item numbers are not necessary.

assemble the stock items in a product. Bills of material are sometimes called *parts lists* or *material lists*. (See Fig. 17.)

The headings. The main headings on most bills of material will give the name, brief description, and number assigned to the product; the date issued, the date superseded, and the sheet number. Other headings may be used, depending on plant policy, but these are the essential ones.

The date issued and superseded are important when parts of a product change. The bill of material is marked "obsolete" as of the date the last unit of the product was made from it. The new bill will be dated as of the date the first unit of the new or revised product is processed using the new bill.

The body. The body of a standard bill of material will be columnized and have spaces for:

1. The item number.
2. The part number.
3. The part name, including necessary descriptions.
4. The part material identified by name or code number.
5. The part quantity required in the product.

An effective bill of material need contain no more information than this, although large companies will have columns for prices, material specifications, and other data.

The item numbers are always in numerical sequence and are useful for quick identification when referring to parts in plans or operation sheets. The part name and number also correlate the components of a product with plans and operation sheets. The purchase department finds the material information column valuable when ordering raw material for the product. The quantity of each part is also necessary in ordering and in computing the total parts to manufacture for a stipulated number of assemblies.

There is no definite priority for listing parts in a bill of material, but a logical sequence will list purchased subassemblies first, then parts manufactured in the plant from raw material, then purchased parts that require additional processing, then purchased stock items like washers, bolts, rivets. Whatever sequence is used, it should be followed consistently for all bills the company prepares, especially for one product.

Bills of material are vital records in any production venture. They must be assembled accurately and kept up to date. Any errors should be promptly corrected since the bills are used by many departments where mistakes may be reflected disastrously. Original bills of material are usually filed in a vault for security purposes.

Instruction Sheets

Although maintenance men and other production personnel may require instructions concerning their jobs, detail instruction sheets are normally prepared only for on-the-the line equipment operators. A typical instruction sheet will contain:

1. A description of each step the operator must perform in a machine operation, including dimensions and tolerances he must work to.
2. The weighted time values estimated for each step.
3. A list of tools necessary to perform the operation.
4. A drawing of the part, showing the machined surfaces.
5. Identification data, such as part name and number, machine number, order number, etc.

An instruction sheet should provide that the best machine methods, tool layout, and operator motions are used. Instruction sheets should be prepared by personnel experienced in the operation being performed; they must also have experience in time and motion principles. Instruction sheets are normally posted near the operator's work station and sometimes contain safety instructions also.

Company usage. Some companies prefer not to use instruction sheets because of the expense of maintaining them. The operator is entrusted to devise his own machining procedure or the foreman may show him. Some companies use special "demonstrators" to instruct operators in new operations, although this method may not be successful if the demonstrators are skilled operators but cannot organize and impart their knowledge effectively.

For complex operations some companies utilize movies to instruct their operators. A good movie will have an operator at the machine performing while the narrator explains his functions. Using movies is more effective if the operators are allowed to follow the operation at their machine while the operator in the movie demonstrates. Movies are used mostly in instructing inexperienced operators. Operations requiring movies are usually of long duration, although complex, short-lived operations can be put on film if the expense is not prohibitive.

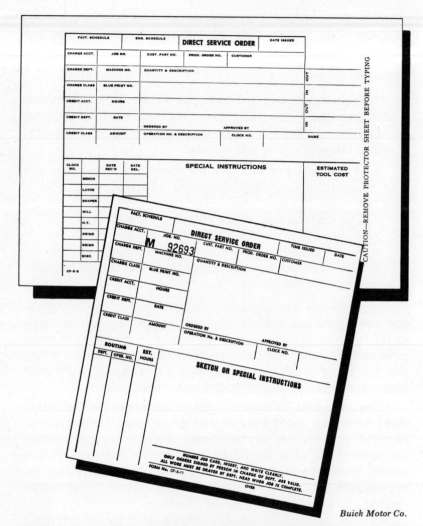

Fig. 18. Typical route sheet blanks. Several copies of each order are made for distribution to various departments.

The amount of instruction companies provide their machine operators depends on the complexity of the operation, the cost of instruction, and the influence expense has on the overall cost. Obviously a complicated operation will require the issue of extensive instructions. On the other hand, extensive instructions are not warranted if their cost cannot be recovered through the savings in labor they will give. In other words, instruction material can be overstressed as well as understressed. Using detail instruction sheets offers a good compromise between these extremes.

Route Sheets

A route sheet is primarily a form that indicates where materials, parts, and subassemblies of a product go for successive processing operations. It is especially valuable in processes that consist of machining and assembling numerous parts, such as in the manufacture of automobiles, typewriters, or computing machines. Strictly speaking, the necessity for routing is eliminated in products which require few machining and assembling operations, and in plants with a high degree of automatic handling. Fig. 18 shows typical route sheets.

A typical route sheet will contain this information:

1. Order number and other identifying data.
2. Sequence of operations, numbered and described.
3. Machines and tooling necessary to process the product.
4. Beginning, completion, and delivery dates.
5. Weighted time values estimated for each operation.
6. Section or department assigned to each operation.

Typical plant routing. In most plants a copy of the route sheet accompanies the material, parts, or subassemblies, actually routing them from point to point through the process. When the routing is completed an inspector or foreman usually initials the route sheet, attesting to the quality and quantity of the sheet's contents. The sheet is then returned to the production department.

In a complex manufacturing process a well-planned route sheet is essential in promoting a smooth flow of work. However, it should never become a substitute to laying out the process itself smoothly. A route sheet cluttered with figures and specifications is doubtlessly acting as an operations sheet and process plan in addition to its intended purpose.

CHAPTER SEVEN

Developing the Process

In this chapter we are going to attempt a presentation of the major problems facing the tool engineer from the moment he receives the product designer's plans until he resolves those problems, which will be shown by a manufacturing process capable of processing the designer's product. The plans the designer submits consist of notations, configurations, and a mass of data that forms a language of its own. The tool engineer and others involved in production must be able to read and interpret these plans. In fact, they must be able to "see" the finished product while it is still in plan form.

FORMING THE OPERATIONS

What all must be "seen" by the plan interpreter? Probably the first thing he looks for are the surfaces to be machined. What problems the various geometric shapes of the surfaces present, the degree of finish desired, the tolerances, the dimensions between surfaces—between plane surfaces, curved surfaces, rough and finished surfaces. The plan interpreter expects all these facts to be indicated on the plans; if they are not, he is justified in querying the product designer.

Next, the geometric relationships are studied more closely. Similarities among surfaces, parallelism, concentricity, roundness, squareness are noted. The allowable limits are noted, the number of holes, their sizes, the number and sizes of fillets, external diameters, etc., are noted. When these are firmly in mind, the experienced reader of plans checks for the kinds of materials and their physical properties. With metals he wants to know about hardness, malleability, ductility, general toughness, and other traits which determine the surface treatment that can properly be made, including plating and painting.

Next, the plans are inspected to determine the actual machine operations that must be made. The problem is not so much one of selection as that of orderly sequence. What operations can be combined, what operations can be integrated and performed simultaneously, what

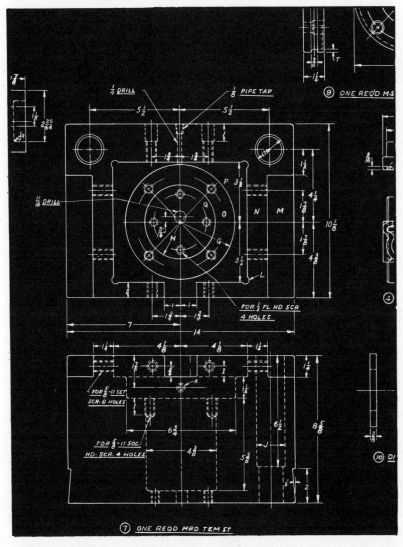

Fig. 1. This is a portion of a modern operation drawing. Notice the drawing is in blueprint form.

operations can be eliminated altogether? Is there any chance of improving the design so that the product can be processed with less expense? What refinements will have to be made, such as burring, chamfering, and polishing? After these questions have been answered, the final question is: what is the best sequence of the remaining operations?

When the problem of operations and their proper sequence is resolved, the last step is to complete the translation of the product designer's plans by preparing operation sheets, bills of material, instruction sheets, route sheets, and any other information necessary to establish the process (see the chapter on Processing Details). Machine equipment and material handling equipment are selected and installed, material for the product ordered, a plant layout made, assembly personnel hired and trained. When these preparatory operations are completed, the processing is ready to begin. How well the tool engineer and his associates have translated the designer's plans into reality will now become evident.

Drawings and Specifications

The plans the product designer develops are called *operation drawings*. They are organized and laid out according to long-standing procedures for preparing plans and usually appear in blueprint form. A great majority of the information the designer sets down conforms to written specifications. These specifications may come from the American Standards Association, the American Institute of Mechanical Engineers, or from other trade associations intent on assuring conformity within their field.

Associations of this nature, including various government agencies, devote much time and expense to producing accurate, complete, and practical specifications, which in most cases are wholly reliable. This mass of reliable information serves as the bridge between the designer on the one side and the tool engineer on the other. The designer develops certain information that conforms to certain specifications, and records this information on the plans. When the tool engineer or anyone else connected with production reads the plans he is aware of this conformity to specifications. Many questions about the design he may have can probably be resolved by consulting the appropriate specifications.

An investigation of operation drawings and specifications is outside the scope of this book. The important point to remember is the great reduction in misunderstandings that result when good drawings

GEAR NOMENCLATURE

4.03 The *Root Cylinder* is the imaginary cylinder tangent to the bottoms of the tooth spaces in a cylindrical gear. (See Fig. 24.)

4.04 The *Face Cone* of a bevel gear contains the tops of the teeth. (See Fig. 25.)

4.05 The *Root Cone* of a bevel gear is an imaginary cone tangent to the bottoms of the tooth spaces. (See Fig. 25.)

4.06 The *Back Cone* of a bevel gear is at the outer ends of the teeth, with its elements perpendicular to those of the pitch cone. The surface of the gear blank at the outer ends of the teeth is customarily formed to such a back cone. (See Fig. 25.)

4.07 The *Front Cone* of a bevel gear is at the inner ends of the teeth, with its elements perpendicular to those of the pitch cone. The surface of the gear blank at the inner ends of the teeth is customarily formed to such a front cone, but sometimes may be a plane on a pinion or a cylinder in a nearly flat gear. (See Fig. 25.)

4.08 The *Crown Circle* in a bevel gear is the circle of intersection of the back cone and face cone. (See Fig. 25.)

GROUP 5   PRINCIPAL PLANES

5.01 The *Axial Plane* of a pair of gears is the plane that contains the two axes. In a single gear, an axial plane may be any plane containing the axis and a given point. (See Fig. 26.)

5.02 The *Pitch Plane* of a pair of gears is the plane perpendicular to the axial plane and tangent to the pitch surfaces. A pitch plane in an individual gear may be any plane tangent to its pitch surface. The pitch plane of a rack or crown gear is the pitch surface. (See Fig. 26.)

5.03 A *Plane of Rotation* is any plane perpendicular to a gear axis. (See Fig. 27.)

5.04 A *Transverse Plane* is perpendicular to the axial plane and to the pitch plane. In gears with parallel axes, the transverse plane and plane of rotation coincide. (See Figs. 26 and 27.)

5.05 A *Tangent Plane* is tangent to the tooth surfaces at a point or line of contact. (See Figs. 28 and 38.)

5.06 A *Normal Plane* is in general normal to a tooth surface at a pitch point, and perpendicular to the pitch plane. In a helical rack, a normal plane is normal to all the teeth it intersects. In a helical gear, however, a plane can be normal to only one tooth at a point lying in the plane surface. At such a point, the *normal plane* contains the line normal to the tooth surface and is normal to the pitch surface. (See Fig. 28.)

Important positions of a *normal plane* in tooth measurement and tool design in helical teeth and worm threads are:
   (a) the plane normal to the pitch helix at side of tooth,
   (b) the plane normal to the pitch helix at center of tooth,
   (c) the plane normal to the pitch helix at center of space between two teeth.
In a spiral bevel gear, one of the positions of a *normal plane* is at a mean point and the plane is normal to the tooth trace 7.20.

5.07 The *Principal Reference Planes* are a pitch plane, axial plane, and transverse plane, all intersecting at a point and mutually perpendicular. (See Fig. 26.)

5.08 The *Central Plane* of a worm gear is perpendicular to the gear axis and contains the common perpendicular of the gear and worm axes. In the usual case with axes at right angles, it contains the worm axis. (See Fig. 29.)

GROUP 6   PRINCIPAL DIRECTIONS

These are directions in the pitch plane and correspond to the principal cross sections of a tooth.

6.01 The *Axial Direction* is the direction of the intersection of the axial plane. (See Fig. 30.)

6.02 The *Transverse Direction* is the direction of the intersection of the transverse plane. (See Fig. 30.)

6.03 The *Normal Direction* is the direction of the intersection of the normal plane. (See Fig. 30.)

GROUP 7   ELEMENTS OF GEAR TEETH

7.01 The *Tooth Surface* forms the side of a gear tooth. (See Fig. 31.)

7.02 A *Tooth Profile* is one side of a tooth in a cross section. Usually a profile is the curve of intersection of a tooth surface and a plane or surface normal to the pitch surface, such as the transverse, normal, or axial plane. (See Fig. 31.)

7.03 The *Fillet Curve* is the concave portion of the tooth profile where it joins the bottom of the tooth space. (See Fig. 31.)

7.04 *Involute Teeth* of spur gears, helical gears, and worms, are those in which the profile in a transverse plane (exclusive of the fillet curve), is the involute of a circle. (See Fig. 32.)

American Society of Mechanical Engineers

Fig. 2.   A typical page from the specifications on gear nomenclature, sponsored by the American Gear Manufacturer's Association and the American Society of Mechanical Engineers. These specifications are broken into groups; each group is broken into numbered sections.

The Cross Co.

Fig. 3. Since this drive housing will not be used in high stress applications, it has been cast instead of forged or fabricated.

and specifications are used. As with all methods of communication, the prime purpose of operation drawings and specifications is providing ways and means of transmitting information as accurately and simply as possible. If this goal is achieved, the obscure, incomplete, and even inaccurate information on plans and in specifications cannot exist; also, the time wasted in interpretation will be saved.

Methods of Processing

Generally speaking, the method of processing a product is inherent in its design. For example, a steel product with a complex design, which we know will be subject to considerable stress in service, is best made a forging. Any surfaces requiring high precision are then machined after the forging operation. Crankshafts, connecting rods, and other parts subject to great stress are produced in this manner. Other steel products which do not require high strength can be cast and machined, or fabricated.

Sometimes in organizing the process ways are seen to improve it by altering the product's design. If this can be accomplished without introducing exorbitant costs or endangering the product's quality or functions, the tool engineer may turn the plans back to the product designer, who redesigns the product according to the improved processing it will give.

An illustrative example of improving a process without sacrificing the product is in the manufacture of steel wrist pins. The conventional method is to machine them from bar stock of low carbon steel on automatic screw machines, carburize them, followed by heat treating and finally grinding them to exact dimensional specifications. The improved method is to cold extrude pins from low carbon steel, followed by the same operations as for the conventional process. The improved process saves an appreciable amount of material and machining without lowering the quality of the wrist pins. Fig. 4 illustrates this processing method.

There are other examples of improving a process without lowering the product's quality. A recent forging development by the Curtiss-Wright Corp., uses a rotary process to save in material, weight, and cost of finished forged parts. The technique utilizes four die-faced hammers to forge a vertical, rotating billet of steel or other premium alloy into its final shape. It works hot or cold, using round, square,

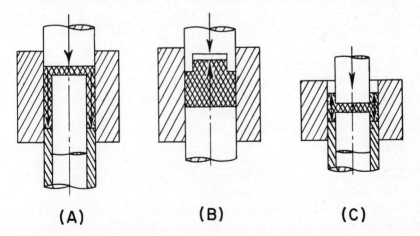

(A)   **(B)**   **(C)**

Fig. 4. Three methods of metal extrusion commonly employed. (A) Forward extrusion in which the metal flows ahead of the die orifice. (B) Backward extrusion in which the metal flows opposite to the punch. (C) Combined forward and backward extrusion in which the extruded metal flows in two directions.

solid, or hollow billets. A typical operation forges seven outside and four inside diameters of a part in forty seconds with appreciable savings in material. Splining or internal gearing is formed with no need for boring or broaching afterwards.

Another interesting technique is the process of pressure bonding aluminum to stainless steel, which results in a final product of superior quality and reduced cost. The new process of bonding aluminum to stainless steel was developed by Aluminum Company of America and incorporated into the manufacture of electric frying pans. The process offers many possibilities for the uses of aluminum in combination with such metals as carbon and alloy steels, other aluminum alloys, and copper. To construct the frying pan, aluminum was tie forged under exacting conditions to a stainless steel pan body, which serves as the inside cooking surface. The new process makes it possible to obtain the heat conducting superiority of aluminum and to readily apply a heating element to a stainless steel pan.

Translating the Design Information

After the tool engineer and others involved in production have examined the product designer's plans and understand fully what he desires, their next job is to translate the information into materials, operations, equipment to perform the operations, men to operate the equipment, arrangement of equipment, and sequence of operations. To the uninitiated it will probably seem like a complex, laborious procedure but fortunately materials, operations, and equipment can be classified.

The material which will go into the product can be determined and selected from a vast array of standards, specifications, and listings published by manufacturers, government agencies, and private organizations specializing in material testing and grading. Materials are classified according to size, weight, strength, composition, price, machinability, heat resistance, conductivity, hardness, malleability, melting point, tensile and comprehensive strength, and a host of other classifications. (See Fig. 5 for a typical classification. Here stainless steels are specified by composition.)

Selecting the best material for the product without introducing exorbitant costs can be a real problem. Usually the designer will specify a number of qualities he will desire in a certain material. (For example, a low-alloy cast steel, type C-Mn, of composition 0.32C, 1.43 Mn, 0.40 Si, normalized heat treatment of 1700°F., a yield point of not under 50,000 psi, a tensile strength of not under 90,000 psi, elongation of 20%.) To select a material that has all of these qualities at a minimum cost means investigating the market and comparing one material against another and the prices of various suppliers until the best material is found. This best material should prove the most economical and possess qualities which fall within the product designer's specified limits. Comparable materials may have certain qualities that are superior to the chosen materials, but other qualities will be unsuitable and the overall cost exorbitant.

Alloy Type	ANALYSIS						Structure Annealed
	Chromium—%	Nickel—%	Other Elements (See Note 4)	Carbon—%	Manganese—%	Silicon—%	
502	4.0-6.0	0.5 Max.	....	0.10 Max.	0.60 Max.	0.75 Max.	Pearlite-Ferrite
501+Mo	4.0-6.0	0.5 Max.	0.50 Mo	Over 0.10	0.60 Max.	0.75 Max.	Pearlite-Ferrite
410	11.5-13.5	0.5 Max.	....	0.15 Max.	0.60 Max.	0.75 Max.	Pearlite-Ferrite
414	11.5-13.5	2.0 Max.	....	0.15 Max.	0.60 Max.	0.75 Max.	Pearlite-Ferrite
416	12.0-14.0	0.5 Max.	0.45-0.60 Mo	0.15 Max	0.75-1.20	0.75 Max.	Pearlite-Ferrite
420	12.0-14.0	0.5 Max.	....	0.30-0.40	0.50 Max.	0.75 Max.	Pearlite
431	14.0-18.0	2.0 Max.	....	0.15 Max.	0.50 Max.	0.75 Max.	Pearlite-Ferrite
430	16.0-18.0	0.5 Max.	....	0.12 Max.	0.50 Max.	0.75 Max.	Pearlite-Ferrite
430-F	16.0-18.0	....	S,Se .07 Min.	0.12 Max.	0.75-1.20	0.30-0.75	Pearlite-Ferrite
440	16.0-18.0	0.5 Max.	0.45-0.60 Mo	0.65-0.70	0.35-0.50	0.75 Max.	Pearlite
440	16.0-18.0	0.5 Max.	....	1.00-1.10	0.35-0.50	0.75 Max.	Pearlite-Carbide
446	23.0-30.0	1.0 Max.	....	0.35 Max.	1.50 Max.	0.75 Max.	Ferrite-Carbide
301	16.0-18.0	7.0-9.0	....	0.09-0.20	1.25 Max.	....	Austenitic
302	17.5-20.0	8.0-10.0	....	0.08-0.20	1.25 Max.	0.75 Max.	Austenitic
304	18.0-20.0	8.0-10.0	....	0.08 Max.	2.00 Max.	0.75 Max.	Austenitic
303	17.5-20.0	8.0-10.0	S,Se,P (Note 1)	0.20 Max.	1.25 Max.	0.75 Max.	Austenitic
316	16.0-18.0	10.0-14.0	2.00-3.00 Mo	0.10 Max.	2.00 Max.	0.75 Max.	Austenitic
317	18.0-20.0	10.0-14.0	2.00-4.00 Mo	0.10 Max.	2.00 Max.	0.75 Max.	Austenitic
321	17.0-20.0	7.0-10.0	Ti (Note 2)	0.10 Max.	0.75 Max.	0.75 Max.	Austenitic
347	17.0-20.0	8.0-12.0	Cb (Note 3)	0.10 Max.	2.00 Max.	0.75 Max.	Austenitic
309	22.0-26.0	12.0-14.0	....	0.20 Max.	1.25 Max.	0.75 Max.	Austenitic
310	24.0-26.0	19.0-21.0	....	0.25 Max.	1.25-1.75	0.75 Max.	Austenitic

Note 1—Sulphur or Selenium .07 Minimum. Phosphorus .03–.17
Note 2—Minimum Titanium content=4 times % Carbon.
Note 3—Minimum Columbium content=10 times % carbon.
Note 4—Sulphur and Phosphorus shown in this column when sufficient; not shown if normal.

Allegheny Ludlum Steel Corp.

Fig. 5.   Stainless steel specifications—composition.

The task of specifying materials, of course, is the product designer's. He must know the specifications of each material he selects and make certain that it matches the qualities and functions demanded in his design. The task of selecting and purchasing material is the purchasing agent's. Besides having a thorough knowledge of material specifications he must know his suppliers; in other words, which ones specialize in certain materials, and which ones are likely to give him good prices.

In most plants the tool engineer acts as an inspector, or checker, with respect to materials. If he sees materials designated on plans that he judges are inferior or overly expensive, he informs the designer; if he sees materials in the plant that appear inferior or do not conform to specifications, he checks with the purchasing agent. In all cases he is expected to take measures that will result in the best material at the most economical cost.

TYPES OF OPERATIONS

Classification by Related Groups

Machine operations are conveniently divided into seven major types. Each of these classifications includes a group of related activities that contribute to the manufacturing process. These operations are:

1. Forging and forming.
2. Material handling and storing.
3. Critical machining.
4. Nondimensional.
5. Tie-in.
6. Assembly.
7. Inspection.

Forging and forming operations. These operations are where metals of plastics are molded, forged, cast, formed, etc. Products of these operations are castings, forgings, plates, bars, or strip stock which serve as the raw materials for subsequent machining operations. Forging and forming operations are relatively specialized processes in themselves. Most manufacturing plants do not perform forging and forming operations in addition to machining operations. Instead they purchase their raw material from steel mills, foundries, and the like.

Although forging and forming operations rarely appear on the

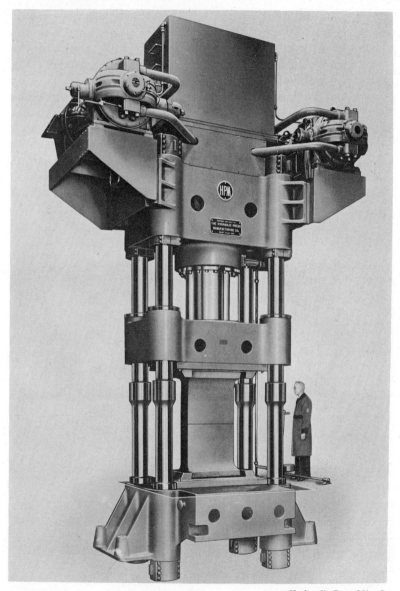

Hydraulic Press Mfg. Co.

Fig. 6. A hydraulic press used in typical forging and forming operations. The press is rated at 1,000 tons and has a 42-inch ram travel.

process plans or operation sheets of manufacturing plants, knowledge of how they are performed is important. For example, forgings are structurally stronger than castings, but usually cost more. The tool engineer, for one, must realize the difference and avoid using forgings for parts that do not require high strength applications.

Material handling and storing operations. These operations are the primary concern of the process engineer and material custodian respectively. The problems connected with the handling of materials is covered adequately in Economic Processing. Basically, the problem is moving materials so that bottlenecks and slack periods are eliminated. Also, methods must be used so that materials are moved cheaply; frequently automated equipment is recommended for this purpose.

Storing of raw materials, stock items, machined parts, and the

The Do-All Co.

Fig. 7. The part to be machined is held in the chuck jaws. Note that surfaces jaws hold have been machined.

finished product sometimes present tremendous obstacles. Except in unusual situations, storage space is at a premium in manufacturing ventures today, especially where plants are located in large and congested cities. Receiving, shipping, and storage arrangement schedules demand the best efforts of top level men. Part of the problem is solved by processing in lots, by adroitly arranging material so that easy removal is assured, by maintaining accurate inventory and ordering records, by using efficient, up-to-date storing equipment. Truly successful storage, however, requires the utmost cooperation of management. If the market is accurately investigated as to demand for the product, and products in manufacture are scheduled in lots and quantities that are realistic, shipments will be regular and frequent, which tends to reduce storage requirements to a minimum.

Critical machining operations. These operations treat the surfaces that provide the part with accurate locations in the work-holding device. They are truly critical operations since any accuracy to be machined into the part stems from reliable and definite locations with respect to the working-holding device. A principle of manufacturing requires that the critical areas be established and machined first, especially on rough parts. These four rules are applied in an analysis of critical areas:

1. Variations in the part's dimensions must be found so that provisions for "truing up" the part can be made, if necessary.

2. To obtain the highest and most consistent accuracy, critical surfaces and as many related surfaces as possible in each part should be machined from the same locators in one setting. Inaccuracies may be introduced by resetting the part or adjusting the holder.

3. The part must be located so that a uniform removal of material can be made among like finished surfaces of all parts, therefore assuring these surfaces will be cleaned.

4. The part must be located so that any surfaces to go unfinished will not be askew. Although surfaces not requiring machining may seem unimportant, by allowing them to become too thin or odd-shaped they may cause interference when the part is performing its intended function.

Nondimensional operations. These operations are ones not concerned with critical dimension and tolerance requirements. Material qualities, protective coatings, chamfering, plating, cleaning, painting, burring are nondimensional operations. Frequently one or several re-

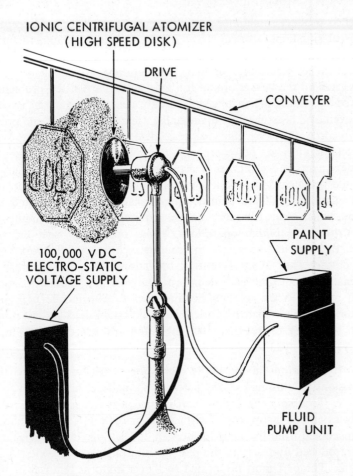

IONIC CENTRIFUGAL ATOMIZER
(HIGH SPEED DISK)

DRIVE

CONVEYER

100,000 VDC
ELECTRO-STATIC
VOLTAGE SUPPLY

PAINT
SUPPLY

FLUID
PUMP UNIT

Fig. 8. Here is a typical nondimensional operation.

lated nondimensional operations represent an auxiliary process within
the overall process. For example, a galvanizing process is a series of
operations which subjects a part to chemical treatment, protecting
designated surfaces with a zinc alloy. Another example, in localized
casehardening, by one method the areas to be left soft are carburized
in an oversize condition and the excess material is removed before
hardening; by another method the soft areas are copper-plated to
exclude carburization and are deplated after hardening.

In modern so-called nondimensional operations, the specialization
and experience required to design these operations cannot be ex-

pected of the average tool engineer. It requires the assistance of specialists; designing and placing the process in operation becomes a joint effort of the process and tool engineer, and the specialist. In many plants the specialist acts as a consultant to the process engineer, outlining the steps of the process while the process engineer attends to the details and execution of the setup operations.

Tie-in operations. These operations are determined by the shapes and sizes desired after the completion of the critical machining and nondimensional (if any) operations. The results of tie-in operations must meet the requirements of later nondimensional operations or the specifications of the finished part. Machining of gear teeth, grinding of noncritical surfaces, or any other machining of a noncritical nature are called tie-in operations. These six rules serve to define tie-in operations and their relationship in the overall process:

1. For consistent and uniform control in tie-in operations, use the critical machining surfaces as reference surfaces.

2. In the event the critical surfaces are no longer reliable as reference surfaces, due to distortion by previous operations such as welding or annealing, re-establish the critical surface by returning to

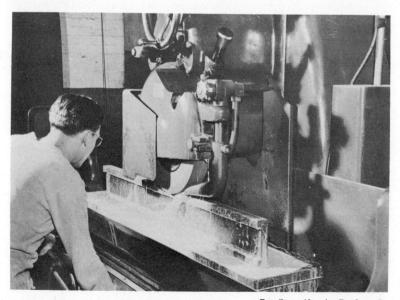

Bay State Abrasive Products Co.

Fig. 9. Here is a typical tie-in operation.

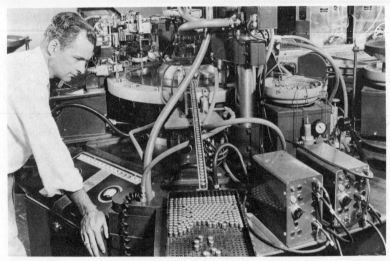

Multra Corp.

Fig. 10.   An automatic assembling machine discharging completed parts.

the original rough-part locators or any secondary locators related accurately to the critical surfaces.

3. Tie-in operations should be processed, if possible, before operations which are likely to be damaged by them. For example, holes should be drilled before a galvanizing operation, or grinding before an annealing operation.

4. Dimensional variations caused by prior operations such as annealing or plating should be determined and controlled.

5. Tie-in operations should be planned to dovetail with prior and subsequent operations so that they remain an integral part of the process.

6. Tie-in operations, since they are noncritical, should be combined with other operations, if possible. For example, a grinding operation should be eliminated from a process if a milling operation, already essential to the process, can give the noncritical dimensions.

Assembly operations. Assembly operations are concerned with uniting previously machined parts to form the desired product. These operations can be very simple, as in the case of a mechanical pencil, or very complex, as in the case of an automobile. For any assembly operation certain procedures, which cannot be covered here, are necessary to assemble products in an orderly and systematic fashion. The assembly line is a good example of a modern, organized assembly operation. Fig. 10 shows an automatic assembling machine discharging completed parts, which are mercury batteries. The assembly sequence is organized into a ten-station work cycle.

Inspection operations. These operations occur at many points in the process and can present many problems. A few of the factors that influence inspection operations are the degree of accuracy desired, the skill of the inspector, the size and policies of the company, the quality of the raw material, the tolerances required by the product designer. Types of inspection tools are covered in Tool Economy. Fig. 11 shows a micrometer comparator in an inspection operation.

Classification by Conventional Divisions

Processing operations are sometimes further broken down. The activities carried on within the scope of fundamental operations—such as forging and forming, critical, and tie-in operations—can be segregated according to natural and/or conventional divisions within the field. These divisions come about largely because of the limited range of action of most machine equipment, excluding intricate transfer equipment and other multi-operation machines, although even they can be considered as a collection of individual operations.

Drill presses are machines which are called upon to drill holes,

Federal Products Corp.

Fig. 11. An inspection operation with a supersensitive micrometer comparator.

lathes to turn parts where cylindrical shapes are desired, milling machines and shapers where plane surfaces are desired. Other natural and conventional divisions enter into heat treating, protective coatings, forging, and other fundamental operations. The point to remember is, by recognizing these specialties of performance, the designing and scheduling of various processing operations can be determined within closer limits. A detailed breakdown of this nature may also reveal situations where operations can be eliminated altogether or combined with others.

DEVELOPMENT OF INDIVIDUAL OPERATIONS

Once the tool engineer and his associates in production have examined the plans and settled upon the operations required (according to the classifications mentioned in the previous section) the next step, and perhaps the most important one, is selecting the equipment. Since World War II almost all processing, particularly metal processing, has become so heavily dependent upon machine equipment that operations cannot be analyzed independently of it. Once the production equipment is selected, the remainder of the planning is centered around developing the sequence of operations based on the selected equipment's specifications.

In this section we are going to be concerned with selecting the proper machine equipment based on the operations it must ultimately perform. This is going to involve developing operations into similar or complementary groups, combining them where possible, arranging them in as natural an order as possible so that equipment selection is reduced to a number of essentials. Knowing these essentials will limit the equipment eligible for selection. The final selection will be a comparison of equipment on a cost and functional basis.

Initial Factors

Prior to the final selection, the factors that must be considered in the course of selecting equipment are these:

1. The nature of the operations that must be performed.
2. The duration of the process.
3. The characteristics of the part.
4. The functional requirements of machines based on individual processing operations and parts.
5. Miscellaneous factors.

The nature of the operations. If a great amount of machining is required, the first factor can become very complex. Basically it divides into four considerations. The first and most important consideration is tolerances. The closer the tolerances the more exacting the equipment needed. In some cases close tolerances may require additional operations, as when grinding and polishing is necessary to attain an ultra-smooth surface finish. Another problem of close tolerances is the integration of cuts that should be planned to avoid inaccuracies in changing machines, locators, etc. Still other problems include the necessity of more refined inspection equipment, cutting tools, and operator skill.

The second consideration is the number of choices in the formation of each operation. In metal processing in particular this means the number of related surfaces to be machined. For one surface there can only be one operation. For two surfaces, there can be two separate operations or one simultaneous operation; in other words, there are two distinct choices. With three surfaces, there can be three separate operations, three distinct combinations of two together and one separate operation, or all three operations together; in other words, five distinct choices. Following this reasoning, for four surfaces there are fifteen distinct choices, and so on. Although the majority of these

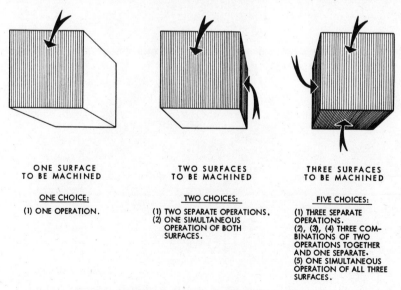

ONE SURFACE
TO BE MACHINED

TWO SURFACES
TO BE MACHINED

THREE SURFACES
TO BE MACHINED

ONE CHOICE:

(1) ONE OPERATION.

TWO CHOICES:

(1) TWO SEPARATE OPERATIONS.
(2) ONE SIMULTANEOUS OPERATION OF BOTH SURFACES.

FIVE CHOICES:

(1) THREE SEPARATE OPERATIONS.
(2), (3), (4) THREE COMBINATIONS OF TWO OPERATIONS TOGETHER AND ONE SEPARATE.
(5) ONE SIMULTANEOUS OPERATION OF ALL THREE SURFACES.

Fig. 12. Machining choices in development of operations.

choices will have no practical importance, the tool and process engineer must be aware of them all to be assured of not overlooking the best formation of operations. (See Fig. 12.)

Another important consideration is the similarity or dissimilarity of operations in the same classification. For example, a dozen holes in a part may have identical diameters and depths, or some or all may be different. If the holes are all exactly the same, a simple, single-spindle drill press is the solution. If the holes are of different diameters and depths, a multi-spindle drill press with adjustable stops for each spindle is needed. Drill speeds may present problems, since the drills for large and small holes will turn at different speeds. Holes of varying depths may require different machining techniques in order to clear chips properly. In general, as the dissimilarity of operations

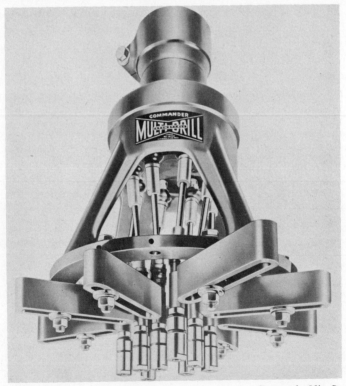

Commander Mfg. Co.

Fig. 13. This complex multi-drill is used in applications requiring varying-diameter holes of varying depths.

within a classification increases, the cost and functional complexity also increases. (See Fig. 13.)

The fourth consideration is the relative positions of all machine surfaces. It is easier to machine surfaces that are parallel or symmetrical than ones that are oblique. Unusual surfaces generally require a special arrangement of equipment to place the cutting tool in the proper position for machining. Unmachined surfaces should also be noted, since their shape may influence the functioning of the part when assembled.

The duration of the process. In the final analysis, the duration depends primarily on market demand. There are two distinct types of demand: short term and long term. Products with short term demand are usually governed by changing fashions or standards; in other words, management does not expect recurring orders for manufacture of these products. Products with long term demand are either seasonal or relatively stable, so that management can judge its permanency, schedule fairly accurate lot sizes, and expect to manufacture the product for an indefinite period of time.

Short term and long term demands for a product dictate the selection of different types of equipment. Economic Selection of Machine Equipment explores the influence of market demand on production equipment. Briefly, a long term demand will allow greater expenditures for high capacity equipment and all the expenses at-

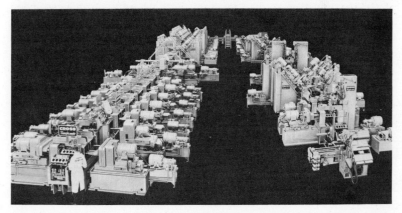

The Cross Co.

Fig. 14. A sectionized automation line for machining engine blocks. This type of equipment is valuable in long term, high volume production.

tending the use of equipment on a long run, high volume basis. Short term market demand means relatively inexpensive equipment must be purchased or the equipment might not be paid off before the break-even quantity is processed.

Long term, high volume production is a special situation in manufacturing. Even the fundamental concepts of machine equipment characteristics may be cast aside because of high capacity. Integration of operations, the introduction of transfer equipment, the addition of attachments and special devices, are all warranted in this type of manufacturing.

Short term, relatively low volume production is the reverse situation. Here is where the tool engineer must use all his ingenuity to process the product to specified tolerances and quantities without introducing expenses that might make the production a losing proposition. It is in this type of production that the new methods of low-cost manufacturing are most often discovered and utilized to the advantage of the company, the industry as a whole, and the buying public at large. This type of manufacturing offers the greatest challenge to the tool engineer.

The characteristics of the part. This factor has three main considerations. The size of the part is important where special handling must be planned because of great bulk and weight. With large, heavy parts it is wise to arrange operations so that as many machining operations as possible can be conducted in one place. The geometry of the part must be studied in those parts where their shapes dictate the design of special jigs and fixtures. The material of the part must be known, especially its hardness and machinability. Very hard material requires different treatment than soft material. Grinding operations are different with materials of different hardnesses. As a rule, the machining of hard material of high tensile strength consumes more power, shortens the life of cutting tools, and requires that equipment be of a more durable nature.

The functional requirements of machines. Each individual process and product may influence the functional requirements of machines in unexpected ways. Machines that are capable of processing parts at a low rate with good efficiency may not process the same parts efficiently at a higher rate. Some machines are designed for repetitive work, others for general-purpose work, although both types may be able to machine the same part to the same specifications.

The range of the machine with respect to part size must be known.

Machines with comparable capacity ratings may vary greatly in the size of the part they can process efficiently. Most machine manufacturers furnish catalogs containing detailed charts and specifications that cover the range-capacity relationships of each machine made. In addition, such data as worktable size and travel, clearance distances, table speeds and feed rates, spindle speeds and feed rates, and

Baird Machine Co.

Fig. 15. An automatic multiple transfer press designed for volume production of small parts. The machine uses mechanical transfer fingers for feeding parts to the dies.

driving motor sizes are given. Besides being helpful in selecting the machine itself, this information is valuable as a guide for designing the cutting tools and other attachments that go with the machine.

The general ruggedness of the machine must be determined if the part it must process is heavy or requires heavy cutting forces, or the production rate is high. On the other hand, a light part requiring light cutting forces needs only lightweight machinery, which should be sought as a cost-cutting measure. For instance, power presses are rated by the compressive forces they will deliver. Since the cost of the press is roughly proportional to the amount of force it will deliver, it is important the amount of force the part actually requires be in that range. The size and weight of machinery also depends to some extent on the plant's layout and the strength of its flooring. Fig. 15 shows a multiple transfer press, valuable for pressing small parts in quantity.

The power requirements of machine equipment must be known to see (1) if it can perform the operation at all, and (2) if it can operate in the intended process with efficiency. Any investigation of power requirements must take into account the power consumption of the specific operation and the inherent power losses of the machine. Exact power requirements for specific operations cannot be calculated exactly, primarily because of fluctuating conditions, but reasonably close estimates can be made. Tables, charts, and load-power graphs are supplied by machine manufacturers from which power losses can be estimated with reasonable accuracy. Power into the equipment must equal the power out plus losses.

Miscellaneous factors. Other factors that influence machine equipment selections depend on particular installations and plant policies. Some plants may deal with the same machine manufacturers for all their purchases; others may deal with only those manufacturers with well-established names and reputations. The situation is similar to car owners who buy the same make of car year after year because of the satisfaction previous ones have given. Many excellent machine manufacturers today have equipment available for all types of installations, large and small, automated and nonautomated. There is no reason to assume one is superior to all others for all kinds of equipment.

Machine equipment selections may be influenced by safety factors, especially safety to the operator, the dependability certain makes have given in the past, the ease with which equipment may be operated and the amount of human skill required, the record of accuracy over a prolonged period, the record of maintenance over a prolonged period, and other factors dependent on particular processes.

When equipment selection is confined to machines on hand or even in use in the plant, a new set of conditions exist which depend greatly on individual installations and plant policies. In general, however, the important factors to consider include the equipment's availability at the time it is needed, its existing workload if the desired operation must be run off it, the location of the equipment, its condition both as to obsolescence and state of wear, the amount of adapting that must be done, the amount of reworking of the process, especially with material handling equipment.

THE OPERATIONAL SEQUENCE

This is the third step in the formation of a manufacturing process. The first step was to analyze and determine the operations from the product designer's plans. The second step was to organize and specify these operations. To accomplish the first two steps it was necessary to understand the information on the designer's plans and translate

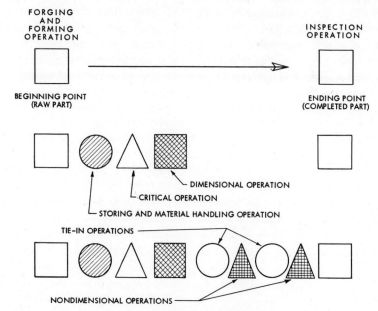

Fig. 16. Development of a typical sequence of operations. Bottom diagram shows the completed sequence.

it into practical methods for processing. Also, it was necessary to differentiate between the various operations and class them according to natural function and convention.

The Beginning and End Points

Developing the operational sequence stems from the product designer's plans, which specify what is desired at the beginning and end points of the process. The beginning point will show the dimensions of the raw part after the forging and forming operation has been completed, the end point will show the requirements desired in the final inspection operations. Between these anchor points the best sequence of operations must be organized; the whole will constitute a manufacturing process. (See Fig. 16 top.)

The first operation after forging and forming is receipt of the raw parts, which includes proper notation of their arrival, and disposition in the plant. The next operation is performing the machining necessary to establish the critical areas for the dimensional machining. (Fig. 16 middle.) After the dimensional machining operation the next operation may vary from plant to plant and for different processes, but it is usually a tie-in operation of some kind, like cutting of gear teeth or drilling noncritical holes. Following the tie-in operation there is usually a nondimensional operation like plating or carburizing. Most processes will consist of several tie-in and nondimensional operations, either together or intermingled. (Fig. 16 bottom.) The final operation is inspecting the part. Inspection operations may also be interspersed throughout the steps of the process.

CHAPTER EIGHT

Tool Design

The function the tool designer fulfills in industry today is probably an outgrowth of the design function of the old time toolmaker, whose duties were, and still are, to construct, repair, maintain, and calibrate the jigs, fixtures, and instruments of the machine shop. With new production methods, the average toolmaker was hard pressed to construct tools which would meet the requirements of these methods. As a result, many companies, especially those in the midst of vast expansion programs, assigned the duties of designing tools to one man who had the experience and ingenuity to cope with the challenges created by new production techniques. These specialists came to be called *tool designers*.

What are the functions of the modern tool designer? To answer this question we must first classify tools. In the chapter on machine equipment selection we said tools were cutting tools, jigs, clamps and other fixtures, hand tools and inspection equipment; in addition, we classed lathes, milling machines, and larger machinery as machine tools. In industry large machinery is usually not called a *tool* alone, but rather, a *machine tool* or *machine equipment*. The designer of this equipment is more properly called a *machine tool designer* or *machine designer*.

Tools are defined most simply as devices capable of machining a material into some predetermined shape, holding the material during the machining, or measuring the material during and after the machining. Therefore, the *tool designer* is a specialist in the design of devices that perform these functions. At the same time his aim is to design these tools so that economical manufacturing can be achieved.

The tool engineer may or may not be a tool designer, depending on his background. In any event he must know enough about design work to supervise those who specialize in it and pass on their designs. Since many tool designers graduate into the broader field of tool engineering, it follows that in industry today many tool engineers, although adept in all phases of their field, specialize in tool design.

A complete investigation of tool designing is well beyond the scope of this book. All we can accomplish here is a presentation of the highlights, pointing out typical design situations and problems. On this basis, the chapter can be divided into three sections: (1) Elemental considerations of tool design, (2) the tool designer's qualifications, duties, and the general procedures he follows in his job, and (3) the types of tools and typical problems the designer encounters.

BASIC CONSIDERATIONS

Steps In Tool Designing

Although the design requirements for each tool present their own problems, there are general considerations that cover almost all tool designs. To begin with, six basic steps the tool designer follows in his work are:

1. An analytical study of the product requiring tooling.

2. An investigation of the scope and purpose of the production process in which the particular machining operation will perform.

3. A determination of the nature of the operation in which the tool is to be used.

4. A determination of precisely what the tool must accomplish; also, its limitations.

5. The design of a tool to suit the requirements of its intended use.

6. The development of the tool so that it is economical to make and also gives economical performance.

Aside from the necessity of examining the product designer's plans for dimensions and shapes, the tool designer studies them to become familiar with the product's intended function, the level of its quality, its general ruggedness, strength characteristics, etc. Step 1 therefore is important as a means of introducing the designer to the eventual end result of his endeavors.

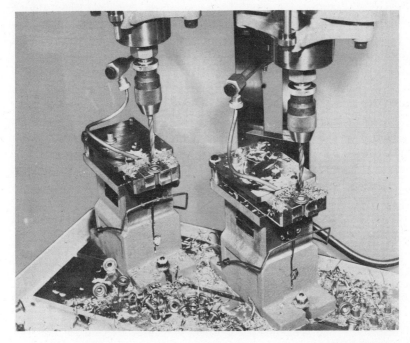

Snow Mfg. Co.

Fig. 1. By mounting an air vise with fingertip control on each drill spindle, the hourly gross was increased from 510 to 780, an ingenious method for increasing production.

Step 2 means the process plans, operation sheets, bills of material, instruction sheets are examined to get a rough perspective of the scope of the process. Although some of this information may itself be in the planning stage only, the tool designer should avail himself of whatever data he can. Steps 3 and 4 require a thorough examination of the process and operation plans. Operations are identified, grouped, and placed in sequence either by the tool engineer or process engineer. In turn, these operations become the focal point on which the tool's design is based. At this early stage it is wise to learn of any limitations the tool may have, such as distortion above a certain temperature or molecular breakdown after a certain length of time.

Step 5 is where the designer brings all his ingenuity and experience into action (see Fig. 1). He must fulfill the requirements of the design and at the same time meet the specifications the various societies and other organizations in his field have established (see the chapter on processing details for a section on specifications). Always he attempts to incorporate into his design features which will make the tool inexpensive to manufacture and also allow economical operation (step 6).

Influencing Factors

An important consideration in tool design is the capacity and range of machine tools. Once these machines are selected, the tools used in conjunction with them must be designed to conform to the machine's specifications. Designs of drills and other cutting tools are heavily influenced by the ratings of the machines for which they are intended, besides the designs they must have to produce desired shapes and surfaces.

Other factors influence the design of tools and must be considered by the tool designer. The material of the product has a definite influence, both in the tool's shape and its composition. In general, the harder the product material, the harder must be the tool material and the more rugged the design.

The speed with which the tool will move affects its design; for example, high-speed drills must be harder and less subject to heat distortion than medium-speed drills. The force exerted on the tool definitely affects its design. Comparatively large forces call for rugged tools, which may present other problems if the tool must be moved about frequently.

Once the tool's general shape, size, and strength characteristics are determined the tool designer has recourse to tables, speed-load graphs, charts, and various specifications which present mechanical, electrical, and physical relationships; typical machine and tool dimensions; strengths and composition of materials, stock part sizes, and other data in easily readable form. The combination of ingenuity, experience, and utilization of tabulated data are the designer's personal tools for doing his job in the best and most efficient manner possible.

Controlling the Variables

Certain variables may introduce errors in machine operations. The tool designer must be aware of these variables and also the means of controlling them. In other words, the tools which perform machine operations must be designed to keep the variables within desired limits. The following variables may introduce errors into machine operations:

Dimensional variations. Parts may come to the operation with varying dimensions. At any point in the process parts must conform to certain tolerances. Variations near the maximum tolerances may adversely affect the choice of location of the part, the size of the cut, and the forces on the tools. The designer must build enough flexibility into his tools to account for these variations.

Material variations. Parts may come to the operation with varying material compositions which, in turn, requires the designer to specify that his tools have enough range in hardness and toughness qualities to overcome fluctuations in thermal expansion, deflection, etc., caused by material variations.

Tool variations. Although minor variations cannot be avoided, the designer must strive toward tolerances in his tools that roughly match those of the parts they are to machine. A part with wide tolerance measurements does not require a tool with close tolerances, and vice versa. Here is another reason the tool designer must carefully inspect the product designer's plans. Sometimes a compromise must be made in cases where the cost would become excessive due to very close tolerances.

Wear variations. Wear is a variable that must be accepted as inevitable. In some types of tools it is slight and easily controllable; in other types, rapid and impractical to control. In the latter case, the amount of wear for any period of time or use, based on empirical data, is accounted for. In general, cutting tools are subject to the most rapid and least predictable amounts of wear; tool holders present the next greatest variations due to wear. With jigs, fixtures and other holding tools, and gages it is usually advisable to insert wear-resistant materials in those areas subject to large and rapid amounts of wear, to avoid specifying large wearable areas, and to design tools so that wear forces, including friction, are at a minimum. With cutting tools, it is a question of using materials and designs that apply closely to the use intended.

The introduction of ceramics for use in cutting tools is an excellent example in the search for wear-resistant materials. Before 1900, cutting tools were constructed from relatively inexpensive oil-hardening steel with the shape shown in Fig. 2(A). The development of high-speed steels brought on the design in Fig. 2(B); in addition, machine tools were redesigned to provide more power and higher cutting speeds. The introduction of these cutting materials followed: cast-alloy (Stellite) tools in the 1920's, cemented-carbide tools for cast

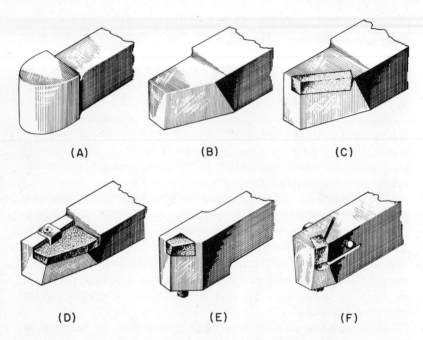

Fig. 2. These tool bits depict the advancement in tool design through the years. (A) Forged tool at turn of century, (B) high-speed rectangular tool introduced about 1910, (C) brazed-carbide tool introduced in early 1930's, (D) clamped-carbide tool introduced in 1950, (E) multi-edged clamped-carbide tool introduced about 1952, and (F) multi-edged, clamped, throw-away ceramic tool introduced in middle 1950's.

iron in the 1930's, cemented-carbide tools for steel in the 1940's, cemented-oxide (ceramic) tools for very hard steels in the 1950's.

Each improvement in tool material was accompanied by an increase in hardness, brittleness, and cost, but made it possible to work at higher cutting speeds. Because of the expense of cemented carbide, it became necessary to braze tool tips to a steel shank, as in Fig. 2(C). Next came the clamped-carbide tip, shown in Fig 2(D), followed by the multi-edged clamped tool shown in Fig. 2(E).

At the present time the ultimate in cutting tool designs is shown in Fig. 2(F), a multi-edged, clamped, throw-away ceramic tool. The throw-away feature arose when tool tips, due to improved manufacturing methods, could be decreased in thickness until it was no longer practical to regrind them. In other words, it is actually more economical to throw the tips away when all the edges have been worn out.

Ceramic tools are valuable in applications calling for light cuts in hardened steels. At high cutting speeds the tendency toward brittleness is reduced in ceramic tools because rising temperatures (caused by high speed) decrease the brittle nature of this material. In addition, ceramic tools are potentially less expensive to manufacture. Both ceramic and cemented-carbide tools are classed as wear resistant, which means, in effect, they will give acceptable accuracy over extended periods of use. The length of this period is called the tool life (see the chapter on Tool Economy).

Distortional variations. Distortion is a variable which may be caused by handling, part holding, or cutting action. To some extent these forces in tools can be predicted and the amount of distortion controlled. Distortion can never be eliminated, since tools are always subject to stresses and strains, but it can be reduced to controllable limits.

The correct methods of part holding and clamping are covered adequately in the Clamping chapter; the Tool Economy chapter also discusses correct clamping procedures. If a part is fragile and deflects easily, extra precautions must be taken, such as: making lighter machine cuts, operating the cutting tool at higher speeds, keeping the tool sufficiently sharp, providing internal bracing to the part, arranging the clamping equipment so that deflection-inducing forces are transmitted to rigid members of the clamp and not the part.

Expansional variations. Expansion caused by heat can produce very definite variations in modern, close tolerance, high-speed machining. Precautions which help bring this excessive expansion under control are: a well-designed coolant supply, which will cover all heat areas with adequate fluid; provisions for adequate heat dissipation from tools; thermostatically-controlled plant temperatures; use of well-designed cutting tools, so that a minimum of energy is lost as heat waste.

BASIC FUNCTIONS

The Plant

Different plants organize their tool design sections in different ways. Many factors enter into the formation of a good design organization. Among them are the size of the plant, the length of the run, the number of products the plant manufactures, the type and quality

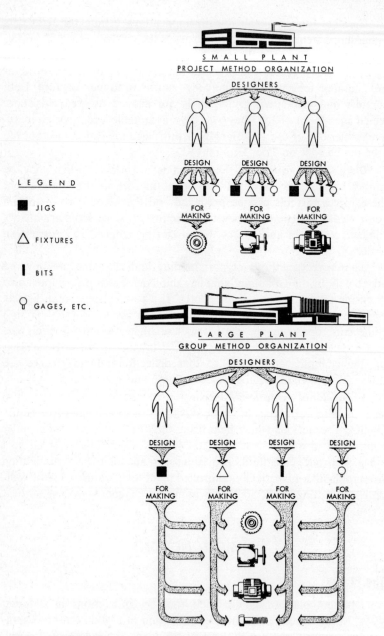

Fig. 3. Simplified diagrams contrasting typical small and large plant tool design organizations.

of the products, and even the ability of the men within the department.

Small plants commonly assign each tool designer all the tools for a part or a product; this is called a *project method* organization. Large plants often assign each of their designers a specific class of tools, like clamps, dies, or gages; this is called a *group method* organization (see Fig. 3). Some plants will utilize a combination of these methods, assigning their best designers to special projects, and others, especially new and untested men, to more routine designs.

A large lot size and a large number of products to be manufactured suggests a subdivision of duties to the point where one designer may handle only jigs, another only cutting tools, another only clamps which the machining of each part of one or several products may require. Perhaps the subdivision may be by machine: one designer handling one or all of the milling machines, another, the lathes, etc. The danger of a highly subdivided design department is the loss in efficiency that tends to occur. However, a plan that integrates the duties of all the designers within a group so that neither time nor endeavor is wasted, can make subdividing design duties just as efficient as any other method; furthermore, the accomplishments are likely to be greater.

The Designer

Aside from a sound background in the technical phases of his job, the good tool designer must possess other assets, some acquired, others inborn. Since practical experience is invaluable for all types of designing, an acquired asset would be experience as a toolmaker.

Another acquired asset is a familiarity with the various manufacturing processes and with the methods and procedures of a modern production organization. The good tool designer should have a fair knowledge of the methods used by management, by purchasing, by inspection, by the product design department, and other departments. Knowing what their duties consist of may help the tool designer avoid introducing impractical designs into tools they must deal with.

Another acquired asset is maintaining up-to-date information on tools, operations, and techniques that are constantly being written up in trade journals and technical magazines, and presented at technical meetings and conventions. To this end the good designer subscribes to the magazines and journals in his field and is a member of technical organizations devoted to the furtherance of tool design.

The ingenious approach. A more or less inborn quality is the ingenious approach the good tool designer must display in many of the design problems he encounters. In this regard he must be original in thought and not be hampered by tradition or set in his ways. He should be inventive and not afraid to exhibit his ideas, no matter how different they may seem. An inventive, ingenious mind can visualize. In the case of the designer he must be able to visualize the solution to a design problem and set down his "vision" so that others can understand it. A designer with good visual perception actually "sees" the finished tool as soon as the problems concerned with the tool's functions are solved.

Another asset that is partly inborn, partly acquired is a cost consciousness concerning the expenses involved in making a tool and also the tool's influence on the product's overall expense. Generally speaking, the most economically-designed tool is one that will perform its intended function correctly, but in some cases economically-designed tools do not machine products so their overall cost is the most economical. The tool designer must be aware of this, and also the expenses involved in quality tools, especially ones that must function with a minimum of resharpening or repairing. The tool engineer is also cost conscious with respect to tool designs; not only the tool must be economical but also the product it processes.

Accuracy in communication. The tool designer must be a fair draftsman. His plans must be legible, easy to understand, and thorough. In addition, he must be able to express himself in written reports so that his designs are never misunderstood. He must be able to make freehand sketches from which designs can be drawn up. Above all, no matter what form of communications he uses, he must be accurate. To assure this, besides being careful initially, he must cultivate the habit of rechecking his work. A quick re-examination will often eliminate many little errors that might not otherwise be caught until the last stages of production.

TYPES OF TOOLS

This section will cover cutting tools, jigs and fixtures, dies, molds, and gages. Machine tools will not be covered. Because of space limitations only important features of each type of tool will be mentioned, together with typical design problems encountered in practice. This section should not be construed as a survey even of tool types, but rather as an introduction—an "eye-opener"—into the design of tools.

Cutting Tools

Due to the wide variety of materials in general use today, the design of cutting tools presents many problems to the tool designer. In the metal-working industries alone the various types of metals and metal alloys run into the thousands. Numerous factors must be considered in the design of cutting tools. The four most important factors are:

1. The product to be machined.
2. The material of the product.
3. The number of parts to be machined.
4. The type and size of the machine tool in which the cutting tool will be used.

Aware of these factors, the designer can begin his planning. An illustrative example of this planning might proceed like this: If the part is to be machined in a drill press, the cutting tool, such as a drill or borer, is selected on the basis of the material of the product and on the dimensions necessary to machine the product. If, for example, the part is cast iron, the cutting tool can be of high-speed steel; if the lot is large, a tool with a tungsten tip for economical operation is recommended.

If the part is a casting, bad scale conditions on its surface may dictate the selection of carbide-tipped tools even on low-volume lots. On the other hand, some parts may require internal intermittent cuts; this being the case, there would be openings in the hole or bore and the cutting tool would not be in contact with the metal at these openings. A condition of this nature often prevents the use of a carbide-tipped tool because it is not capable of resisting the shock effects which are experienced in internal, intermittent cuts. For this type cut a high-speed tool is better suited to withstand the shock. Each step of the design requires similar judgments, weighing the advantages and disadvantages of each alternative, rejecting one for the other until the design is complete.

Good design judgment. Fig. 4 shows the result of exercising good judgment in a tool design. The tool is a subland drill having two lands on one diameter and two other lands on a different diameter. Both sets of lands extend the full flute length of the drill. The original tool manufacturer establishes both diameters for this full length and the operation never grinds on diameter. Sublands having as many as twelve different diameters have been used; three and four are common.

Fig. 4.   Subland drill with two lands on one diameter and two other lands on a
different diameter.

The purpose of subland tools is to allow the economical machining of two or more diameters with one tool in one pass. Subland tools also eliminate the necessity for separate tools, spindles, heads, or even machines for each diameter, thereby reducing costs. The tooling cost, the direct and indirect labor costs are also reduced when using these tools.

Another example of good design judgment, Fig. 5 shows a tool which can be adjusted rapidly and accurately to precise limits utilizing the micrometer and vernier principle. This multi-purpose cutting tool is valuable in high volume, high precision applications. It reduces downtime through quick adjustment of each cutting tool point to the required part dimension. Fig. 6 shows an electric motor housing, an aluminum part machined by the multi-purpose tool. The tool is mounted in a precision boring machine, where nine surfaces are machined in one pass.

Due to the large number of cutting tool manufacturers today, designers can often find the tools they require without resorting to

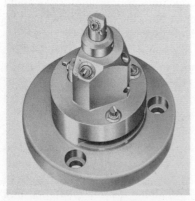

DeVlieg Machine Co.

Fig. 5.   A multi-purpose, high-precision cutting tool. Quick adjustment of each tool point reduces downtime.

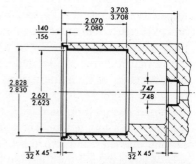

DeVlieg Machine Co.

Fig. 6.   An aluminum electric motor housing. The multi-purpose tool of Fig. 5 machines it to the tolerances shown.

special designs. A perusal of tool manufacturers' catalogs will give the designer a fair acquaintance with the standard tools available on the market. Because they are usually less expensive than special tools, the designer should check into the possibility of using standard tools before he begins his design work.

Special designs. If no standard tool will accomplish the machining operation required, then the designer must develop his own design. A special tap design recently developed overcomes four major tapping problems: pick up, loading, welding, and galling. These characteristic problems in tapping operations are solved by a special preventive treatment of the tap. A highly ductile lubricating deposit is firmly bonded to the surface of the tap and anchored into the ground pores. Under operating pressures this deposit is further compressed into the pores and burnished to a bright, slippery consistency. Since the lubricant becomes an integral part of the tap, high pressures during operation will not force it out, as with conventional lubricants.

Another special design, Fig. 7, shows five sections of carbide-

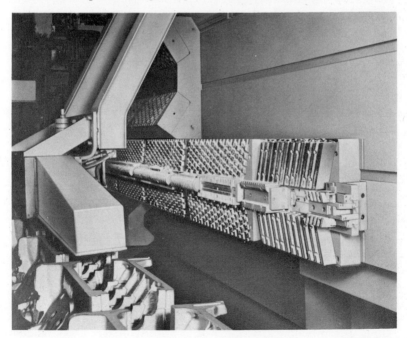

Ex-Cell-O Corp.

Fig. 7. Five sections of carbide-tipped broaches.

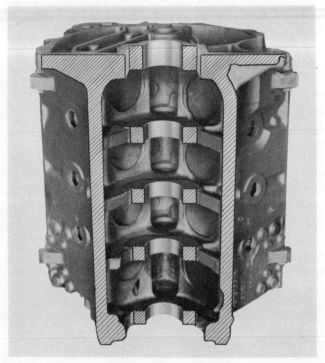

Ex-Cell-O Corp.

Fig. 8. An engine block, which is machined where shown by the broaches of Fig. 7.

tipped broaches, which give greater production and reduced down-time where used in a large automotive plant. The tooling in this plant is set up for the broaching of the pan rail, half bores, bearing locks, and parting faces of engine blocks (Fig. 8). A maximum of ³⁄₁₆″ stock is removed in a single pass by the five-section, combination half-round and face broach, which uses carbide-tipped tool bits and broach inserts. The results desired in this high volume operation were relatively high accuracy, a long tool life, and a minimum of downtime. The designer solved this by using inserts and 100% carbide-tipped tools. As a result, between re-sharpenings (the tool life) 20,000 to 25,000 cast-iron blocks are finished and semi-finished.

Fig. 9 shows how a selection of a properly-designed tool holder and carbide or ceramic inserts gives a reduction in tooling and machining costs. The removal and replacement of the insert is ac-

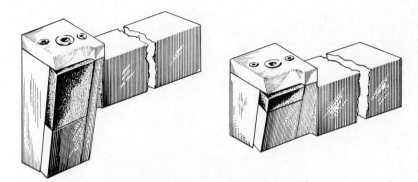

Fig. 9. The left tool holder is for carbide or ceramic inserts up to 1½" in length. The right tool holder is for throw-away inserts.

complished in seconds without adjustment of the tool holder. If the inserts should for some reason be of different thicknesses, they can still be positioned quickly without any readjustment of the tool holder in its post. If throw-away inserts are used, no regrinding is necessary.

Jigs and Fixtures

As stated previously, a jig is a device for holding a part while an operation is being performed and at the same time guiding the cutting tool that performs the operation. Jigs are recommended for such operations as drilling, reaming, boring. There are many kinds of jigs, such as plate jigs, box jigs, shaft-drilling jigs, index jigs, etc.

Shaft-drilling jigs. To drill holes in shafts sometimes poses a problem to the tool designer, especially when there are various diameters of shafts. Usually it means designing individual jigs for each shaft, but there are still other problems. Due to the difficulty in having the drill locate exactly in the center of the shaft, and to prevent runout of the drill, it is necessary to bring the drill guide bushing down close to the top of the shaft. A standard design of the shaft-drilling jig is shown in Fig. 10 (top). With a jig of this type stationary and sliding V-blocks are provided. An adjustable work stop is also provided on the rear end of the jig so that the distance of the hole from the end of the shaft can be accurately maintained. Rest buttons are placed beneath the top plate of the jig so that the height of the drill bushing to the top of the shaft can be properly located, thereby preventing runout of the drill.

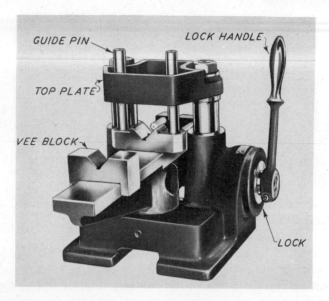

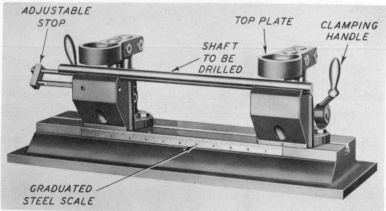

Fig. 10.   A standard shaft-drilling jig (top). A jig for drilling two or more holes in a shaft in one setup (bottom).

By using a jig of this design, various sizes of V-blocks can be interchanged and an extra liner-bushing put into the top plate. This will allow a number of drill bushings to be used, which will give a variety of hole sizes that can be drilled. Different size jigs will accommodate different diameter shafts.

Another adaptation of the shaft-drilling jig just described is one with two smaller jigs on each end of a base, as shown in Fig. 10 (bottom). These are adjustable lengthwise, permitting two or more holes to be drilled in the shaft at the desired locations. A hardened steel measuring scale is mounted on the jig base, which will measure any center distance desired within the range of the jig. In some production operations five or more of these small jigs are mounted on one base and used on multiple-spindle drill presses, making it possible

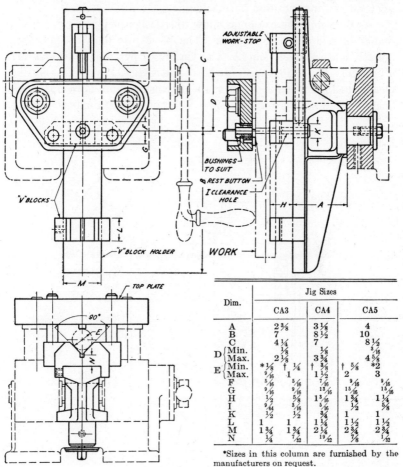

Dim.		Jig Sizes		
		CA3	CA4	CA5
A		$2\tfrac{3}{8}$	$3\tfrac{1}{8}$	4
B		7	$8\tfrac{1}{2}$	10
C		$4\tfrac{1}{4}$	7	$8\tfrac{1}{2}$
D	Min.	$\tfrac{1}{8}$	$\tfrac{1}{8}$	$\tfrac{3}{16}$
	Max.	$2\tfrac{1}{8}$	$3\tfrac{3}{4}$	$4\tfrac{5}{8}$
E	Min.	*$\tfrac{1}{8}$ †$\tfrac{1}{4}$	†$\tfrac{3}{8}$	†$\tfrac{5}{8}$ *2
	Max.	$\tfrac{5}{16}$ 1	$1\tfrac{1}{2}$ 2	3
F		$\tfrac{5}{16}$	$\tfrac{5}{16}$	$\tfrac{9}{16}$
G		$\tfrac{9}{16}$	$\tfrac{13}{16}$	$\tfrac{15}{16}$
H		$\tfrac{1}{2}$	$1\tfrac{3}{8}$	$1\tfrac{1}{4}$
I		$\tfrac{9}{64}$	$\tfrac{5}{16}$	$\tfrac{1}{2}$
K		$\tfrac{1}{2}$	$\tfrac{1}{2}$	1
L		1	$1\tfrac{1}{4}$	$1\tfrac{1}{2}$
M		$1\tfrac{3}{4}$	$2\tfrac{1}{4}$	$2\tfrac{3}{4}$
N		$\tfrac{1}{4}$	$\tfrac{19}{32}$	$\tfrac{7}{8}$

*Sizes in this column are furnished by the manufacturers on request.

†Sizes in this column are standard *V* blocks.

The Cleveland Universal Jig Co.

Fig. 11. Details of shaft-drilling jigs, showing a variety of sizes.

to drill all the holes in the shaft at one time. Numerous combinations of this type jig can be utilized depending on the operation and the ingenuity of the tool designer. (See Fig. 11.)

All-purpose, high-capacity jigs. Other types of jigs are designed on the index principle for rapid production. Besides drilling, they may be used in allied operations such as reaming, counterboring, countersinking, spot-facing, and tapping. In a typical setup parts are fed to the cutting tool on a circular table, which automatically rotates, placing each part into position for machining.

As the foregoing examples show, the design of jigs is primarily a matter of individual applications. The basic principles of jig design are few and relatively simple. The variety of jigs required today are a challenge to the ingenuity of the tool designer. He must apply the basic principles ingeniously, meet the dimensional and tolerance specifications, and not permit his designs to become uneconomical. To this

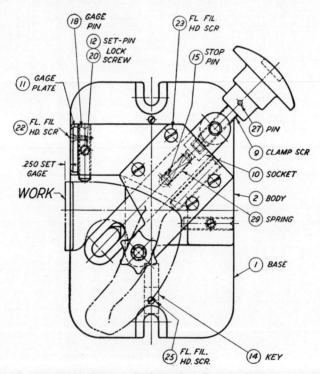

Fig. 12.   An assembly drawing of a fixture for milling a surface on a gear shift lever quadrant.

extent, these factors will determine the type of jig that can be designed.

The basic principles of jig design were presented in the chapter on Tool Economy. Although these principles are time-tested and applicable to most designs, they should not be construed as being iron-clad. A tool designer with adequate experience, judgment, and ingenuity may do what he sees fit, despite the rules.

Typical milling fixtures. Fig. 12 is an assembly drawing of a typical milling fixture. The machine is for milling a surface on a gear shift lever quadrant. The part is also shown on the drawing. Since no machining or great strength is required, the body of the fixture is an iron casting. The body has an elongated slot machined in it to accommodate a clamping bar. This type of fixture presents a design problem of holding the irregular-shaped casting (the part) securely in the correct position. To account for this difficulty, all points on the fixture against which the part comes in contact are hardened and ground, and clamping screws are provided where necessary to hold the work securely for the milling operation.

In the manufacture of automatic clothes washers a number of parts are milled, one of which is the gear housing. Fig. 13 shows a fixture for face milling four of these housings at one time, an example

Cincinnati Milling Machine Co.

Fig. 13. A fixture for face-milling four gear housings for automatic washers at one time.

of good fixture design. The part has been bored in the lower section
prior to the milling operation. The four gear housings are then located
in the milling fixture by means of fixed and movable locating plugs that
are actuated by levers, which can be seen on the extreme left in Fig. 13.
The housing rests against hardened pins inserted in the fixture, and
two clamps are provided, each clamp holding two parts, one part on
either side of the fixture. Additional clamping screws are also provided to prevent movement. This milling fixture design permits rapid
loading and unloading of parts.

Influencing factors. What holds true for jig design also holds true
for fixture design: the basic principles are the same, the designer must
often be ingenious, the rules are not steadfast. As mentioned previously, fixtures hold the part only, and in many applications take a much
heavier thrust because they must be fed into the cutting tool. Therefore, they require sturdy designs, and must be as close to the work table
as possible, holding the part securely without introducing distortion.
Clamps must be stronger than jigs and the locators more positive.

Besides the cost factor, the type of fixture to use in any situation
depends upon the machine on which the fixture will be mounted.
There are milling fixtures, lathe and turret lathe fixtures, boring fixtures, drilling and tapping fixtures, broaching fixtures, etc. Different
type machines call for different type fixtures, and each class of machine
calls for still further fixture refinements. In addition, there are vise
fixtures, face plate fixtures, V-block fixtures, and many other fixtures
used in conjunction with auxiliary tools.

Most large plants and even smaller plants have personnel in their
tool design departments who specialize in jig and fixture design. Management has come to attach great importance to those design features
which they once considered minor. In this age of specialization and
cost control, they know the significant savings that can result in good
jig and fixture designs. The field is diverse enough to challenge the ·
best tool designers.

Dies

In modern metalworking plants the use of metal stampings has
been constantly increasing due to the fact that stampings produced
from flat sheet metal have proved more economical than castings on
a great many kinds of parts. Formerly, castings were used extensively
because the size of power punch presses was a limiting factor in
stamping operations. Now the size of power punch presses is limited

only by the requirements of the metalworking plants. Because of their cost, forgings, fabrications and other forming operations never could approach the high-volume processing of castings and stampings. Stampings have an advantage over castings: when a stamping is produced by means of dies and punch presses, the part is finished or almost finished. This is not true of castings, which usually require several subsequent machining operations.

Basic points. In designing dies, certain basic points should be given careful consideration by the tool designer. These points are:

1. The type of die to be designed.
2. The number of parts to be produced.
3. The capacity of the power punches available.

Name of press............	Toledo	Consolidated	Consolidated	Consolidated	Verson	Bliss	Niagara	Niagara	Bliss
Size....................	5	6	5	3	3	54	156	510	5S
Mach. No...............	1964	976	899	2810	2836	2820	2808	2843	2825
Stroke of ram.......	2½	3½	3	2	2	1½	10	12	......
Adjustment of ram..	5½	5	4	2	2	None	5	4	......
Maximum die space.	8½	9¼	8	6⅜	6¼	9½	10	14½	......
Bolster width F-B...	18¼	22	17	12	12	12	19½	32	38
Bolster length R-L..	27½	34	29½	20	21¾	16	19	28½	33
Bolster thickness....	2	2¼	2	1¼	1½	1½	2⅜	3	4
Opening in bolster F-B and R-L......	6 D.	9¼D.	5¾D.	5 D.	6 D.	4	6½	6½x7	4
Opening in machine bed F-B and R-L..	12x16	17 D.	14 D.	8½ D.	8½ D.	7	*	16x16	25
Ram width F-B....	......	......	......	......	......	......	7¼	19	......
Ram length R-L....	......	......	......	......	......	......	9¼	23	......
Diameter of punch shank............	2½	2½	2½	1⁹⁄₁₆	1⁹⁄₁₆	1⁹⁄₁₆	2	3	......
Height of punch shank	2½	3	2½	2⅜	2⅜	2⅜	2½	3	......
Max. diameter of knockout pin....	......	1	¾	⅝	⅝	No	⅝	1	......
Max. ht.—K.O. pin above P. shank...	......	2	2½	1¼	1¼	No	3	5	......
Throat distance from C.L.▲ of ram.....	......	11	8¼	6	6¾	6	......	......	......
C.L.▲ of ram back to C.L.▲ of guide pin†.	......	6.	4½	3	3	‡	‡	‡	......
C.L.▲ of ram R and L to C.L.▲ of guide pin†.	......	7	5½	4½	4½	‡	‡	‡	......
Length of air cushion pins§............	......	......	......	......	......	......	......	7	......
Opening in sub-bolster......	......	......	......	......	◄	......	......	12x12	......
Thickness of sub-bolster............	......	......	......	......	......	......	......	4	......
Tonnage of press....	87½	56	36	22	26½	36	43	188	215

*Must use bolster.
†Applies only when guide pins protrude above upper die shoe.
‡Must be below closed die.
§Minimum below shoe when die is open.
▲Center line.

Fig. 14. Data sheet showing the critical dimensions of a number of punch presses.

204 TOOL DESIGN

Since the tool designer has no control of points 2 and 3, determining the type of dies to use, based on the product's design, and actually designing the die is his primary responsibility.

The types of dies most frequently used in average plant production are piercing, drawing, cutoff, parting, die casting, and forging dies, some of which will be covered in this section. Fig. 14 shows a typical data sheet containing the necessary dimensions of a number of punch

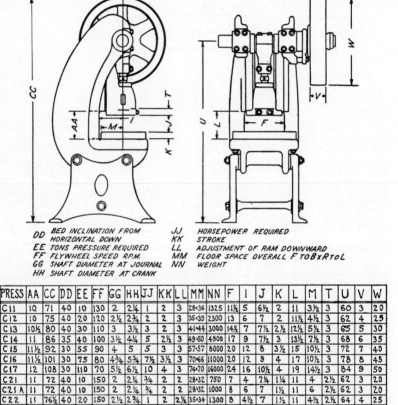

DD BED INCLINATION FROM HORIZONTAL DOWN
EE TONS PRESSURE REQUIRED
FF FLYWHEEL SPEED R.P.M.
GG SHAFT DIAMETER AT JOURNAL
HH SHAFT DIAMETER AT CRANK

JJ HORSEPOWER REQUIRED
KK STROKE
LL ADJUSTMENT OF RAM DOWNWARD
MM FLOOR SPACE OVERALL F TO B x R TO L
NN WEIGHT

PRESS	AA	CC	DD	EE	FF	GG	HH	JJ	KK	LL	MM	NN	F	I	J	K	L	M	T	U	V	W
C11	10	71	40	10	130	2	2¼	1	2	3	28×36	1325	11½	5	6½	2	11	3½	3	60	3	20
C12	10	75	40	20	120	2½	2¾	2	2	3	35×39	2300	13	6	7	2	11½	4½	3	62	4	25
C13	10½	80	40	30	110	3	3½	3	2	3	41×44	3000	14½	7	7½	2½	12½	5½	3	65	5	30
C14	11	86	35	40	100	3½	4¼	5	2½	3	49×50	4900	17	9	7½	3	13½	7½	3	68	6	35
C15	11½	92	30	55	90	4	5	5	3	3	57×57	8000	20	12	8	3½	15	10½	3	72	7	40
C16	11½	101	30	75	80	4¾	5¾	7½	3½	3	70×66	11000	20	12	9	4	17	10½	3	78	8	45
C17	12	108	30	110	70	5½	6½	10	4	3	74×70	16000	24	16	10½	4	19	14½	3	84	9	50
C21	11	72	40	10	150	2	2¼	¾	2	2	28×32	750	7	4	7¼	1¼	11	4	2½	62	3	20
C21 A	11	72	40	10	150	2	2¼	¾	2	2	28×32	1000	8	6	7	1½	11	6	2½	62	3	20
C22	11	76½	40	20	150	2½	2¾	1	2	2½	35×34	1300	8	4½	7	1½	11	4½	2½	64	4	25
C22 A	11	76½	40	20	150	2½	2¾	1	2	2½	35×34	1600	9½	6½	7	1½	11	6½	2½	64	4	25
C23	12	81	40	30	125	3	3½	2	2	2½	41×40	2400	9½	6½	7¾	1¾	12	6½	2½	66	5	30
C23 A	12	81	40	30	125	3	3½	2	2	2½	41×40	2900	13	9	7¼	2	12	9	2½	66	5	30
C24	13	87½	35	40	100	3½	4¼	3	2½	3	49×46	4300	13½	9½	7½	2½	13	9½	3	70	6	35
C25	14	87½	30	55	100	4	5	5	3	3	57×52	5300	12½	9	8	2½	14	9	3	70	7	40
C25 A	14	93½	30	55	100	4	5	5	3	3	57×52	10000	15	11	7¾	2¾	14	11	3	73½	7	40

Fig. 15. An open-back inclinable punch press with data sheet showing critical dimensions for various size presses.

presses. By looking at this data sheet, the tool designer can usually determine what press the die under consideration should be designed for. If the die has certain specifications that can't be altered, the machine tool designer may be called upon to design a special machine. The open-back inclinable punch press (shown in Fig. 15) is one frequently used in industrial plants. The accompanying data sheet gives the designer all the necessary information. By referring to the data sheet in Fig. 14, the various specifications and dimensions can be identified.

Basic conditions. In die design the following conditions must be observed:

1. The die should fit comfortably into the die space of the press designated for the operation.

2. The height of the die in its closed or lowest position should be such that the jaw of the press is also at its lowest position of the press stroke.

3. The die's shape should be such that the press stroke will allow sufficient clearance to load and unload parts from the die.

Verson Allsteel Press Co.

Fig. 16. The die stations of an automatic transfer press for stamping drawers.

4. The die's design should make the most economical use of material; in other words, insure that wastage after pressing is kept to a minimum.

Fig. 16 shows finished stampings from a 450 ton automatic feed press designed for stamping of metal drawers in one operation. To produce these drawers in one operation on one integrated machine represents the latest in automatic stamping methods. Previously, five separate machines were needed to perform the operation. The press is mechanically operated and electronically controlled.

Die casting dies. Fig. 17 shows a die casting die, which consists of two matching halves of polished alloy steel cut to form a cavity between them shaped exactly like the final part desired. The choice of steel depends largely on the metal to be die cast. While zinc die casting calls for intermediate grades of die steels, which have been heat treated for long production runs, the higher melting point alloys of aluminum, magnesium, and copper require special die steels.

Die casting dies may have a single cavity for making one casting for each cycle of the die casting machine or, when comparatively

American Zinc Institute, Inc.

Fig. 17.   A die casting die.

small parts with simple shapes are to be cast in large quantities, several cavities may be incorporated in the die. If such cavities are duplicates, the die is known as a combination die, which is well suited in the production of different die castings for use in a single-product assembly.

Because of the high precision with which steel die cavities can be machined and polished, a very high degree of surface smoothness and dimensional accuracy can be obtained in the die castings; also, every die extrusion in a long production run will be sufficiently identical in size and shape.

Drop Forging Association

Fig. 18. One of the steps in the fabrication of forging dies.

Forging, sub-press dies. Fig. 18 shows one of the steps followed in the fabrication of forging dies, which are machined from rectangular die blocks. The operation illustrated is the outlining of the finishing impression on the machined face of the die block. It consists of first laying out the template of the finishing impression, which is to sink in the die block, on its machined face. A color background is provided on the face of the die block to secure a convenient surface for the marking of the outline of the forging. For shaping a forging to exact contour, the location of the finishing impression in each die block is usually arranged in such a way that the weight center of the forged product is at the geometric center of the ram, or mid way from side to side and from front rear of the ram.

Dies which use leader pins are called sub-press dies, an example of which is shown in Fig. 19. The product formed by this particular sub-press die, an automobile clutch disk, is shown in Fig. 20. Leader

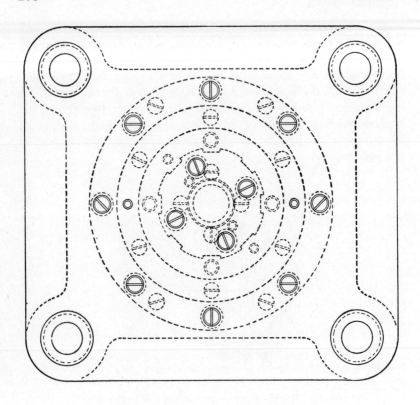

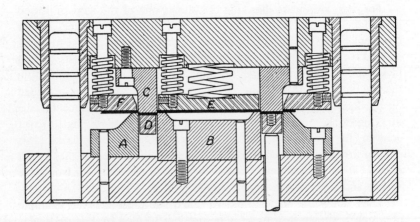

Fig. 19.   Top and side views of a sub-press blanking die for a clutch disk.

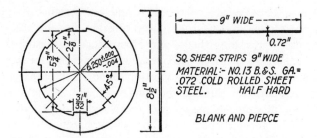

SQ. SHEAR STRIPS 9" WIDE
MATERIAL :- NO.13 B.&S. GA.=
.072 COLD ROLLED SHEET
STEEL.   HALF HARD

BLANK AND PIERCE

Fig. 20. An automobile clutch disk. This is the part machined by the blanking die of Fig. 19.

pins hold the upper and lower die members in perfect alignment while the stamping operation is in progress, thereby processing parts that fit properly when assembled.

The blank shown in Fig. 20 is cut to shape from a sheared strip nine inches wide. The diameter of the hole and the spacing of the notches must be accurate. This is achieved by using a die set having four leader pins and four bushings, as shown in Fig. 19. The main components of this die are: *A,* outer die ring, which cuts the outside diameter; *B,* central die section, which cuts the inside diameter and notches; *C,* punch, which is made in the form of a ring and so designed that it can pass freely between die sections; *D,* pressure ring, which is spring operated, its purpose being to eject the finished blank from the dies; *E,* spring-operated plate which ejects the center slug from the punch; and *F,* spring-operated ejector plate, which removes the remainder of the strip from the outside surface of the punch.

Drawing dies. These dies are designed to suit a wide range of operations. Some dies are very simple and consist only of a punch and die for drawing shallow cup-shaped objects from flat blanks in one

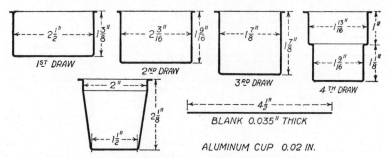

Fig. 21. Layout of the drawing operations for an aluminum cup.

operation. Other dies are complicated and are designed to perform several operations in one stroke. Deep-drawing dies are designed to produce deep cups, long shells, and other deep-drawn shapes, some of which cannot be drawn in one operation because the drawing punch diameter would be so small in proportion to the depth of the draw that the punch would tear through the stamped metal. To produce such shapes, several drawing passes are necessary, and periodically the metal must be annealed because of cold-work hardness developed as the metal is subjected to the drawing operations. When developing a deep draw, the usual practice is to lay out and analyze the sequence of drawing operations. Fig. 21 presents a layout of operations whereby an aluminum cup is produced from a flat blank.

Progressive dies. Progressive piercing and blanking dies are used extensively in producing stampings. *Progressive dies* are so called because of the sequence of operations performed in a single die. Usually the perforating station in a die is the first operation, followed by notching, blanking, or cutting-off operations. Fig. 22 shows a rectangular part, made from a piece of flat brass, with an elongated slot punched in it. The piercing and blanking punches are shown in section views. The stripper, for removing excess material from the die or

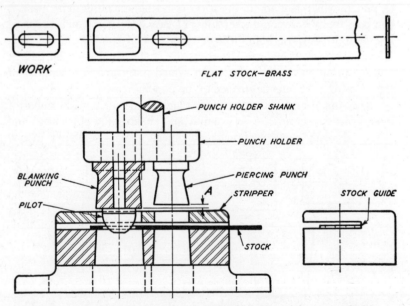

Fig. 22.   A simple progressive piercing and blanking die, and the part machined.

punch, is mounted directly to the top of the die section in the die. A guide is provided at the rear of the die so that when the strip has traversed through the die it will be guided in the correct position for performing the various operations. The blanking punch is provided with a pilot so that it will locate properly in the elongated slot produced by the piercing punch.

To cover even the general types of all the die designs currently available on the market would require an entire book. What we have presented gives an idea of the scope of the field. As with cutting tool and jig and fixture design, the design of dies is often, especially in large plants, assigned to personnel who specialize in it. The field of die design is a challenging one; as with all phases of tool design it requires judgment and ingenuity of the personnel engaged in it.

Molds

Although the tool engineer and tool designer in our context are not directly concerned with molds, they should be acquainted with the field since molded products oftentimes serve as the raw material

PLASTICS COMPARATOR

PLASTIC MATERIAL	Toughness (Impact Strength)	Flexural Strength	Tensile Strength	Color Suiting	Cold Flow	Water Resistance	Acid Resistance	Caustic Resistance	Solvent Resistance	Dimensional Change on Aging	Heat Resistance (Continuous Heat)	Flammability	Heat Insulation	Specific Gravity	Hardness	Loss Factor	Resistivity	Dielectric Strength	Moldability Around Inserts
Phenolic: General Purpose	10	3	3	7	1	6	3	4	1	4	2	3	2	8	5	10	7	4	2
Phenolic: Low-Loss	11	3	7	7	1	3	4	4	1	2	3	1	7	12	3	4	3	3	2
Phenolic: Heat-Resistant	9	4	8	7	1	3	4	4	1	1	1	1	7	13	2	○	8	8	2
Phenolic: Acid and Alkali-Resistant	10	6	8	7	1	4	2	3	1	5	3	2	2	5	4	○	○	7	3
Phenolic: Shock-Resistant	2	1	5	7	1	7	4	5	1	6	3	4	3	10	5	○	9	8	1
Phenolic: Transparent	7	1	3	7	1	4	3	3	1	5	3	2	2	6	4	7	5	6	3
Urea	8	1	1	1	2	9	4	4	1	7	7	5	5	11	1	9	4	2	4
Polystyrene	7	2	7	4	4	1	1	1	3	3	6	6	1	1	6	1	1	1	6
Cellulose-Acetate	4	6	9	3	8	11	4	6	3	9	5	6	4	7	9	8	6	5	5
Aceto-Butyrate	1	5	10	3	6	8	4	4	3	8	4	6	6	4	8	3	○	○	5
Ethyl-Cellulose	3	2	6	6	7	10	4	2	3	8	5	6	4	2	8	2	2	1	5
Methyl-Methacrylate	6	1	4	2	5	5	2	2	3	8	9	6	2	3	7	5	○	2	6
Vinyl (No Filler)	5	1	2	5	3	1	1	1	2	3	8	5	2	9	7	6	2	1	5

Bakelite Corp.

Fig. 23. This plastics comparator table shows the relative merits of the various materials and facilitates selection of materials which are outstanding in the properties desired.

for their product; also, tool designs will be influenced by the shape and composition of the raw material. Molds are the tools used in foundry practice, which may be described as that branch of engineering dealing with the melting of metal and the subsequent pouring of this molten metal into molds to form castings.

Castings are made in large quantities in two general classes of metals or their alloys. The largest and most important class is made from the iron (ferrous) group of alloys, consisting of gray cast iron, malleable cast iron, carbon steel, and alloy steel. The secondary class is the non-ferrous group, consisting of the copper-base alloys—brass and bronze; aluminum alloys; zinc-base alloys; and tin- and lead-base alloys. In addition, an increasingly important role is being played by plastic-molded products: the phenolic, polystyrene, vinyl, and other plastics. (See Fig. 23.)

Types of molds. There are two general types of molds: those made of sand and those of metal. When judged on a tonnage basis, most molds are of sand. Metal molds are being used in increasing numbers, particularly for making small castings in large quantities, in die casting of zinc or aluminum alloys, and in centrifugal casting of metals. Sand molds are divided into three groups: green sand molding, dry sand molding, and loam molding. Metal molds are made of heat-resistant metals such as alloy steels, carbide steels, and even cast iron, and the casting surface coated with china clay and lamp black.

Aside from the design they must impart to the casting, molds and cores can be extremely critical in design. The mold must be properly vented, supported, and good gating must be provided; also, adequate risers are needed to compensate for shrinkage. A good molding process, including the mold design, will produce:

1. Sound castings, those free from internal impurities, such as blowholes, porous spots, shrinkage, etc.

2. Clean castings, those free from imperfections, such as slag and sand.

3. Smooth castings, those having a uniform surface free from scabs, buckles, cold shuts, swells.

The raw material the manufacturing plant receives is inspected for quality before being sent out into the plant. In the case of castings, the inspector should accept only those that are sound, clean, and smooth. (To this end he is justified in calling for X-rays or magna-

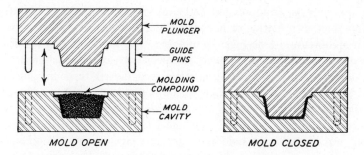

Fig. 24. In the compression molding process the material is placed in a mold cavity by the press operator. When the mold is closed, the molding compound is compressed to the part's shape and held in this form until it hardens.

fluxing of random castings.) Castings with excessive amounts of blow-holes, sand, and impregnated slag will not be as strong structurally as acceptable castings.

   Plastics molding. Plastics molding is similar in most respects to

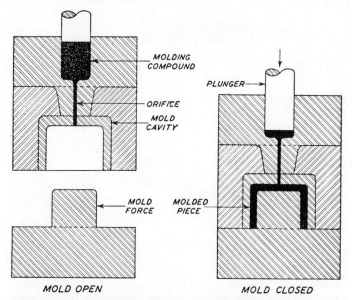

Fig. 25. In the transfer molding process material is loaded in a well above the mold. This well connects with the mold cavity through a small orifice. When the molding press closes, it brings the two mold halves together and holds them firmly. Additional pressure compresses the compound, which flows through the orifice and fills the mold cavity.

molding metals. Compression and transfer moldings are used extensively for thermosetting or hot-set plastics, which harden or set under heat and pressure (see Figs. 24 and 25). The thermosetting materials may also be injection molded in special injection machines. The hardening of thermosetting materials is achieved through chemical change in the resin which takes place under heat and pressure. The press and mold hold the compound under great pressure while this action is in process. After the chemical change is effected, the cured resin will continue to hold the filler particles of the compound in compression when the mold pressure is released. The part has then been formed to the shape of the mold.

Injection molding is used primarily for thermoplastic or cold-set plastics, which are plastic when heated and solid after cooling. In molding thermoplastic products, the material is melted by heat and

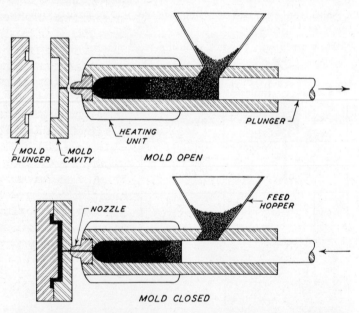

Fig. 26. Injection molding is done by an automatic machine. The molding material is loaded in a feed hopper. When the mold opens, the plunger permits an additional supply of material to drop into the cylinder. On the closing stroke, the machine closes and locks the mold halves tightly together. When the plunger moves to the left, new material from the hopper is forced into the heating unit, where it is melted. This added volume forces material out of the nozzle and into the mold cavity to form a molded part. The mold is cooled so that the compound hardens quickly. When the mold is opened, the part is freed.

pressure. The plastic mass of hot material is injected into a relatively cold mold, causing the material to harden and retain the shape of the mold.

Thermoplastic materials may be extended into continuous lengths of regular cross sections, such as tubes, channels, and rods (see Fig. 26). This is accomplished by forcing the hot plastic material through a die which shapes the product. The process is similar in effect to the forming of a ribbon of toothpaste as the substance is squeezed from the tube.

Gages

As mentioned in the Tool Economy chapter, inspection tools are classified as: (1) inspection gages, (2) reference gages, which are used to determine sizes of other gages or to calibrate instruments, and (3) working gages, the feelers, calipers, and similar gages used by the operator for any gaging necessary to the operation he is performing (see Fig. 27). The Tool Economy chapter defines and classifies various inspection gages.

Influencing factors. Briefly, in gage design certain factors which are applicable to all types of designs must be considered. Certain prin-

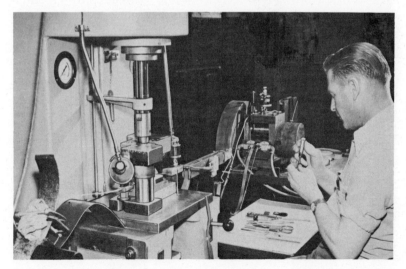

American Brake Shoe Co.

Fig. 27. The operator is using a micrometer gage. In this application the instrument is called a working gage.

ciples, especially those of good design practice and economy, must be adhered to. The product, its quantity and quality, and the manufacturing process require close scrutiny. While gages which give accurate readings are essential, practical tolerances must be figured into the design. With use gages will wear and the readings they give will change. Although it is not practical to maintain exactly the same level of accuracy, it is necessary that predictable accuracy be designed into gages.

The limits to which a gage should be constructed is specified by the designer. A rule-of-thumb figure for gage tolerance is ten percent of the tolerance desired in the part, although this is not always feasible in certain high-precision products being designed today. The tool designer should never specify a dimension without tolerance, because such needless precision, even if the dimension is not critical, will increase the gage's cost beyond economical bounds.

Design goals. Gages should be designed that are as foolproof, as durable, and as easy to manipulate as possible. Since some types of gages are subject to abnormal abrasive action, the designer should specify materials able to resist this type of year. Hardened steel is satisfactory for the points of contact of most gages. Where extreme wear is likely, inserts of cemented carbide, ceramics, or other ultra-hard materials are advised. In certain applications it is even advisable to make the wearing points disposable, as is done with certain cutting tool tips. This policy may prove economical overall, since gage maintenance becomes simpler, with reduced downtime and labor costs.

CHAPTER NINE

Locating and Clamping

Although locating and clamping are two distinct subjects, we will consider them together here since one follows the other in machine setups. Strictly speaking, locating and clamping are related only to the extent that clamping procedures are partly influenced and determined by location. The choice of locating points, however, should not be based on available clamping devices. The points of location should be decided on first, then the clamping means chosen that will complement the locating points according to accepted principles.

Because of time limitations, locating and clamping procedures take on a special importance. This chapter emphasizes those procedures which give rapid, sure, and accurate means of locating and clamping.

Machining Forces

When a part is machined it is subjected to a combination of forces the direction and intensity of which depend upon the type of machining operation. In this chapter we will merely recognize that drilling, turning, milling, grinding, broaching, and other distinct machining operations create distinct machining forces that differ not only in magnitude but also in the direction in which they are applied. For example, if holes are drilled in a part, the force created is one of continuous pushing and twisting. This machine force is known as combined thrust and torque. On the other hand, if a part is milled, the forces exerted are a series of rapidly repeated impacts, composed of either push-and-lift or pull-and-push-downward forces, depending upon whether conventional or climb milling is employed. For the tool designer, a good policy is to design the work-holding device so that the cutting force will tend to push the part against the enclosure in the holding device and not away from it.

LOCATING PRINCIPLES

In volume manufacturing it is essential that parts be accurately located in their work-holding devices in order to achieve consistent results when machining them. The success of interchangeable manufacture depends on a consistent uniformity of parts, which means locators must be durable, mechanically sound, and the points suitably located. A proper setup initially means all the parts in a lot can be identically positioned, thereby allowing part uniformity.

For best results, a sufficient number of surfaces on each part must have locating points so that the part can be contained securely in the work-holding device. The locating points must be arranged to suit each part design, whether the geometric form of the part be simple or complex. To best study this, our investigation will be concerned with typical examples that point out good locating practices.

Part Location

Locators are essential elements in work-holding devices. They engage the locating points on the part for accurately positioning it with respect to the holding device and the cutting tool. Locators are mounted on the body of the holding device so they may be easily removed for replacement or repair, as shown in Fig. 1. A hand-clamped fixture and locators are illustrated, which locate and hold a cylinder head while four slots and two side bosses are milled simultaneously. Fig. 2 shows the part in place, the location of surfaces to be milled, the milling cutter, locating points, and the gage block. This

Cincinnati Milling Machine Co.

Fig. 1.   A hand-clamped fixture and locators, used in holding and locating a cylinder head for milling operations.

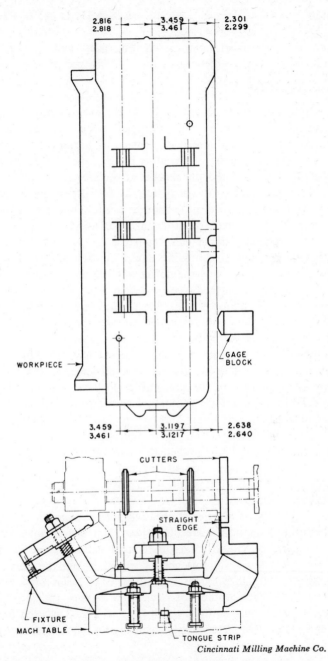

Cincinnati Milling Machine Co.

Fig. 2. Drawing of the fixture in Fig. 1, showing the part in place, the location of surfaces to be milled, the milling cutter, locating points, and the gage block.

material and illustrations on locating parts and locators has been adapted from the excellent treatise *Milling and Milling Machines*.[1]

Locating Points

Locating points accurately locate the part in the jig or fixture and establish the location of the surfaces to be machined with respect to the reference surface. In the fixture of Fig. 1, the locating points are two pins which fit into locating holes of the cylinder head, thereby locating the slots and the machined surfaces of the bosses with respect to the reference gage in Fig. 2. These pins are inserted in the fixture frame and held in position by a nut. They can be removed for replacement or repair when damaged or worn out.

A reference surface (also called a gaging or setting surface) is usually provided in a holding device for setting the cutting tool in proper relationship with the device and the part. In the fixture of Fig. 1, the reference surface is provided in a gage block held on an extension of the fixture frame. The surface is accurately located from the locating pins, and is aligned to give the exact location of the finished surface of the bosses, seen in Fig. 2.

By means of spacing collars and shims, the milling cutters are located on the arbor at the accurate distance given in Fig. 2. The fixture is aligned on the machine table by means of tongue strips, which are located under the fixture and fit into the table T-slots. The alignment between cutters and part is now obtained by adjusting the machine slides and holding a straight edge against the reference surface of the gage block. When the side cutting face of the side mill, for milling the bosses on the cylindrical head, is in line with the straight edge, the cutters will be in position to mill the slots and the surface of the bosses.

Fig. 3 shows a series of locating holes situated in a straight line, thereby simulating a plane. It is important to remember that two or more surfaces should not be used for location in one definite direction. An example to this general rule is when the part's accuracy achieved through previous machining is in terms of a more liberal tolerance, which would not interfere with the specified dimensional accuracy of the part. The drilling jig in Fig. 3 is used in drilling a steel plate. The plate is held against only one imaginary plane (in

---

[1] *A Treatise on Milling And Milling Machines*, THE CINCINNATI MILLING MACHINE CO., Cincinnati, Ohio, 1951, Third Ed.

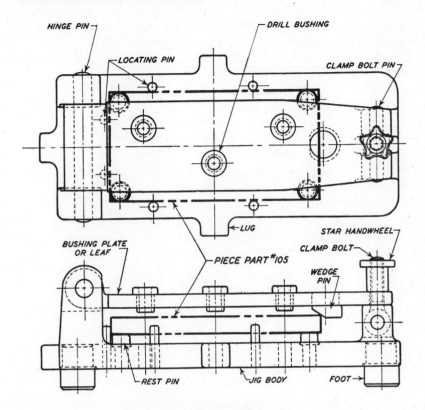

Fig. 3.   A leaf drill jig for drilling a plate.

one direction), which is formed by drawing a tangent line to the two locating pins shown at the left of the figure.

Requirements for Selecting Locating Points

Proper selection of locating points is very important, since they determine the accuracy with which the part will be machined in all the operations to be performed on it. For this purpose it is desirable, as far as possible, not to destroy locating points but to keep the locating points the same for all operations in which the dimensions are related to each other. Therefore, no accumulation of error can result, as would be the case when the part's location is shifted from one set to a different set of locating points.

Locating points should be placed as far apart as possible, and arranged to insure optimum accuracy of the part. The basic require-

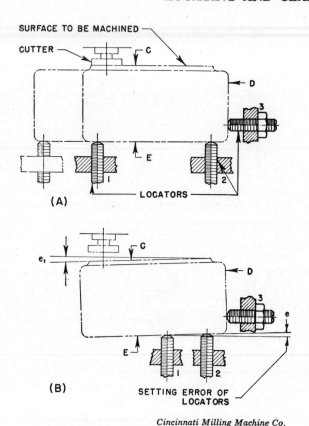

Fig. 4. A line diagram showing the desirable placement of
locators when positioning the part from an external surface.

ments governing the selection of locating points, both on the work-
holding device and on the part, may be illustrated by the following
hypothetical condition, shown in Fig. 4.

To machine surface C or the rectangular-shaped part shown in
View A of Fig. 4, the part is located from the previously machined
surfaces E and D by means of locators, indicated by the numerals 1,
2, and 3. To achieve stability and accuracy in the setting of the part,
locators 1 and 2 are placed as far apart as the length of the surface E
will permit. For the same reason, locator 3 on surface D will be
placed near the corner adjacent to surface E.

When locators 1, 2, and 3 have been accurately set in the fixture,
no difficulty will be experienced in accurately locating and machining

surface C in relation to surfaces D and E. If locators 1 and 2 were placed close together, as in View B of Fig. 4, the error e in the setting of locators 1 and 2 would be amplified to a value e_1 over the length of the milled surface.

To obtain the best results, therefore, locators should be placed at a distance which is at least equal to the length of the surface to be machined. On the other hand, if the locating points can be located farther apart than the length of the surface to be milled, as indicated in the phantom section in View A, any inaccuracy of contact between the part and the locators would be correspondingly reduced. Locator 3 determines the longitudinal setting of the part. It will likewise affect the accuracy of part location if placed too far away from the line connecting locators 1 and 2.

Design of Locators

The design of locators is subject to variations which are dictated by a number of factors, including the size of the parts, the character of the operation, and the method of machining used to meet production requirements. Fig. 5 shows an arrangement of locating connecting rods for a cap sawing operation.

The operation is performed in reciprocal milling, with the parts positioned abreast. Each air-operated fixture holds four connecting

Cincinnati Milling Machine Co.

Fig. 5.   A setup for locating connecting rods for a cap sawing operation.

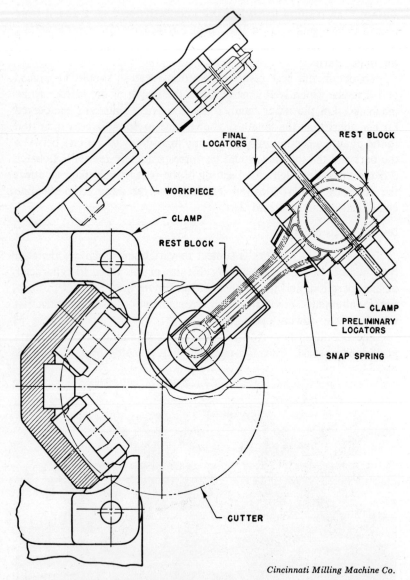

FINAL
LOCATORS

REST BLOCK

WORKPIECE

CLAMP

REST BLOCK

CLAMP

PRELIMINARY
LOCATORS

SNAP SPRING

CUTTER

Cincinnati Milling Machine Co.

Fig. 6. Details of construction of preliminary and final locators used in fixtures shown
in Fig. 5.

rods, one in each of the four stations. The connecting rods are clamped
simultaneously by operating an air valve at the front of each fixture.

To hold the connecting rods before clamping, the four stations are provided with preliminary side locators, shown in Fig. 6. These locators are made in the form of double-slotted blocks loosely fitting the connecting rods around the four machined faces of the clamping screw bosses.

A snap spring holds the connecting rods in the preliminary locator and a rest block supports the rod near the crankpin end. When all stations have been loaded, the operator turns the air valve and the clamping force locates the connecting rods against the final locators, which have two locating surfaces, each serving adjacent rods. The final locators also serve as rest blocks, and are slotted to allow for saw clearance.

TYPES OF LOCATORS

Pin-Type Locators

When drilled or bored holes are used for aligning the part in the fixture, the locators are pins which fit into the holes in the part. The accuracy of locating the part will depend on the arrangement of the pins and also on the fit between the locating holes and locating pins. If these holes and pins are set diagonally to the surface C to be milled, as shown in View A of Fig. 7, a maximum looseness e between the hole and pin X, for example, will result in a smaller displacement e_1 of the part relative to the pin (as the looseness is taken up by rotating the part clockwise around pin Y at an angle to the surface C) than would result if the pins were located as in View B, Fig. 7.

In the latter case, the two locating pins are on a line parallel to the surface C, and the displacement e_1 relative to the pin W will be almost the same as the looseness e between the hole and the pin. This occurs when the part is rotated clockwise around the pin Z, which fits closely in the corresponding hole. It is preferable, therefore, to have a diagonal arrangement of the locator pins whenever possible.

Three locating points are needed to locate a part from external plane surfaces, as shown in Fig. 4. But when the part is located from bored holes, each locating pin is equivalent to two locating points, because it locates the part in any two directions at right angles to each other. Therefore, two solid pins are the equivalent of four locating points; as a result, one of the points is not needed and even if it were used, it would only add to the difficulties of locating the part within

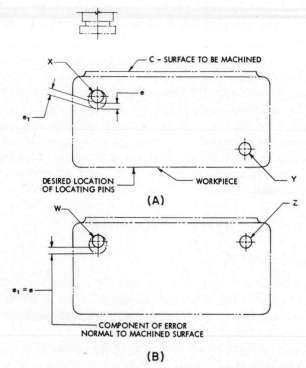

Fig. 7. A desirable location for locating pins when positioning
the part from bored holes.

the fixed distance of the rotating pins. To avoid this condition, the superfluous locating point is eliminated by relieving from one pin most of the cylindrical surface except two diametrically-opposed small circular lands. Then there is only one definite point of location, this being in the direction normal to the small circular land.

The diamond-shaped pin, as shown in Fig. 8, which is usually designed for large locating holes, permits only a slight movement of the part in the direction normal to that of the opposed circular lands of the pin. These two circular lands, as shown in Fig. 9, together with the other pin, determine the location of the part. The relieved sides of the diamond-shaped pin will allow easy positioning of the part, although the distance between the locating holes may vary slightly from one part to the next within the nominal value of the machining tolerances used.

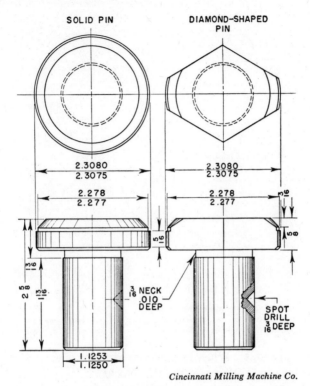

SOLID PIN   DIAMOND-SHAPED PIN

Cincinnati Milling Machine Co.

Fig. 8. A typical design of locating pins for large locating holes.

To facilitate location of the part in the fixture, the height of the solid pin is sometimes made greater than that of the diamond-shaped pin, so that the operator can locate the part on one pin at a time. For purposes of economy and uniformity of design, the dimensions, shapes, and sometimes the sizes of locating pins should be standardized. Designs of typical solid and diamond-shaped locating pins are shown in detail in Fig. 8. The latter type pin is recommended where very small locators are required.

To ease insertion of the pin into the part, both types of locating pins are chamfered on the upper end, and are provided with a lead diameter slightly smaller than the diameter of the locating hole in the part. As mentioned previously, the diamond-shaped pin should be placed with the two circular lands aligned at right angles to the surface to be machined, as shown in Fig. 9. Locating pins are also made with a chamfered end only, as shown in Fig. 10. This takes the place

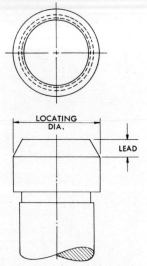

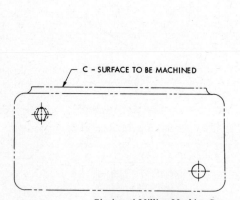

Cincinnati Milling Machine Co.

Fig. 9. Location of a diamond-shaped pin in relation to the surface to be machined. The lands are aligned at right angles to this surface.

Cincinnati Milling Machine Co.

Fig. 10. A variation in locating pin design, using a conical lead instead of a two-diameter lead.

of the lead diameter. When in position, locating pins should project above the bearing surfaces or the rest blocks.

Fixed Locators

Locating pins may be either fixed or retractable. Fixed locating pins are used in the work-holding device shown in Fig. 11. Here the fixed pins locate an aluminum cylinder head set up in a rotary fixture for milling a series of fins. The cylinder head is supported and located on the large diameter stud which centers it on the inside bore. The final location for milling the fins is obtained by means of a diamond-shaped pin, which engages the locating hole in the joining surface of the cylinder head. In this operation, the cylinder head cooling fins are milled to the required depth by guiding the cutting tool with a tracer, which follows the contour of the template as the part is rotated with the fixture.

In this example, it is found that it is not always possible to separate the function of supporting from that of locating, especially when the part is supported on a center hole, between centers, or in V-blocks. In the case shown in Fig. 11, the large diameter shoulder on the fix-

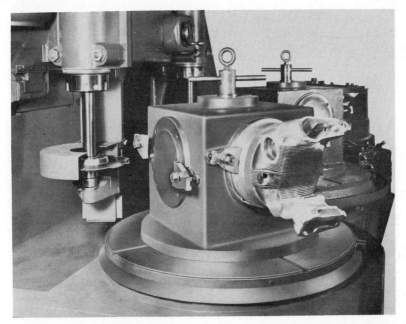

Cincinnati Milling Machine Co.

Fig. 11. Fixed locating pins locate an aluminum cylinder head in a rotary fixture for milling the head's cooling fins.

ture supports the cylinder head and at the same time locates it both vertically and laterally, while the diamond-shaped pin locates it radially. The center stud performs the function of both supporting and locating the cylinder head.

Retractable Locators

Locating pins are sometimes made retractable so the part can be laid down on the rest blocks and then slid into position before inserting the pins. In fact, this design is highly desirable if there is any chance of interference during load and unload operations. Fig. 12 shows an arrangement using this method of locating the part, a cylindrical block. In this arrangement the locating pins are mounted on the ends of a crossbar, which is moved up and down as a centrally-located eccentric is operated by a hand lever. The bar is balanced by two springs placed at equal distances from the eccentric. As shown in Fig. 12, the lever is located at the front of the machine, which is used

Cincinnati Milling Machine Co.

Fig. 12.   Retractable locating pins for locating a cylinder block.

in machining various surfaces on a cylindrical block held in a built-in fixture. The locating pins are normally in the retracted position. When the part is moved into position, the operator rotates the lever to raise the pins, and also moves the cylinder block slightly to ease the engagement of the pins with the locating holes. After the part has been located and clamped, the pins are retracted.

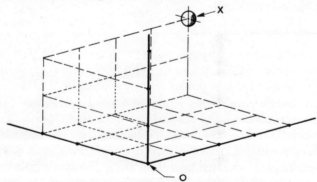

Fig. 13.   The movements the sphere X makes with respect to point O can be resolved into no more than six basic movements.

To further ease the insertion of the pins and reduce the time required for locating the part in the fixture, both locating pins are made with a diamond-shaped head, as shown in Fig. 8, with the circular lands at right angles to the surfaces to be milled. This permits a slight variation in the location of the part in the direction parallel to the surface to be milled. The slight movement of the cylinder block by the operator makes it easier to position the part, and has no appreciable effect on the accuracy of location of the block.

V-Type Locators

Before this type of locator can be described, we must understand the different movements a free body can make with respect to some point in space. Fig. 13 shows a point O in space, through which three co-ordinate axes have been drawn. The sphere X represents a free body. It can be shown mathematically that any movements this body makes with respect to point O can be resolved into not more than six elementary movements: three motions parallel to the co-ordinate axes and three rotations about these axes, each motion and rotation pertaining to one axis. Usually six movements are not necessary to de-

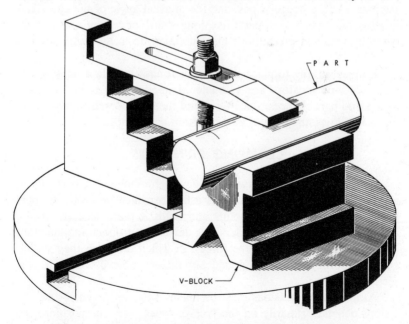

Fig. 14. A V-block used to hold round stock in preparation for drilling.

scribe a part's motions in locating applications. Perfect freedom means all six movements are possible. Some loss of freedom occurs when less than six movements are possible. For complete confinement all six movements must be prevented.

By itself, the V-block locator shown in Fig. 14 eliminates four of these basic movements; the remaining two do not affect the machining operation. Note that the part is round stock, the most usual shape in V-type locator applications. The main object of locating a round body in V-blocks is to position its axis in a definite direction. For many simple or initial machining operations this is all that is required.

A simple V-type locator provides two points for location. A locating point on a radius is necessary for complete confinement. The strap clamp in Fig. 14 provides a third point which, together with the V-block, completely confines the round part. In more refined setups the strap clamp may be replaced by a sliding V-block which gives a more positive locating point, especially with respect to rotational movements.

V-type locators can become quite complicated in design. This is necessary because of variations in the part's diameter or rounded sections, surface irregularities, and the unusual angle of the cut. Also, there is the chance that parts like long shafts or tubing may not be perfectly true and precautions must be taken to account for any deviations.

Besides serving to place the axes of round parts in a definite position, V-type locators are valuable in applications requiring swift setups and part changes, since they lend themselves well to foolproofing possibilities and ease of part insertion and removal.

CLAMPING PRINCIPLES

As stated earlier, a *fixture* is a device for holding a part during a machining operation. A *clamp* is a fixture which positions the part firmly against the locating points and holds it there securely during the machining operation. A clamping device must direct and maintain certain forces. The size of the forces, in which direction they should act, where they must be applied are factors we will cover in this section.

A number of decisions must be made in clamp design. These decisions depend primarily on the type of locator and its position, the part's design, and the cutting forces to be opposed. Other decisions depend on economic considerations (see the Tool Economy chapter), the size of forces available to actuate the clamp, the proportions of a clamp that enable it to develop a desired force and resist excessive counterforces.

Clamps hold the part against the cutting thrust by means of frictional forces set up between the clamp and part at their points of mutual contact. When the cutting thrust is relatively powerful, frictional forces alone may not be adequate to prevent movement of the part; consequently, properly placed positive stops are necessary. The practice in some plants is to use locators as stops. To insure lasting accuracy, however, locators should not be subjected to loads for which they were not designed. In order not to interfere with locators, positive stops are adjustable, like wedges or screws, and placed into position after the part has been located and clamped.

Designing Clamping Devices

A number of rules are observed in the design and use of clamps.

Cincinnati Milling Machine Co.

Fig. 15. A V-block fixture used in supporting a crankshaft from the turned crankpin for milling the contour of crankcheeks.

Although these rules may require modification in individual applications, the following are the most important for general use:

1. If possible, clamps should be located immediately above the rest points or surfaces, as shown in Figs. 1 and 15. If this condition is not observed, the part may spring or lift because each supporting point will then act as a fulcrum. The clamping fixture shown in Fig. 15 is also an example of a V-type centralizing bearing surface, which is used to support a crankshaft for milling the crankcheeks to the contour of the special milling cutter. The 180° location of the cranks permits milling the contour of both cheeks at one setting, using a seven inch diameter shell end mill that is profile ground to the required radius.

2. All side clamps should press downward and inward, so that they will tend to seat the part in the fixture, as shown in Figs. 5 and 15.

3. If possible, clamps should be manipulated from the operator's side of the fixtures. This is a safety measure as well as one of motion economy.

4. When cams and wedges are used for clamping, they should be so arranged that the direction of load tends to tighten rather than loosen them.

5. If possible, clamps should be made retractable so that the operator can load and unload the part without interference from them.

6. Clamps which are liable to move in tightening should be avoided in high volume processing. In other words, clamps should be as foolproof as possible in operations requiring speed or where the operator is relatively unskilled.

7. The clamping force required must be considered along with the clamp's design. A suitable design in all other respects may not furnish enough force to hold the part securely in applications where excessive cutting thrusts or machine vibrations are encountered.

8. The size of the part must enter into clamp design considerations, since some clamps are more suitable for a particular size.

9. The surfaces of the part must enter into clamp design considerations, since rough surfaces, such as unfinished castings, require a greater travel of the clamp in the clamping range.

10. The number of setups must be known in clamp design considerations. A clamp that is comparatively difficult to set up should not be used in operations calling for frequent setups.

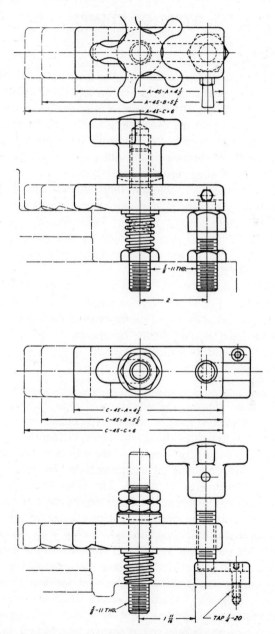

Fig. 16.   The top view shows a clamp with spring; the bottom view shows a clamp with lock nuts and a hand knob in the heel.

TYPES OF CLAMPS

Hand Clamps

Although hand clamps constitute the great majority of clamping devices, we will not discuss them here in any detail because of their relatively simple design. Briefly, hand clamps are levers and are operated in accordance with the usual physical laws for lever action. The fulcrum is located between the heel and the clamping end of the clamp. Fig. 16 (top) shows a clamp with a spring which is widely used on various types of inexpensive jigs and fixtures. It may be purchased as standard equipment and comes in three lengths. The clamp washers and rest are hardened, the stud is alloy steel, heat treated for toughness, and the hand knob is made of steel. There is a coil spring underneath the clamp so that the clamp springs away from the part when the hand knob is loosened, permitting the rapid removal of the part from the fixture.

Fig. 16 (bottom) shows a clamp similar to that in the left view, but it is capable of a wider range of adjustment. The clamp is of a different design, being mounted on the base of the fixture. The clamp proper is fastened to the fixture by means of a stud that has a spherical washer with two lock nuts.

Plain Clamps

Besides hand clamps, the simplest and most generally used type of clamp is the plain-sliding or wrench-type clamp, so called because a wrench is used to tighten the clamp. Here, the centrally-located stud bolt and nut combination performs the function of acting as the fulcrum and also producing the clamping force. Examples of this type clamp are shown in Figs. 1 and 15. The latter clamp is a prismatic bar with a central, longitudinally-elongated opening for passage of the clamping stud bolt. The opening is long enough to allow sufficient sliding movement of the clamp for positioning it on the part and retracting it when the part is loaded and unloaded in the fixture. On the clamp heel, a slot is provided to engage the clamp rest. This guides the clamp during the in-and-out movement incident to its use. The clamp rest is a headless shank set screw which can be adjusted in height to support the clamp at the level of the clamping end.

When the clamp is released, a spring, inserted on the stud bolt, holds the clamp up so that it moves away from the part. To avoid bending of the stud bolt by uneven contact of the washer under the clamping nut, and also to improve operation of the fulcrum, a combination of spherical washers is used under the clamping nut. This will also provide equalization of the clamping force of the nut on the clamp when the clamp is in a slightly tilted position. As shown in the figure, the heel of the clamp may be provided with a hand grip or handle.

When clamping by tightening the nut at the fulcrum point of the clamp, which is halfway between the clamp and part as shown in Fig. 15, the clamping pressure is only half of the pressure produced by the clamping nut. To increase the clamping pressure on the part to more than half of the clamping nut pressure, the clamping bolt and the fulcrum may be placed nearer to the part than to the clamp rest.

Dog-Point Clamps

Dog-point clamps are used for clamping round or flat parts, such as shafts and plates, which cannot readily be clamped with the sliding-type clamp. Dog-point clamps produce a clamping force which tends to seat the part against the locating and supporting surfaces. The clamp in Fig. 17 is retracted from the part when unclamped by pivoting on the fulcrum. It can be applied in less space than is required by the sliding-type clamp. By making clamping units to standard dimensions for this type clamp, so that they are readily

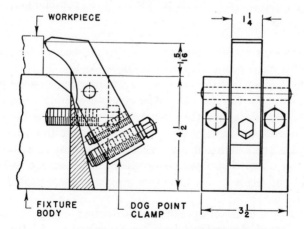

Cincinnati Milling Machine Co.

Fig. 17. A standard, self-contained, dog-point clamp unit designed for bolting to the fixture body.

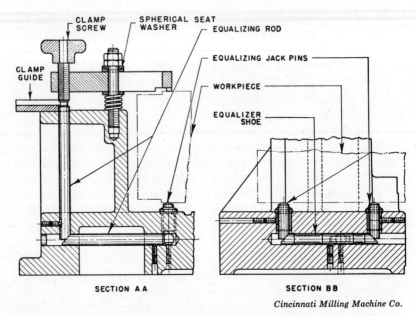

SECTION A A   SECTION B B

Cincinnati Milling Machine Co.

Fig. 18. A hand-operated fixture, showing a quick-acting clamp in combination with equalizing jacks. Clamping is produced by turning a hand screw on the heel of the clamp to reduce effort in clamping the part.

available when needed, simple and economical fixtures of compact design can quickly be made up to suit the given condition.

Quick-Acting Clamps

By transferring the clamping action to the heel of the clamp by means of a hand-operated screw, as shown in Fig. 18, the force required to clamp is now the same as the clamping force on the part and half of that at the fulcrum. This type clamp is operated more quickly and with less effort than the plain type, thereby saving the time required to pick up and lay down the wrench; for this reason, it is known as a quick-acting clamp. When the clamping screw is located on the heel of the clamp, the clamp guide, which is used to keep the clamp in line when it is retracted, is a separate heat-treated unit, as shown in Fig. 18.

A retractable, lever-operated, quick-acting clamp is shown in Fig. 19. The clamping lever is spline-connected to the head of the clamping screw to permit adjusting its angular position to the most convenient location for its operation. The use of a lever has the further

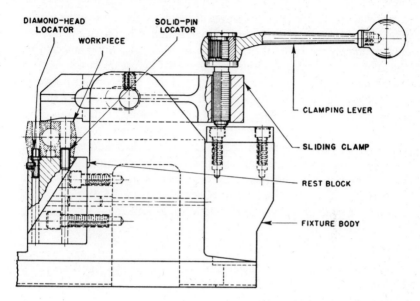

Cincinnati Milling Machine Co.

Fig. 19.   A quick-acting clamp.

advantage of increasing the clamping force with a minimum of effort on the part of the operator.

Cam-type, quick-acting clamps. A clamp of this type is used in

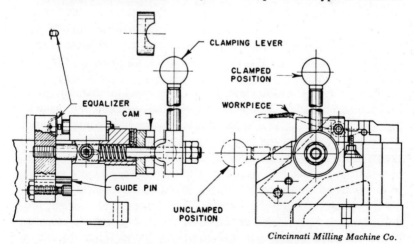

Cincinnati Milling Machine Co.

Fig. 20.   Detail of a quick-acting mechanical clamp.

a two-station fixture. Fig. 20 shows a detail of the quick-acting mechanical clamp for the fixture. The clamping force is applied at
approximately the center of the clamp by a stud, rigidly connected to
the clamp at the fulcrum point and actuated by a cam which, as the
clamping lever is rotated, forces the clamp into the clamped position.

The clamp nose is provided with a mechanical equalizer in the
shape of a half-round piece, pivoted at the middle of the span. The
contacting points are two small areas separated by a recess and located at the extreme ends of the equalizer, which straddles the half-
plier hole and provides equalization of clamping pressure around the
supporting pin. An adjusting screw is located at the heel of the clamp
to permit setting the clamp in proper alignment with the points of
contact. A guide pin engaging a hole in the clamp keeps the clamp in
the required position.

Automatic Clamps

The following factors determine whether to use hand-operated
or automatic clamps:

1. The production rate.
2. The number of parts to be clamped.
3. The frequency of clamping.
4. The shape of the part.

If the first three factors are high, or any one of them, automatic
clamps should be used. If the part's shape is not overly complex,
automatic clamps can be used. Between these extremes, the choice
of manual or automatic clamps depends on individual applications.
Automatic clamps are classified as (1) automatic mechanical clamps,
(2) pneumatically-operated clamps, and (3) hydraulically-operated
clamps.

Automatic mechanical clamps. Fig. 21 shows a mechanical clamp,
actuated automatically in conjunction with the operation of a machine
that clamps poppet valves. In the station at the right, the milling cutter
is engaged in milling the slot in the valve head, and the clamp is
shown in the clamping position. The clamp is held on a bracket supported from the machine overarm. The heel of the clamp contacts a
spring-actuated plunger which, as the poppet valve contacts the clamp
nose, is rotated around the fulcrum. The spring is compressed, producing the clamping force on the valve head. The distance traveled
by the part to mill the slot completely is very short, so that the clamping force remains nearly constant during the milling operation. As

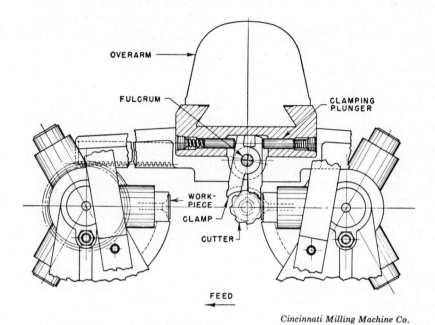

OVERARM

FULCRUM

CLAMPING PLUNGER

WORK-PIECE

CLAMP

CUTTER

FEED

Cincinnati Milling Machine Co.

Fig. 21. An automatic mechanical clamp for clamping poppet valves for reciprocal milling a slot in a valve head.

soon as the cut has been completed, the table rapid-reverses to the right and the clamp is automatically released up to a limiting stop.

Pneumatically-operated clamps. In this type clamp, a piston-and-cylinder combination actuates the clamps by means of air and mineral oil, respectively, which is directed under pressure to the cylinder by a control valve. In pneumatic-type clamps, constant clamping force is maintained against variations in the air pressure in the supply line by inserting a pressure-reducing valve in the circuit to maintain a constant unit pressure in the fixture line.

For safety of the operation, it is desirable to provide such means as will prevent the release of the clamp if the supply line should accidentally be cut off or if the line pressure drops below the operating pressure of the fixture. One method of preparing for such an emergency is to insert a pressure switch in the supply line, which will stop the machine automatically if the supply is cut off or the pressure drops below a safe limit. For small parts and light cuts of short duration, the clamp may be kept in position directly by the force developed in the cylinder.

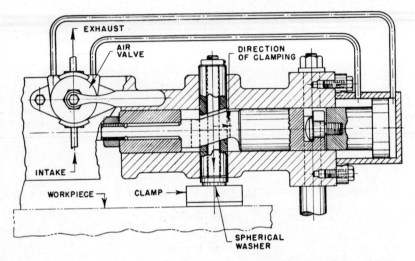

Cincinnati Milling Machine Co.

Fig. 22. Detail of a pneumatically-operated clamping mechanism, showing the cam design used to apply and release the clamping force.

A method frequently used is to have the clamping force produced by the cylinder applied through self-locking devices, such as wedges or cams. These will hold the clamps engaged in the clamped position even though the pressure in the cylinder may drop to zero. This arrangement is used in the pneumatically-operated clamp shown in Fig. 22. Here, the clamping force from the cylinder is transmitted to a horizonal plunger in which two opposed sloping surfaces may engage alternately with corresponding surfaces on a vertical plunger. The plunger actuates the clamping pad through a set of spherical equalizing washers. The operation of the clamp is controlled by an air valve, as shown in the figure.

When clamping, the sloping surfaces which come into engagement are inclined at the friction or locking angle for dry surfaces, so that the clamping force can be maintained even without the help of the cylinder pressure. When unclamping, the air valve is turned to direct air under pressure to the right hand side of the piston. As the piston moves the horizontal plunger to the left, the clamping pressure is released, and further movement of the piston to the left then causes the upper pair of sloping surfaces to come into engagement and lift the clamping pad from the cylinder.

Hydraulically-operated clamps. Fig. 23 shows a fixture which

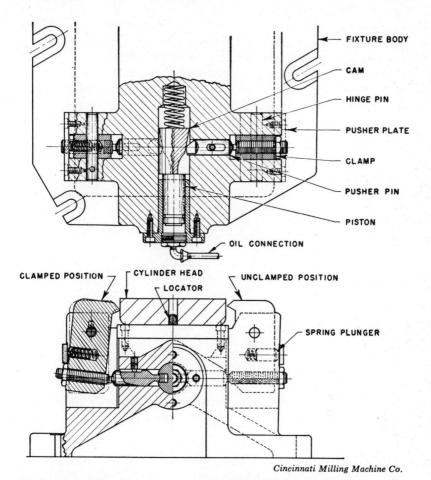

FIXTURE BODY

CAM

HINGE PIN

PUSHER PLATE

CLAMP

PUSHER PIN

PISTON

OIL CONNECTION

CLAMPED POSITION — ┌ CYLINDER HEAD   ┌ UNCLAMPED POSITION
                   └ LOCATOR

SPRING PLUNGER

Cincinnati Milling Machine Co.

Fig. 23. Hydraulically-released, dog-point clamps applied to a fixture for holding a cylinder head. The clamps are moved into clamping position by means of a spring.

holds a cylinder head to mill the joining face. Unclamping is done hydraulically by sending oil under pressure to a piston which moves the cam to compress the loading spring. This releases the clamps, which are rotated away from the part by spring plungers acting on a pusher plate.

With the fixture in Fig. 23, opposed dog-point clamps are operated simultaneously by a spring-loaded cam, which operates two push pins in contact with the heels of the clamps. Therefore, an approximately constant and equalized clamping force is applied to the part. Equalization is obtained through lateral adjustment of the cam in relation to the differential movement of the two pusher pins. When more than one clamping point is used, equalization of the intensity of the clamping forces is necessary to avoid inaccuracies resulting from the differential deflection produced by clamping forces of unequal intensity.

CHAPTER TEN

Dimensions and Tolerances

The tool engineer is more concerned with dimensions and tolerances on drawings from the machinist's point of view than from the draftsman's. He is interested in the mechanics of drafting only in so far as they enable the process engineer, tool designer, machinist, and other production personnel to perform their duties easily and accurately. In his capacity as tool engineer he seldom, if ever, actually does any drafting work; however, he must be able to interpret and translate into other media the information given on plans and in specifications.

The tool engineer is not a plan checker, as such. A checker's duties include inspecting plans for correctness of dimensions and tolerances, notes, parts lists, scales, and dimensions that tie in with related parts or assemblies. The checker makes no drawing corrections; he is not responsible for design. On the other hand, the tool engineer is involved very closely with design and with plans that are accurate, complete, and easy to interpret.

PRINCIPLES OF DIMENSIONING

This chapter is concerned with the dimensions and tolerances that appear on plans and in specifications. That they may be accurate and complete is not enough for the tool engineer. He must also be sure that the design is functional and that the dimensions and tolerances indicated are practical. Impractical dimensioning is one of the chief causes of manufacturing difficulties. Since interchangeable manufacture is based on practical methods, the consequences of unsound dimensioning can be disastrous.

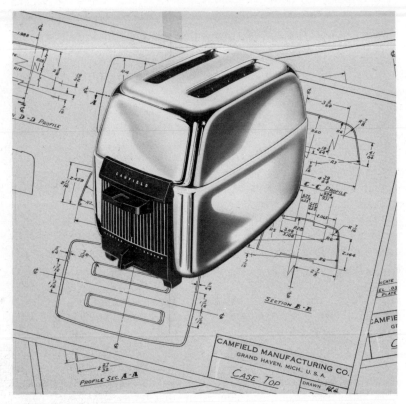

Camfield Mfg. Co.

Fig. 1. Even a comparatively simple product like a toaster requires precise dimensions and tolerances.

Plans and specifications may sometimes show designs that are not in agreement with processing requirements, or at least economical and practical requirements. These plans will depict idealized designs that cannot be manufactured according to accepted methods. It is the tool engineer's job to spot these shortcomings while the designs are still in the plan stage and not when the component parts reach the test stage, where their deficiencies become glaringly evident.

The purpose of this chapter is to examine dimensions and tolerances on plans with a view toward assuring practical tooling and manufacturing methods. The mechanics of drafting and what the plan checker must look for will not be discussed. A brief introduction to the rules of dimensioning is necessary to serve as a point of departure for our discussion. The following sections will be presented from the tool engineer's standpoint.

General Rules for Dimensioning

Any number of rules can be listed for proper dimensioning. The important ones stress accuracy of meaning and ease of interpretation. The following general rules have these factors as their goals:

1. Enough dimensions must be included so that even the dimensions of complicated parts can be determined without calculating or assuming any distances.

2. Dimensions must be shown clearly, so they can be interpreted in only one way.

3. Dimensions must be shown between points, lines, and surfaces that have a definite relationship to each other or that influence the location of other parts (see Fig. 2).

4. Dimensions must be selected and laid out with a view towards avoiding accumulations of tolerances that might cause various interpretations and lead to unsatisfactory mating of parts and failure in operation.

5. Each feature must be dimensioned in the view where it appears in profile, if possible, and where its true shape appears.

6. Each dimension should only be shown once, except in unusual cases where failure to do so might lead to misinterpretation.

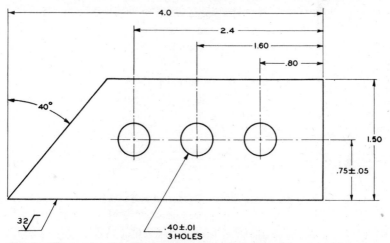

Fig. 2. This part has been dimensioned to show the points, lines, and surfaces that have a definite relationship to each other.

7. Wherever possible, dimensions should be specified to make use of readily available materials and tools.

Specific Rules for Dimensioning

Although still concerned with conveying accuracy of meaning and ease of interpretation, a few specific rules are necessary as an adjunct to good dimensioning. When he examines drawings the tool engineer expects to see certain rules and conventions being used. The following rules are widely accepted in industry and agree with American Standards Association recommendations:

1. Dimensions are shown by the (a) *unidirectional method,* placing dimensions to be read from the bottom of the drawing only, or (b) *aligned method,* placing dimensions along their dimension lines (see Fig. 3).

2. Dimension lines should be aligned, if possible, and should be grouped for uniform appearance.

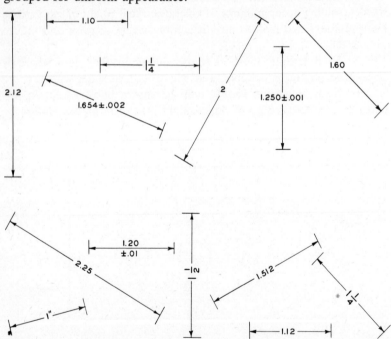

Fig. 3. At top are shown dimensions labeled by the unidirectional method. At bottom are dimensions labeled by the aligned method. Whichever method is selected should be used exclusively on a drawing and all related drawings.

3. Abbreviations should be used only if they are common and agree with accepted standards.

4. Linear and angular dimensions should be expressed in accepted units and properly and consistently indicated.

5. In decimal dimensions, the number of significant places must agree with conventions based on tolerance limits. For example, where tolerance limits of ± 0.01 or more are permitted, two-place decimals are used; for limits of ± 0.010 and less, decimals to three or more places are used.

6. On drawings of parts produced in large quantity for interchangeable assembly, only dimensions and notes for the final forms and sizes should be shown, without indicating methods of manufacture. For example, only a hole's diameter is given, without indicating whether it should be drilled, reamed, punched, etc.

7. On drawings showing how one or more preliminary operations are performed, the dimension for each preliminary operation should be given, with a proper allowance for stock removal and with suitable tolerances.

8. In selecting a datum, points, lines, or surfaces on a part should be used that are accessible during manufacture, so that meas-

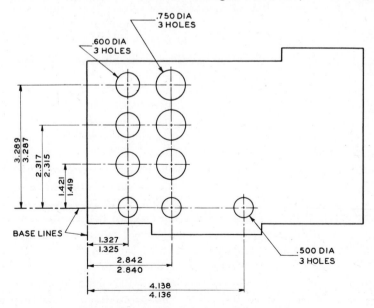

Fig. 4. Dimensioning holes by the baseline method.

urements from it can be readily made; also, any mating parts should have matching datums to insure proper assembly and to facilitate tool design.

9. Reference surfaces should be more reliable than any locations established by measuring distances from the datum.

10. To avoid accumulation of errors, the base line method for laying out dimensions should be followed (see Fig. 4). Since any finished surface may serve as a base line, the machinist lays out all his measurements from reliable surfaces.

11. A part should be dimensioned in the three co-ordinate directions so that its important features are completely defined. The co-ordinate directions are at right angles to each other; the three directions correspond to height, width, and depth.

12. Maximum material conditions should be specified in dimensioning. For example, in a bearing and shaft assembly, the bearing should be specified at its minimum size with tolerance in the positive direction; the shaft at its maximum size with tolerance in the negative direction. (See the sections on cylindrical fits later in this chapter.)

Tolerances and Limits

Dimensions without tolerance used for information purposes only are commonly called *reference dimensions*. The total amount a stipulated dimension may vary is called *tolerance*. Tolerance notations should be expressed in the same form as their corresponding dimensions. In this age of precision measurements, the tool engineer must be especially watchful of tolerance notations that are not precise enough; in other words, of decimal figures that are not at least to the same number of places as the corresponding dimension.

In a series of dimensions with tolerances, total variations in position that occur should equal the sums of the tolerances of the individual distances. As mentioned earlier, datum dimensioning avoids accumulative overall error, but the tolerance on the distance between two series-type dimensions equals the sum of the tolerances on two dimensions from the datum. Where the distance between two points must be controlled closely, the distance should be dimensioned directly with the controlling tolerance. Fig. 5 (top) shows a series of dimensions where tolerances accumulate between points A and B. Fig. 5 (middle) shows the same accumulation with different tolerances. Fig. 5 (bottom) shows the distance to be controlled dimensioned directly with its controlling tolerance; this method is advised.

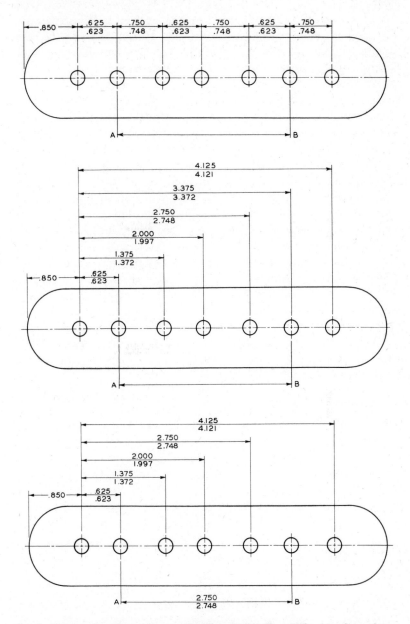

Fig. 5. The top view shows point-to-point dimensioning. The middle view shows datum dimensioning. The bottom view shows distance AB dimensioned directly with its controlling tolerance.

Three systems of tolerance are widely accepted in industry today: (1) the unilateral system, (2) the bilateral system, and (3) the limit system. The kind of manufacturing and the type of machine operation determines to a great extent where each is best suited.

The unilateral system. This system of tolerances, which has been exclusively-adopted in modern standard systems of fits, allows dimensional variations in only one direction from the design size. Stating tolerance in this fashion is especially suitable where critical sizes are approached as material is removed during manufacture; for example, close-fitting holes and shafts are often given unilateral tolerances. On drawings unilateral variations are indicated by two tolerance numerals, one either plus or minus, the other zero in both cases. A unilateral variation is sometimes expressed without stating that the variation in the other direction is zero (see Fig. 6-top).

The bilateral system. This system of tolerances allows dimensional variations in both directions from design sizes. Bilateral variations are usually stated with locating dimensions, or with any dimension that can be allowed to vary in either direction. On drawings bilateral variations are indicated by two tolerance numerals, one plus and one minus, or if the plus and minus variations are equal, a combined plus and minus sign followed by a single tolerance figure. "MIN" and "MAX" are often used in dimensional notations where the other limit is not critical (see Fig. 6-middle).

The limit system. This system indicates only the largest and smallest permissible dimensions. There is no design size as such, and the machinist's responsibility is to reach a size which lies somewhere

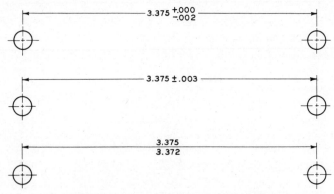

Fig. 6. The top dimension is by the unilateral tolerance system; the middle, by the bilateral system; the bottom, by the limit system.

between the limits. The tolerance is the difference between the limits. The tool engineer must make certain these limits are practical and functional. On drawings limit sizes are indicated by a high and low limit. The high limit is above the low limit where dimensions are given directly, and the low limit precedes the high limit where dimensions are given in note form (see Fig. 6-bottom).

DIMENSIONING FOR FITS

In any discussion of tolerance we must remember that the main purpose of specifying upper and lower limits is to allow a mass standardization of parts. If mating parts could be custom fit as was done in the days before mass production, there would be no point in specifying tolerances, since any ill-fitting parts discovered during assembly could be reworked until a proper matching of parts was realized, or rejected altogether. For standardizations of parts, also called interchangeable manufacture, the tolerances on critical dimensions should be such that an acceptable fit will result upon assembly of mating parts which have any combination of sizes that are within the tolerances.

Standard Systems for Cylindrical Fits

In determining and controlling fits between mating parts, two terms are used, allowance and tolerance. *Allowance* is the intentional difference permitted in dimensions between mating parts in order to achieve a desired fit. It is obtained by computing the difference between the dimensions of the largest internal fitting part and the smallest external fitting part. By doing so, the tightest possible fit is obtained between mating parts.

When specifying allowance, either a physical clearance or interference between the mating parts is obtained, depending on the functional requirements. The *basic hole* and *basic shaft* sections following explain this exactly. In the case of shaft clearance, the largest possible shaft diameter desired is still smaller than the smallest hole diameter in the bearing with which it is fitted. On the other hand, with interference the opposite is desired: the largest hole should be smaller than the smallest mating shaft.

As already mentioned, *tolerance* is the amount of variation permitted in the size of a part. Its acceptance is derived on the practical basis that it is not wise economically to strive to process parts at

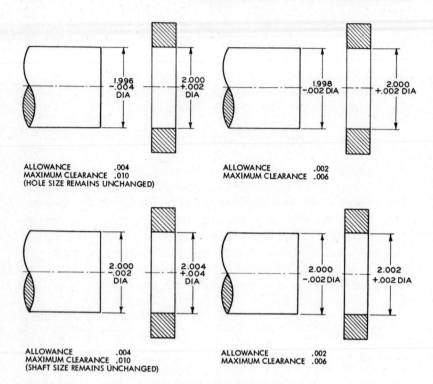

Fig. 7. At top is shown typical "basic hole" fits. At bottom is shown typical "basic shaft" fits.

exactly the specified dimensions. The permissible variation is controlled and used in conjunction with allowance to obtain a desired fit.

"Basic hole" system. To specify dimensions and their tolerances of an internal and external cylindrical surface so that the surfaces will fit together as desired, it is necessary to assume either the minimum hole size or the maximum shaft size before beginning calculations. A *basic hole system* is a system of fits in which the design size of the hole is the reference size and tolerance is calculated for the shaft (Fig. 7-top).

Limits for a fit in the basic hole system are determined by specifying the minimum hole diameter, finding the maximum shaft size, and adjusting the hole and shaft tolerances to obtain the desired maximum clearance or minimum interference. For a clearance fit, the maximum shaft size is obtained by subtracting the minimum clearance, which is the desired allowance, from the minimum hole size; for an interference fit, by adding the maximum interference to the minimum hole size. Costs of tooling can often be reduced by calculating from the basic hole size, providing the size selected can be produced by a standard cutting tool and inspected with standard gages. The tool engineer should strive to make these conditions possible.

"Basic shaft" system. Limits for a fit in the *basic shaft system* are determined by specifying the maximum shaft size, finding the minimum hole size, and adjusting hole and shaft tolerances to obtain the desired maximum clearance or minimum interference (see Fig. 7-bottom). For a clearance fit, the minimum hole size is obtained by adding the minimum clearance to the maximum shaft size; for an interference fit, by subtracting the minimum clearance from the maximum shaft size. This system is recommended only where standard sizes can be utilized; for example, standard size shafting.

Allowances and Tolerances for Cylindrical Fits

The American Standards Association (ASA) recommends the use of certain terms which apply to cylindrical fits and also the procedure of specifying such fits. Standardization of fits is valuable in processing, since controlled quality means parts can be manufactured without special inspection procedures. The following classification of fits has been approved by the ASA[1]:

Loose fit (Class 1). *Large allowance.* This fit provides for considerable freedom and embraces certain fits where accuracy is not essential. Examples: machined fits of agricultural and mining machinery; control apparatus for marine work; textile, rubber, candy, and bread machinery; general machinery of a similar grade; some types of ordnance material.

Free fit (Class 2). *Liberal allowance.* For running fits with speeds of 600 rpm or over, and journal pressures of 600 psi or over. Examples: electric motors, internal combustion engines, many machine tool parts, and some automotive parts.

Medium fit (Class 3). *Medium allowance.* For running fits under 600 rpm and with journal pressures less than 600 psi; also for sliding fits and accurate machine tool and automotive parts. (See Fig. 8.)

Snug fit (Class 4). *Zero allowance.* This is the closest fit that can be assembled by hand and necessitates work of considerable precision.

---

[1] Extracted from *American Standards Association Standard 84a-1925* with the permission of the publisher, THE AMERICAN SOCIETY OF MECHANICAL ENGINEERS, 29 West 39th Street, New York 18, New York.

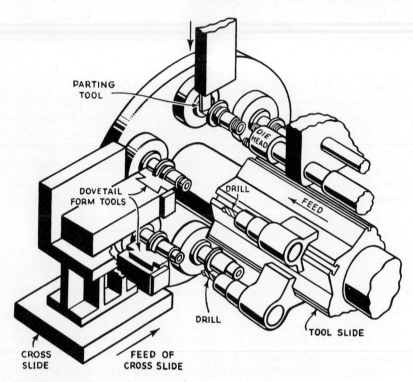

Fig. 8. The shaft-bearing fits in the sectional view of this six-spindle automatic screw machine are mostly class 3, or medium allowance fits.

It should be used where no perceptible shape is permissible and where moving parts are not intended to move freely under load.

Wring fit (Class 5). *Zero to negative allowance.* This is also known as a tucking fit and is practically metal to metal. The assembly of mating parts is usually selective and not interchangeable.

Tight fit (Class 6). *Slight negative allowance.* Light pressure is required to assemble these fits and the parts are more or less permanently assembled, such as the fixed ends of studs for gears, pulleys, rocker arms, etc. These fits are used for drive fits in thin sections or on extremely long fits (such as hub length) in other sections, and also for shrink fits on very light sections. This class fit is used in automotive, ordnance, and general machine manufacturing.

Medium force fit (Class 7). *Negative allowance.* Considerable pressure is required to assemble these fits and the mating parts are considered permanently assembled. These fits are used in fastening

TABLE I

CLASS OF FIT	METHOD OF ASSEMBLY	ALLOWANCE CLEARANCE	INTERFERENCE	HOLE TOLERANCE	SHAFT TOLERANCE
1. LOOSE	STRICTLY INTERCHANGEABLE	$.0025\sqrt[3]{D}$		$+.0025\sqrt[3]{D}$	$-.0025\sqrt[3]{D}$
2. FREE	STRICTLY INTERCHANGEABLE	$.0014\sqrt[3]{D^2}$		$+.0013\sqrt[3]{D}$	$-.0013\sqrt[3]{D}$
3. MEDIUM	STRICTLY INTERCHANGEABLE	$.0009\sqrt[3]{D}$		$+.0008\sqrt[3]{D}$	$-.0008\sqrt[3]{D}$
4. SNUG	STRICTLY INTERCHANGEABLE	$.0000$		$+.0006\sqrt[3]{D}$	$-.0004\sqrt[3]{D}$
5. WRING	SELECTIVE ASSEMBLY		$.0000$	$+.0006\sqrt[3]{D}$	$+.0004\sqrt[3]{D}$
6. TIGHT	SELECTIVE ASSEMBLY		$.00025D$	$+.0006\sqrt[3]{D}$	$+.0006\sqrt[3]{D}$
7. MEDIUM FORCE	SELECTIVE ASSEMBLY		$.0005D$	$+.0006\sqrt[3]{D}$	$+.0006\sqrt[3]{D}$
8. SHRINK	SELECTIVE ASSEMBLY		$.001D$	$+.0006\sqrt[3]{D}$	$+.0006\sqrt[3]{D}$

The American Society of Mechanical Engineers

Formulas for allowances and tolerances.

locomotive wheels, armatures of motors, and crank discs to their axles or shafts. They are also used for shrink fits on medium sections or on long fits and are the tightest which are recommended for cast iron holes or external members, as they stress cast iron to its elastic limit.

Heavy force and shrink fit (Class 8). Considerable negative allowance. These fits are used for steel holes where metal can be highly stressed without exceeding its elastic limit. This class fit causes excessive stress for cast iron holes. Shrink fits are used where heavy force fits are impractical, as on locomotive wheel tires, heavy crank discs of large engines, or other components operating under similar conditions.

Table I shows the eight classes of fits in column form, with allowances and tolerances recommended by the American Standards Association and generally accepted by industry. For each class of fit the corresponding method of assembly is included. A simple method of computing allowances and tolerances of mating parts in terms of their diameters is indicated.

DIMENSIONING FOR PRODUCTION

Dimensions and Tolerances on Tool Drawings

Fig. 3 of the Tool Design chapter presents two typical design organizations, one primarily for big plants, the other for small plants. The making of work-holding, inspection, and hand tools is also divided along similar lines. In other words, the toolmaking department in one plant is organized so that each toolmaker does all or nearly all the construction on one tool; in another plant, the organization is more specialized, one man handling all the lathe operations on many tools, another all the milling operations, etc. The former setup is primarily for small plants; the latter, for big plants.

How the plant's toolmaking department is organized will influence the dimensions and tolerances required on tool drawings. In a small plant organization, skilled and reliable toolmakers are essential, since the practice is to leave matters of tolerances and the tools required in construction in their hands. A good example of this is in surface finishes. The skilled toolmaker can be relied upon to impart a degree of finish to a surface that will suit the overall requirements of the part. The tool engineer, or whoever handles his duties in a small plant, may specify what degree of finish he desires, based on the part's function.

On the other hand, in a typical big plant organization not very much can be left to the discretion of the toolmakers. Since they are usually specialists they do not follow any tool through to completion, and they seldom know the end result of the particular operations they perform. This type of setup is geared toward high capacity production; therefore, the dimensioning of tool drawings must be complete and accurate, and follow the accepted standards found on production drawings.

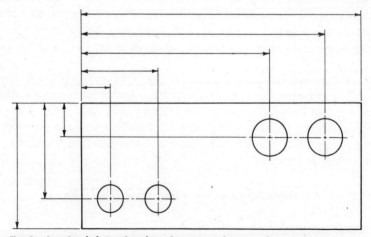

Fig. 9.   Locating holes and surfaces by means of rectangular coordinates. Sometimes dimensioning by this method can lead to more than one interpretation.

Dimensions and tolerances on tool drawings should not be specified more closely than is absolutely necessary. As we found while studying machine tools, the higher the machining accuracy required, the higher the expense. A gage that will measure accurately to one ten-thousandth of an inch is not necessary in situations where tolerances of several thousandths of an inch are allowed. On a cost basis, the added precision designed into the tool is wasted.

We see that the tool engineer must thoroughly understand the organization and capabilities of his toolmaking department. In a large plant especially he must make certain that the drawings the department receives are as accurate and complete as possible. In addition, he must not allow tools to be built with a precision beyond what the parts require.

Positional Tolerances

Formerly, locating by means of rectangular coordinates has been primarily with individual tolerance notations as, for example, in Fig. 9. Nowadays the designer's intent can often be expressed more exactly if locations are given as *true positions,* with appropriate tolerances to show how far actual positions can be displaced from true positions. What are called *positional tolerances* designate locations by stating in the general notes the allowable variation.

For instance, holes or bosses may be permitted to vary from the desired position in any direction from the true position axis, while

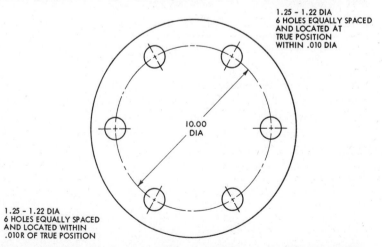

1.25 - 1.22 DIA
6 HOLES EQUALLY SPACED
AND LOCATED AT
TRUE POSITION
WITHIN .010 DIA

10.00
DIA

1.25 - 1.22 DIA
6 HOLES EQUALLY SPACED
AND LOCATED WITHIN
.010R OF TRUE POSITION

Fig. 10. The notes indicate two methods of specifying true position dimensioning.

slots or keyways may be permitted to vary from the desired position on either side of the true position plane. From these two differences we see that there are two methods for designating positional tolerances.

First method. (See Fig 10.) Where significant surfaces of parts are located by dimensions with respect to their axes and where the location may be permitted to vary in any direction, the area of tolerance will be specified based on the diameter of the circle for the part in Fig. 10 (top note).

Second method. Where significant surfaces of parts are located by dimensions to a center plane or to one portion of the part's surface, the notation shown in Fig. 10 (bottom note) should be followed. Notice that two positions are always established by untoleranced dimensions. Care must be taken by the tool engineer to insure that general tolerance notations are not applied to dimensions establishing true positions.

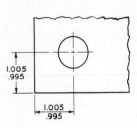

ASME

Fig. 11. Direct tolerances allow variation in the direction indicated by the dimension lines.

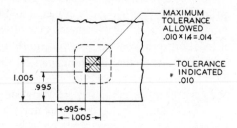

The American Society of Mechanical Engineers

Fig. 12. A square tolerance zone, a result of the dimensioning of Fig. 11. Maximum variation occurs at 45 degrees from the horizontal or vertical direction in which the tolerances are indicated.

True position dimensioning. It is interesting to investigate the standard prepared by the American Standards Association on true position. This standard is the endeavor of the Association to unify the national standards for engineering drawings. Portions of the standard are quoted, as follows[2]:

> True position dimensioning establishes locations by giving distances from datums, to locate true positions, and a tolerance within which an actual location may vary from its "true position" (theoretically exact location).

----

[2] Extracted from *American Standard Drafting Manual, Dimensioning and Notes* (ASA Y14-5-1957), with the permission of the publisher, THE AMERICAN SOCIETY OF MECHANICAL ENGINEERS, 29 West 39th Street, New York 18, New York.

Under another practice in the past, locations are given on drawings by means of rectangular or polar coordinates, each with its own tolerance. Direct tolerances, as shown in [Fig. 11], allow variation in the direction indicated by the dimension lines, which results in a square tolerance zone, as shown in [Fig. 12]. Since variation of the actual location may occur anywhere in the square, the maximum allowable variation from the desired location occurs at 45 degrees from the horizontal or vertical direction in which the tolerances are indicated, and therefore, is greater indicated by tolerance on dimensions.

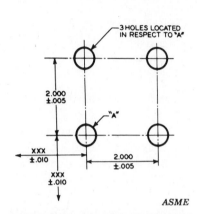

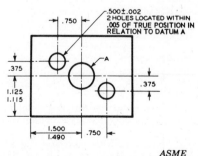

Fig. 13. Using rectangular coordinates to establish tolerance for a group of holes. The tolerances are on the rectangular co-ordinates locating datum A.

Fig. 14. Zone patterns where the datum hole is located at (a) theoretically correct position, and (b) the extreme upper right hand corner of the tolerance zone.

For a group of holes as shown in [Fig. 13], the size and location of the tolerance zone for datum A is established by the tolerances on the rectangular coordinates locating datum A. The size of the tolerance zones for the other holes derives from the tolerances of the coordinates from hole to hole. The positions of these square zones vary as the datum hole location varies.

[Fig. 14] illustrates two of the many zone patterns: (a) where the datum

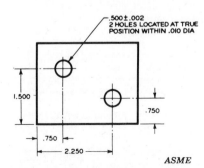

Fig. 15. Proper notation for identifying a true position expression.

Fig. 16. Notation for assuring proper alignment of features between mating parts.

hole is located at its theoretically correct position; and (b) where the datum hole is located at the extreme upper right hand corner of the tolerance zone.

A complete true position expression consists of two, or three parts. First, the basic locating dimensions are given with some indication that general drawing tolerances do not apply. Second, expressions such as "LOCATED AT TRUE POSITION WITHIN .XXX DIA." or "LOCATED WITHIN .XXX R OF TRUE POSITION" are added to the note concerning the feature to be located. See [Fig. 15]. And third, if necessary, a phrase identifying the datum is added.

Where a part and its mating part have matching feature patterns, and alignment between such parts depends upon a functional feature such as a pilot, bore, or surface, this feature should be used as a datum. In such cases the location tolerance note reads "XX HOLES LOCATED WITHIN .XXX R OF TRUE POSITION IN RELATION TO DATUM A," as in [Fig. 16], thus assuring proper alignment of features between the mating parts.

Maximum Material Condition

Maximum material condition of a part is an expression which indicates that the part contains the maximum material; for example, maximum shaft size and minimum hole size. The expression is abbreviated *MMC*. When MMC applies on drawings, the condition can be shown in (1) a general note, (2) in applicable specifications referenced on the drawing, or (3) by adding "MMC" to each applicable dimension.

The American Standards Association has recently defined the concept of MMC. Due to its importance to the tool engineer portions of the standard are included here, especially with respect to positional tolerance[3]. The term *feature* means a hole, slot, boss, or other significant surface.

As a general rule, tolerances of position are determined by the specified maximum material condition of mating features and in many cases the limits of location must be observed regardless of the actual finished sizes of the features concerned. However, in other applications, the limits of center distance may be exceeded if the features are not on their maximum material limits of size, because of the increased clearance between the mating features. This, then, is the interpretation when the symbol MMC is used in conjunction with the location specification.

To carry on interchangeable production efficiently, precautions must be taken to make sure that parts can be freely assembled. Fixed gages, made to simulate mating features at dimensional limits that make assembly most critical, can be used to assure free and proper assembly, by simple and economical inspection methods.

Under some dimensioning systems, there has been a lack of adequate means to indicate proper tolerance conditions. This has permitted various interpretations

---

[3] Extracted from American Standard Drafting Manual, Dimensioning and Notes (ASA Y14-5-1957), with the permission of the publisher, THE AMERICAN SOCIETY OF MECHANICAL ENGINEERS, 29 West 39th Street, New York 18, New York.

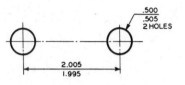

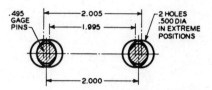

ASME

Fig. 17. Dimensioning holes this way permits more than one interpretation.

ASME

Fig. 18. An interpretation of the dimensioning of Fig. 15.

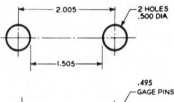

ASME

Fig. 19. A different interpretation from the interpretation of Fig. 16, based on the dimensioning in Fig. 15.

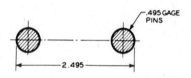

ASME

Fig. 20. A different interpretation of either Figs. 16 or 17, based on the dimensioning in Fig. 15.

of the tolerances, which have not always been in agreement with the designer's intent.

If the holes in [Fig. 17] are exactly .500 in diameter (the maximum material condition, or the smallest size hole permitted by the drawing specification) and are centered exactly 2.000 apart, they will theoretically receive a gage consisting of two round pins fixed in a plate if the pins are centered 2.000 apart and are .500 in diameter.

However, the limits specified on the drawing permit the center distance between the holes to be from 1.995 to 2.005. The pins in the gage would therefore have to be .005 smaller, or .495 diameter, to enter the holes in their extreme positions, as shown in [Fig. 18].

If the holes are exactly .500 in diameter but located at the maximum permissible center distance, the .495 diameter gage pins would contact the inner sides of the holes since the distance between the inner sides of the gage pins is 1.505, [Fig. 19].

Now if the holes are exactly .500 in diameter but located at the minimum permissible center distance, the gage pins would contact the outer sides of the holes if the distance between the outer sides of the gage pins is 2.495, [Fig. 20].

Neglecting gagemaker's tolerances, the gage pins would have to be .495 in diameter and the centers located exactly 2.000 apart. Thus the holes in the part, if they are .500 in size, will fit the gage pins if located within the limit locations specified on the drawing.

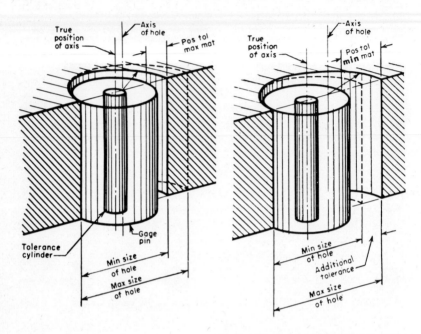

The American Society of Mechanical Engineers

Fig. 21. Using the maximum material concept as an adjunct to positional tolerance dimensioning.

[Fig. 21] illustrates the additional positioned tolerance permissible at minimum material condition for a single hole located from a datum.

Experience has indicated that in all but a few exceptional designs, this additional tolerance is acceptable and desirable. It permits the acceptance of parts which can be freely assembled whether or not the holes or other features are located within the specified positional tolerance. It will be noted that when a hole is larger than its minimum diameter, the total positional tolerance may be exceeded by an amount equal to the difference between the specified minimum size and the actual size of a specific part. [See Fig. 21.] If a particular hole in an actual part is at minimum diameter, the difference is zero, and so the actual location of that hole must be within the positional tolerance stated on the drawing.

This principle of additional tolerance available when parts are at other than their maximum material condition has been recognized and used in manufacturing for many years. This is evident from the fixed type pin gages which have been commonly employed to inspect parts in order to exercise control over the least favorable condition of assembly.

But the practice should not be applied indiscriminately. Its prime purpose should be to facilitate manufacture by permitting inspectors to accept parts that will assemble and function properly but that may otherwise be rejected because the positional tolerances specified on the drawing have been exceeded. The specification on a drawing providing for the additional tolerance indicates definitely that the designer has considered the problems involved, and approved certain deviations larger than the positional tolerances stated. This prevents uncertainty about the intended meaning in any particular situation, and avoids confusion which might be caused by allowing deviations outside the stated limits without specifying which dimensions might so deviate.

Selective Assembly

Sometimes requirements for functional accuracy are so strict that even utilizing statistical methods results in machining tolerances that are not economical. In these cases selective assembly procedures are often applied by the tool engineer.

Selective assembly means that parts are selected from their respective lots for the purpose of mating the smallest shafts with the smallest holes, the largest keys with the largest keyways, etc., to obtain

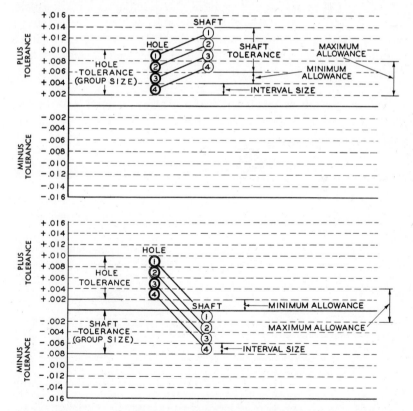

Fig. 22. Shown at top is a selective assembly system for a press fit. Shown at bottom is a selective assembly system for a running fit.

the desired fit. Fig. 22 shows two selective assembly systems, one for a press fit, the other for a running fit. To set up these systems the following steps are necessary:

1. Maximum and minimum allowances are established, based on the functional requirements of the part.
2. Methods of machining the mating parts are decided on to establish their position relative to the basic size.
3. The difference between the minimum and maximum allowances is multiplied by one-half to obtain the interval size.
4. The group size (see Fig. 22) is determined. This size usually depends on the tolerance the least accurate machine will give when machining the mating parts.

If these steps are correctly applied, the resulting selective assembly systems will assure 100% interchangeable assembly for all parts within a stipulated interval size. By increasing the tolerance range, machining costs are reduced. While assembly costs are relatively low, inspection and material handling costs are usually higher using this type system. In other words, although functionally sound, before a selective assembly system is installed in a plant a careful investigation should be made by the tool engineer.

Transfer of References

Transferring references is carried out by the tool engineer to furnish more acceptable reference surfaces on a practical basis than those indicated in the product designer's plans. In this procedure, the tool engineer is examining the plans, as he should be, from the machinist's point of view.

When transferring the reference of a dimension, an elemental rule is not to permit the new tolerances that affect this dimension to exceed

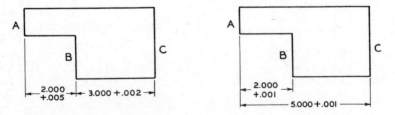

Fig. 23. The left view shows the product designer's method of dimensioning. The right view shows a transfer of references by the tool engineer to provide a more acceptable reference surface.

the tolerance of the original dimension. Fig. 23 (left) shows the original dimensions as provided by the product designer. For machining purposes, Fig. 23 (right) is redimensioned to utilize surface A as the reference surface. To maintain the original tolerances between surfaces B and C, the sum of the tolerances between A and B, and A and C cannot exceed the original tolerance between surfaces B and C.

In Fig. 23 (right), if AB is at the lower limit and AC the upper limit, their dimensions would be 1.999 and 5.001 inch, in that order. Distance BC would become 3.002 inch, the maximum dimension permissible. Any increase in the tolerance of distance AB without a corresponding decrease in distance AC, and vice versa with respect to the distances, will cause distance BC to exceed its upper limit. Any decrease in the tolerance of distance AB without a corresponding

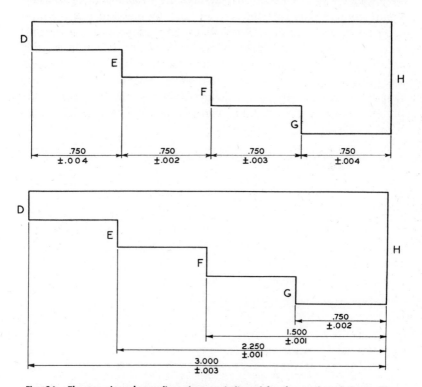

Fig. 24. The top view shows dimensions as indicated by the product designer. The bottom view shows dimensions of the same part as modified by the tool engineer for machining purposes.

increase in distance AC, and vice versa with respect to distances, will cause distance BC to fall below its lower limit.

Fig. 24 (top) shows dimensions as indicated by the product designer; Fig. 24 (bottom) shows dimensions as modified by the tool engineer for practical purposes. Two different solutions are possible in transferring references to surface H.

When starting at D:	When starting at F:
HD = 3.000 ± .0025 inch	HF = 1.500 ± .001 inch
HE = 2.250 ± .0015 inch	HG = 0.750 ± .002 inch
HF = 1.500 ± .0005 inch	HE = 2.250 ± .001 inch
HG = 0.750 ± .0025 inch	HD = 3.000 ± .003 inch

Since the total of the translated tolerances is the same, ± .007 inch, we see that several choices of tolerances are available when transferring references. The best choice is dictated by that which is the most compatible with machine capabilities and economical processing. In our example, the minimum tolerance is ± .0005 inch in the first case, which calls for comparatively high machine accuracy and expensive processing. In the latter case, a minimum tolerance of ± .001 inch requires comparatively low machine accuracy and an inexpensive process. The tool engineer must make certain the best choice for his process is used.

CHAPTER ELEVEN

Estimating Production Costs

Estimating production costs is a special procedure requiring the experience and judgment of highly qualified men. The great majority of manufacturing plants today have one or more men of this caliber devoted exclusively to preparing estimates. The tool engineer is not as concerned with the details of the estimator's job as he is with the results of the estimator's labors. But the results of the estimator's labors are for the most part inseparable from the details of his job. Therefore, the tool engineer must have a grasp of the essentials of cost estimating. The purpose of this chapter is to introduce these essentials.

Why is the tool engineer interested in cost estimates? Obviously the principal reason is his interest in economical production. To attain this goal he must compare the costs: (1) of comparable units of production equipment proposed for his process, (2) of various manpower proposals for operating his process, and (3) of various auxiliary equipment and service proposals. Chapter Two presents an analysis of manufacturing costs and establishes methods for comparing them. The estimator's task is to prepare the cost figures which the tool engineer will use in his analysis and comparisons.

From cost estimates the tool engineer can also determine the most economical method for processing a particular product, the return that can be anticipated from a proposed investment, and the ability of equipment already installed to operate economically. Of course, his final decision must take into account functional requirements and factors that might affect overall economy, like maintenance costs. After considering all factors, the tool engineer will submit his choice for the best proposal to management.

Barber-Colman Co.

Fig. 1. In estimating costs for these high production tools many factors are considered, including chip load, finish required, amount of stock to be removed. Notice the multitude of operations that were necessary to machine these tools to the shapes desired. The estimator must account for every operation in preparing his estimate.

At the very least what should the tool engineer know about estimating production costs? First of all, he should recognize that estimating can be divided into three main groups; that is, estimating of materials, of labor, and of indirect costs. The first two groups can be considered to have two parts: estimating the tooling costs of the process and estimating the product costs. Many manufacturing concerns have estimators who specialize either in tool cost estimating or in product cost estimating. In this chapter we will consider tooling and product estimating together, for both material and labor costs.

MATERIAL COST ESTIMATING

Material costs can be accurately estimated once the tool's dimensions are received from the tool designer and the product's dimensions from the product designer. Estimating material costs consists first of determining the volumes and weights of the component parts of the tool or product. Knowing the type of material, including its forming stage treatment, it is an easy and straightforward matter to calculate the price of each component based on prices per unit of weight or volume that can be obtained from catalogs of distributors of that material.

Theory of Material Cost Estimating

A simple, theoretical example will illustrate material estimating. Fig. 2 shows an object with several standard geometric shapes. Since any tool or product can similarly be broken into standard shapes, the initial step becomes one of computing the volumes of these shapes:

Shape A (a rectangular parallelopiped) $\quad = \quad 1\frac{1}{2} \times 1 \times 2 \quad = \quad$ 3 cu. in.

Shape B (a cylinder) $\quad = \quad \frac{\pi}{4} \times \frac{3}{2} \quad = \quad$ 1.18 cu. in.

Shape C (a right triangular parallelopiped) $\quad = \quad \frac{1}{2}\left(1 \times \sqrt{3} \times 3\right) \quad = \quad$ 2.60 cu. in.

Shape D (a rectangular parallelopiped minus a cylinder) $\quad = 3 \times 5 \times 2 - \left(\frac{\pi}{4} \times 2\right) =$ 28.43 cu. in.

Shape E (a cube) $\quad = \quad 1 \times 1 \times 1 \quad = \quad$ 1 cu. in.

Shape F (a semicylinder) $\quad = \quad \frac{1}{2}\left(\frac{9}{4}\pi \times 2\right) \quad = \quad$ 7.07 cu. in.

$\overline{\quad\quad\quad}$ 43.28 cu. in.

If the material composition of each shape is different, individual costs must be computed. Assuming the shapes in our example have the same composition, the next step is adding the volumes, which totals 43.28 cu. in. If the distributor's catalog lists prices on a per unit of

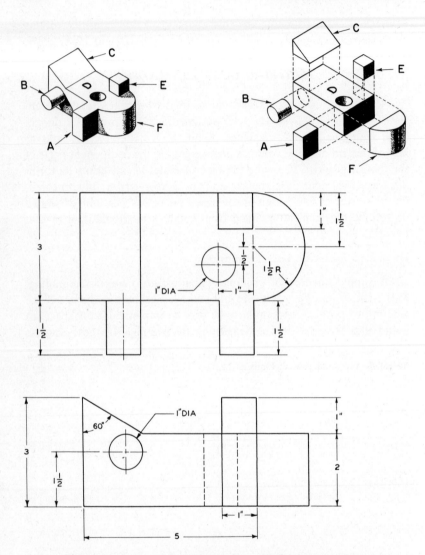

Fig. 2. This purely geometric shape can be estimated for material cost.

volume basis, the last step is multiplying the applicable price by 43.28 cu. in. to give the estimated material cost.

In most cases, catalog prices are listed on a unit of weight basis. This means the object's volume must be converted to a weight measure by multiplying the volume by the density of the material. In our example the weight would be $43.28 \times 490/(12)^3 = 12.25$ lbs. for structural steel having a density of 490 lbs./cu. ft. If the cost-per-pound of structural steel is, say 20 cents, the material cost estimate for our object is $2.45. If the object is a part, the total material cost is the unit cost ($2.45 here) multiplied by the number of parts.

Tables of material densities are readily available for converting volumes to weights, as are catalogs which quote the latest prices. With castings the usual practice is to allow about ten percent overage as a safety factor since foundry conditions cannot be controlled more closely. No safety factor is necessary with forged and formed products.

Material Cost Estimating in Practice

Whenever steel parts require hardening, the cost is added to the material cost. Whether the hardening operation is done within the plant or is subcontracted, the cost is figured on a pound basis for

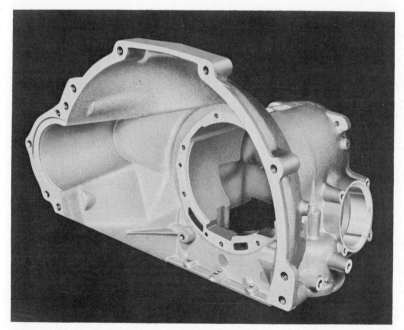

Barber-Colman Co.

Fig. 3. This transmission case is an aluminum casting. Although aluminum is more expensive on a per pound basis than steel, it is less expensive in the long run because its volume is much greater than steel for equivalent weights. A cost estimate reveals this long run saving, which can be capitalized upon providing structural requirements are not critical.

estimating purposes and can be included in the material cost. The price of standard items like screws, jig legs, springs, bushings, etc., can be obtained from manufacturer's price lists.

In estimating product material cost, since the final calculation may serve as the selling price, at least in the beginning, it is important the material estimate be as accurate and complete as possible. For this reason it is important not only to include the amount of material in the finished product but also any material removed in the machining and finishing of the product.

For example, in estimating the amount of material in a sand casting, the metal lost in the heads, sprues, and runners must be accounted for. The same applies to other castings, such as permanent mold and die castings, where surplus metal including the flash must be trimmed away before advancing to the finishing operations; trimming flash away also applies to forgings. In the case of metal stampings there is a reasonable amount of surplus material that must be included in the overall cost estimate.

When ordering material for automatic screw machine work, an extra amount is required in order to account for cut-off and stub end pieces at the end of a commercial bar length. The estimator must remember to allow enough overage of material for machining operations, such as milling and grinding, that require excess material in order to reach stipulated dimensions. He must remember that such operations as drilling and reaming also remove material; although the material removed cannot be classed as excess, it must be accounted for.

The amount of material purchased is determined by the amount required per part multiplied by the total number of parts, with a surplus for spoilage included, which is usually five percent of the net amount. An estimate that is too high will cause overbuying. An estimate that is too low will result in a shortage. Neither condition is desirable, although an excess of material will not be a total loss; it can be used in future operations.

Empirical formulas have been developed that establish the allowance for scrap in different types of operations. For stamping operations the scrap allowance is determined by adding the thickness of the stock to 15/1000 of the blank's diameter, expressed in the same units of measurement.

Material Cost Estimate Example

A practical means of estimating total manufacturing cost is

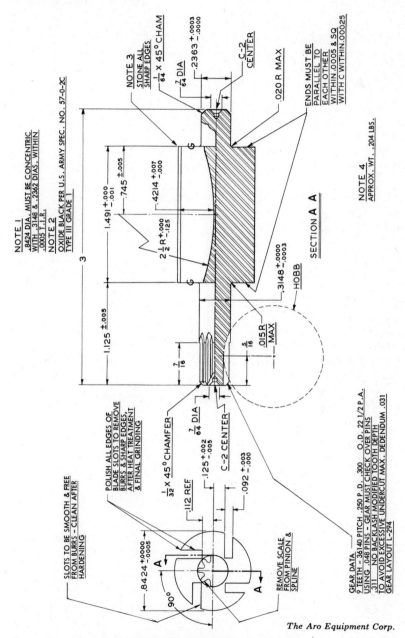

NOTE I
.8424 DIA. MUST BE CONCENTRIC
WITH .3148 & .2362 DIAS. WITHIN
.0005 T.I.R.

NOTE 2
OXIDE BLACK PER U.S. ARMY SPEC. NO. 57-0-2C
TYPE III GRADE 1

NOTE 3
STONE ALL
SHARP EDGES

NOTE 4
APPROX. WT. .204 LBS.

SECTION **A A**

ENDS MUST BE
PARALLEL TO
EACH OTHER
WITHIN .0005 & SQ
WITH C WITHIN .00025

C-2
CENTER

.020 R MAX

.2363 +.0003
−.0000

7/64 DIA

1/64 × 45° CHAM

1.491 +.000
−.001

.745 ±.005

.4214 +.007
−.000

2 1/2 R +.000
−.125

3

1.125 ±.005

.3148 +.0000
−.0003

HOBB

.015 R
MAX

5/16

7/16

POLISH ALL EDGES OF
BLADE SLOTS TO REMOVE
BURRS & SHARP EDGES,
AFTER HEAT TREATMENT
& FINAL GRINDING

SLOTS TO BE SMOOTH & FREE
FROM BURRS − CLEAN AFTER
HARDENING

1/32 × 45° CHAMFER

7/64 DIA

.125 +.002
−.005

C-2 CENTER

.092 +.003
−.000

.112 REF

.8424 +.0000
−.0005

90°

REMOVE SCALE
FROM PINION &
SPLINE

GEAR DATA
9 TEETH − 36140 PITCH .250 P. D. .300 O.D. 22 1/2 P. A.
USING .048 PINS − GEAR MUST CHECK OVER PINS
.311 NO BACKLASH MODIFIED TOOTH DEPTH
TO AVOID EXCESSIVE UNDERCUT MAX. DEDENDUM .031
GEAR LAYOUT L-294

The Aro Equipment Corp.

Fig. 4. This operation drawing is for a four blade, off center rotor. Here is where the estimator begins the calculations for his estimate.

PART NO.	USAGE PER YEAR	NO. RUNS PER YEAR	NO. MACH OPS.	NO. HAND OPS.	NO. INSPECT. OPS.	TOTAL NO. OPS.	MAT COST EACH	LABOR COST EACH	TIME HRS. PER PIECE	MAT COST PER YEAR	LABOR COST PER YEAR
30406	284	1	10	10	5	25	$.285	$ .764	.38	$ 81.94	$ 216.98
30435	2680	2	12	10	3	25	.262	.522	.26	702.16	1398.96
30511	1882	1	10	9	4	23	.233	.559	.28	438.51	1052.04
30745	14419	2	10	6	5	21	.044	.38	.19	634.44	5478.22
30976	1165	3	10	12	5	27	.233	.745	.37	271.45	867.93
30984	1967	4	11	11	4	26	.189	.567	.28	371.76	1115.29
31061	654	2	10	12	5	27	.772	.912	.46	504.89	596.45
31294	261	3	15	16	5	36	1.80	2.50	1.25	469.80	652.50
31563	1026	4	13	10	2	25	.33	.799	.40	338.58	819.77
31593	4312	3	11	13	5	29	.263	.692	.32	1134.06	2768.30
31603	1414	3	10	11	4	25	.184	.693	.33	260.18	979.90
32066	430	1	9	10	5	24	.232	.811	.41	99.76	348.73
32374	378	2	10	12	3	25	.262	.758	.38	99.04	286.52
32598	409	1	15	12	3	30	2.319	2.813	1.41	948.47	1150.52
33026	2735	3	10	17	4	31	.094	.809	.41	257.09	2212.62
33094	1443	3	11	17	5	33	.094	.874	.44	135.64	1261.18
36016	1338	2	11	5	1	17	.022	.437	.22	29.44	584.71
33570	378	4	11	13	5	29	.497	.972	.49	187.87	367.42
33345	230	1	12	11	2	25	.297	.752	.38	68.31	172.96
34577	817	2	11	12	6	29	.317	.690	.33	258.99	563.73
34734	198	1	12	16	4	32	.094	.779	.39	18.61	154.24
31633	1731	2	10	11	4	25	.184	.669	.33	318.50	1158.04

LABOR TIME HRS. PER YEAR	OVERHEAD COST EACH	OVERHEAD COST PER YEAR	TOTAL COST EACH	TOTAL COST PER YEAR	EST. SET-UP HRS. PER PIECE	EST. SET-UP HRS. PER YEAR	EST. SET UP COST PER PIECE	EST. SET UP COST PER YEAR
108	$1.874	$ 532	$ 2.92	$ 829	.063	18	$.189	$ 54.00
697	1.273	3412	2.02	5414	.066	177	.198	531.00
527	1.368	2575	2.16	4065	.021	40	.063	120.00
2739	.946	13,640	1.37	19754	.005	72	.015	216.00
431	1.825	2126	2.80	3262	.103	120	.309	360.00
551	1.395	2744	2.15	4229	.063	123	.189	369.00
301	2.183	1428	3.87	2531	.055	36	.165	108.00
326	6.007	1568	10.30	2688	.264	69	.792	207.00
410	1.956	2007	3.09	3170	.179	184	.537	552.00
1380	1.572	6778	2.48	10694	.029	123	.087	369.00
467	1.711	2419	2.59	3662	.085	120	.555	360.00
176	1.999	860	3.04	1307	.040	17	.120	51.00
144	1.862	704	2.88	1089	.175	66	.525	198.00
577	6.742	2757	11.87	4855	.056	23	.168	66.00
1121	2.010	5497	2.91	7959	.009	24	.027	72.00
635	2.173	3136	3.14	4531	.052	75	.156	225.00
294	1.09	1458	1.55	2074	.075	26	.225	78.00
185	2.368	895	3.84	1452	.275	104	.725	312.00
87	1.844	424	2.89	665	.087	20	.261	60.00
270	1.685	1377	2.69	212	.100	82	.300	246.00
77	1.935	383	2.81	556	.131	26	.393	78.00
571	1.649	2854	2.50	4328	.069	120	.207	360.00

The Aro Equipment Corp.

Fig. 5. This sheet shows the standard machine costs for all comparable rotors produced by the manufacturer. When an estimate is needed for a new-design rotor, it can be prepared quickly using these figures for reference.

shown by the following example. A component part used in an air
rotating tool assembly is shown in Fig. 4. To estimate the total manufacturing cost of this part, a rotor, it is necessary first to estimate the
cost of the material used in the part. We will do this in the same
manner as we did earlier for a purely geometrical shape.

The material for this part is cold rolled steel and it should be
purchased as round stock of ⅞ in. diameter in order to be able to
machine the part to a final size of 0.8424 in. diameter at its largest
section. The finished length according to the drawing is 3 in. Since
the rotor is to be machined first on an automatic screw machine from
a long round bar, an extra amount must be allowed in the estimate
of the bar's length. This extra length depends upon the width of the
cut-off tool used on the screw machine. For a part with this size and
material specifications, a cut-off tool of ³⁄₁₆ in. width is ample. Therefore, the total length of round stock required for the part is $3\frac{3}{16}$ in.

By simple geometry, the volume of a right cylinder ⅞ in. in
diameter and $3\frac{3}{16}$ in. long is $\frac{\pi}{4} D^2 \times L$, where D is the diameter
and L the length, or $\frac{\pi}{4}\left(\frac{7}{8}\right)^2 \times \left(3\frac{3}{16}\right) = 1.94$ cu. in. The weight
g of 1 cu. in. of cold rolled steel is 0.28 lb. The total weight of the
material required for one part is $0.28 \times 1.94 = 0.55$ lbs.

The current price per pound of the material specified is 8 cents.
Therefore, the cost of material per part is $8 \times 0.55 = 4.4$ cents, or
$0.044. Fig. 5, a cost sheet of all comparable rotors made in the
manufacturing plant, shows this cost on the fourth line (Part No.
30745) in the column labeled *Material Cost Each*.

To find the total material cost of the assembly is merely a matter
of estimating the cost of each component in the same way as shown
in our example, and adding these component costs to give the unit
assembly cost. The unit cost is the key factor. Knowing it, we can
compute the material cost over a run, over a year, over a period of
years, etc.

LABOR COST ESTIMATING

Estimating labor cost is similar in many respects to estimating
material cost. Since the cost of direct labor is the primary concern in

FORM 802

OPERATION SHEET

O.S. BY_____ DATE_____ REVISED_____

PART DESCRIPTION_____ ROTOR

SHEET NO. ___2___ OF ___12___

ASSY. NO._____

PART NO. ___B-30745___

MATERIAL REQUIRED

OPTIONAL

(A) See change request #23624 HL 9-22-53
(B) See change request #26926 FC 6-7-54

DEPT.	OPR. NO.	OPERATION - MACHINE & TOOL NAME	SET-UP HOURS	MACH. OR TOOL NO.	STD. HRS RATE	REMARKS
25	(A) 10	Face, holding body length 1.502 - 1.508				
		& form holding O.D. of short stem .244 - .248		785	$2.81	(2.38) 8-25-53
		center drill, recess & burr .842 dia				
		with file.				
		Tool Layout		25502-T		
		M-952 Adjustable Angle Rack tool		Std.		
		Snap gage .248 - .244		"		
		Snap gage 1.502 - 1.508		T-8-30745		
		Recess gage (on 30511)		T-5-30511		
		Collet stop (on 30445)				
		Bore pads in machine				
		Drill bushing (on 31024)		15401-T-6		
		Form tool		8264-T		
		Operation Drawing		25252-T		
		Recess tool bit		25253-T		
		C-2 Center Drill		Std.		
		CONTINUE WITH OPER. 18 ON STD. ROUTING				

The Aro Equipment Corp.

Fig. 6. This is an operation sheet for machining the rotor of Fig. 4. Altogether twelve sheets are necessary to describe the twenty-one operations performed on the rotor.

any manufacturing plant, we will confine our analysis to estimating direct labor cost. This cost is the sum of a number of individual manufacturing operations necessary to shape a part to a predetermined design and make it ready for assembly into the finished unit. In our example the unit is an air tool.

Labor Cost Estimate Example

The part shown on the drawing of Fig. 4 is of a relatively simple design, yet in order to process it completely twenty-one individual operations are necessary. These operations include ten machine operations, six hand operations, and five inspection operations. They are described on standard operation sheets, a sample of which is shown in Fig. 6. There is a total of twelve sheets necessary to describe the operations for the part. Examining the sample sheet we see that every operation listed is composed of a number of minute elements. The time of each must be ascertained by time and motion studies to estimate the total labor cost. How complete this is carried out depends upon how complete an estimate is desired. If the total assembly (the product) is meant for a highly competitive market, the estimate must be detailed and thorough. In any event, the estimate should not include cost computations that won't affect the total cost, nor computations so broad as to be misleading.

For the complete study of an operation and its elements, additional work sheets are supplied, such as the "Operational Setup and Tool Layout Procedure Analysis," a sample of which is shown in Fig. 7, and "Layout and Time Study," a sample of which is shown in Fig. 8. From these the hourly rate paid for a particular operation and various time units of the elements of an operation are obtained. The cost of the total operation is computed by adding the costs of the individual elements.

On the cost sheet, Fig. 5, continuing with Part No. 30745, the direct labor cost of each part is $0.38, which may be found in the *Labor Cost Each* column. The overhead cost of each part is $0.946. Note the high overhead cost due to a limited production of parts per year (see Chapter Two to learn how overhead is determined). The total manufacturing cost of each part is then the sum of the costs of material, direct labor, and overhead, or $0.044 + 0.38 + 0.946 = $1.37.

Comparative Labor Costs

A number of manufacturers prefer to keep records of complete cost analyses not only of a particular component part which goes into an assembled unit, but also of all similar component parts comprising similar assembled units. The results of the analyses are shown in Fig. 5. Twenty-two component parts are listed on this sheet. Appropriate columns are arranged for the following vital information: part

OPERATIONAL SET-UP & TOOL LAY-OUT PROCEDURE ANALYSIS			Part No.	30745
			Tool No.	25502-T
○ Form # 2833			Oper. No.	10
MACHINE NO. W & S #3 #785 DEPT. 25			Sheet 1 of 2 sheet	
Date: Material: 7/8" Rd. C-1118 Name: Rotor				

Description of operation:

Face holding body length 1.502 – 1.508 and form

holding O.D. of short stem .244 – .248, center drill, recess and burr

.842 dia. with file.

STA #	SET-UP PROCEDURE — Tools and Gages	Tool No.	Tool Comb.	TOOL LAY-OUT
1	Face and form tool	8264-T		
2	Center drill C-2	Std.		
3	Adj. angle rack tool	Std.		
	Snap gage .248 – .244	Std.		
○	Snap gage 1.502 – 1.508	T8-30745		
	Recess gage on 30511	T5-30511		
	Collet stop on 30445			
	Bore pads in machine			
	Drill bushing	15401-T-6		
	Recess tool bit	25253-T		

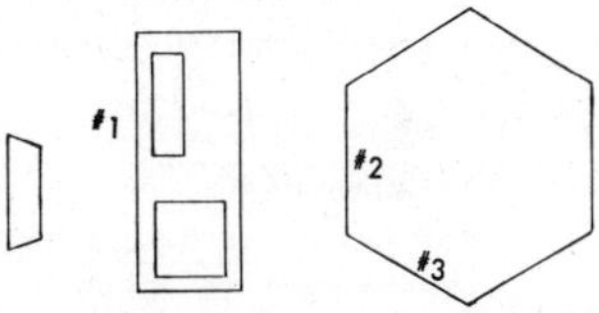

OPERATION SEQUENCE	RPM	FEED
Blow collet if necessary,		
Pick up piece from cross slide		
and mount and lock piece in		
collet		
Start machine and #1 to work		
Face and form	460	hand
Engage feed and change speed and		
face out and #2 to work	920	.0065
Center drill	920	hand
Index #3 and to work		
Recess	460	hand
Reverse index #2		
Burr O.D. with file		
Stop spindle and remove piece		

The Aro Equipment Corp.

Fig. 7. This operational setup and tool layout procedure analysis is necessary for preparing an estimate for the part of Fig. 4.

number, usage per year, number of runs per year, number of machine operations, number of hand operations, number of inspection operations, total number of operations, material cost of each part, labor cost for each part, time in hours for each part, material cost per year, labor cost per year, labor time in hours per year, overhead cost per

FORM 987

LAYOUT AND TIME STUDY
THE ARO EQUIPMENT CORPORATION
BRYAN, OHIO

B-30745

POS.										
PART NO.	B-30745	NAME	Rotor-Four Blade Off Center			MATERIAL		SAE #C-1118		
SIZE STOCK	7/8 RD. CRS		LENGTH	3 1/16		MACHINE NO.	1 1/4 RA-6			
WEIGHT PER FT.	2.044	WEIGHT PER THOUSAND PCS.		565 lbs.		276, 9 ft/M pcs.		LBS.		

POS.	SPINDLE SPEED 553	SURFACE FEET 126	OPER NO.	5	FEED PER REV.	DEPTH OF CUT	REVS.	TOTAL TIME
6th	Feed stock							
	R-form circ. Use tool support					.250		
	Spot drill 5/8					.093		
1st	F-form .875 dia. to .856					.031		
	Use roller support (?)							
2nd	F-form front stem					.250		
	Use roller support							
3rd	Shave front stem to .310 and .326 dia.					.250		
	Use roller support on .856 dia.							
4th	F-form cut off end					.250		
	Drill (A-1 center drill)					.275		
	Use roller support on .326 dia.							
5th	Cut-off				.002	.312	156	18

Spindle Speed Gears	K-30	L-46		CAMS				Index Time	2/2
Feed Gears	A 52	B 48	C 36	D 64	Lead Cam	1/4	4th Pos.	1/4	Total Time	22
Collets	7/8 Rd.			1st Pos.		5th Pos.	5/16		
Feed Shells	7/8 Rd.			2nd Pos.	1/4	6th Pos.	1/4	Hourly Prod.	164
				3rd Pos.	1/4	Acc. Slide	Pos.	Expected Prod.	115

QUAN.		CODE	TOOL NO.	REMARKS
1	R-form tool circ.	DE	12382-T	
1	F-form tool .842 dia. D.T.	BJ	12383-T	
1	F-form tool front stem D.T.	BE	12384-T	
1	Shave tool front stem D.T.	BJ	12385-T	
1	F-form tool cut-off end D.T.	AE	12386-T	
	Operational Drawing		12580-T	
1	Feeler depth gage for 1.120 length		9406-T	

DATE	% EFFICIENCY 70%	BY G. A. L.	CHECKED

The Aro Equipment Corp.

Fig. 8. This layout and time study sheet is necessary in preparing an estimate for the part of Fig. 4.

year, total manufacturing cost for each part, total cost per year, estimated setup in hours per part, estimated setup in hours per year, estimated setup cost per part, estimated setup cost per year.

This information, compiled for handy reference is valuable for estimating the costs of new parts on a comparison basis. In other words, such information may serve as a standard or guide in numerous applications where the parts in question fall within a range as determined by the part's shape, contour, and similar features.

Labor Cost Estimate Sheets

Fig. 9 shows three sheets of a cost estimate of a pump assembly used in an automatic transmission. There are eleven sheets necessary to show all the costs involved in the estimate. The production rate is based on 213 parts net per hour, the labor rate on $2.70 per hour. Sheet Two indicates a shaft, Part No. 50334, on the first line. Operation Ten is indicated on the next line. This operation consists of forming three grooves, chamfer break down and cut off. One operator handles four machines. The production rate per hour per machine is 200 parts. This brings the direct labor cost per 100 parts down to only $0.337, based on the wage rate of $2.70.

The tool cost is indicated in column five; for Operation Ten this cost amounts to $75.00. The next column describes the tools, which are cams for the first operation. Columns Seven and Eight indicate the gage cost and identify the gages; for Operation Ten the cost is $225.00 for two plug and two snap gages. No equipment cost for this operation is shown, since the machines are not new and have been used for some time. For other operations, such as Operation Thirty, the cost of manufacturing equipment amounts to $12,000 for a six-station Kingsbury machine. The installation and freight for this machine is shown in the next to last column as $500.00. Notice that the operations are numbered by tens so that additional operations, if they are included later, may be easily inserted.

From a study of shop drawings of the part, the methods engineer and tool engineer determine the exact sequence of operations to be performed on this part. Most engineering and estimating departments have records of elementary time data from which the standard time for performing a great variety of machine operations can be obtained. For a more exact analysis the standard time is developed in two parts: a setup time for the entire project and a cycle time to process each part. The setup time on the first sheet of Fig. 9 is not indicated

PRODUCTION BASED ON __213__ NET PER HR.
___ ON __2.70__ PER HR.

H. MAR`
M. GABI
P. JONE

| | TOOL | TOOL DESCRIPTIO |

PRODUCTION BASED ON __213__ NET PER HR.
LABOR BASED ON __2.70__ PER HR.

H. MAR`
M. GABI
P. JONE

OP. NO.	DESCRIPTION OF OPERATION	PROD. PER HR.	LABOR PER 100	TOOL COST	TOOL DESCRIPTION
#50123	PLUNGER – RELAY VALVE (CONTINUED)				
20	DRILL #53 (.0595) DIA. HOLE	300	9 00	2 00 00	DRI..
30	REMOVE BURR				

PRODUCTION BASED ON __213__ NET PER HR.
LABOR BASED ON __2.70__ PER HR.

H. MARTI
M. GABBI
P. JONES

OP. NO.	DESCRIPTION OF OPERATION	PROD. PER HR.	LABOR PER 100	TOOL COST	TOOL DESCRIPTION
#50334	SHAFT-LEVELING VALVE				
10	FORM 3 GROOVES, CHMFR. BREAK DOWN & CUT OFF (1 OP. = 4 MACHS.)	200 EA. MACH.	.337	7 5 00	CAMS
20	MILL .086 SLOT (1 OP. = 2 MACH'S)	215	1.25	1 2 00 00	2 VISES WITH JAWS
30	DRILL, CHMFR., TAP & BROACH .020-.030 CHMFR. AT SLOT	300	.90	5 0 00 00	TOOLING FOR 5 STA
40	ROUGH GRIND O.D.	500	.54	2 0 00 00	SPEC. TOOLING
50	FIN. GRIND O.D.	500	.54	- - -	
			3.567	8 2 75 00	
	MAT'L SAE 1132 - 1137 C.R.S. .3906 DIA. X 1½ 92.843 ÷ 1000 PCS.				
#50331	VANE - LEV. VALVE				
10	BLANK THRU	3200	.0845	8 00 00	BLANK DIE
20	TUMBLE FOR 10 HRS. TO DEBURR 20000 PCS. PER LOAD-OPER. REQ'D FOR 2 HRS. ONLY.		.027	6 00 00	
			.1115	14 00 00	
	MAT'L. SAE 1025 C.R.S. .083 +– .002×45/64 × 1.383 ÷ 1 PC.				
#50333	SHAFT & VANE ASS'Y.				
10	ASSEMBLE SHAFT, VANE & SOLDER 5 ASSEMBLIES PER STATION	320	.845	85 00 00	4 STAT. INDEX. FI
			.845	85 00 00	

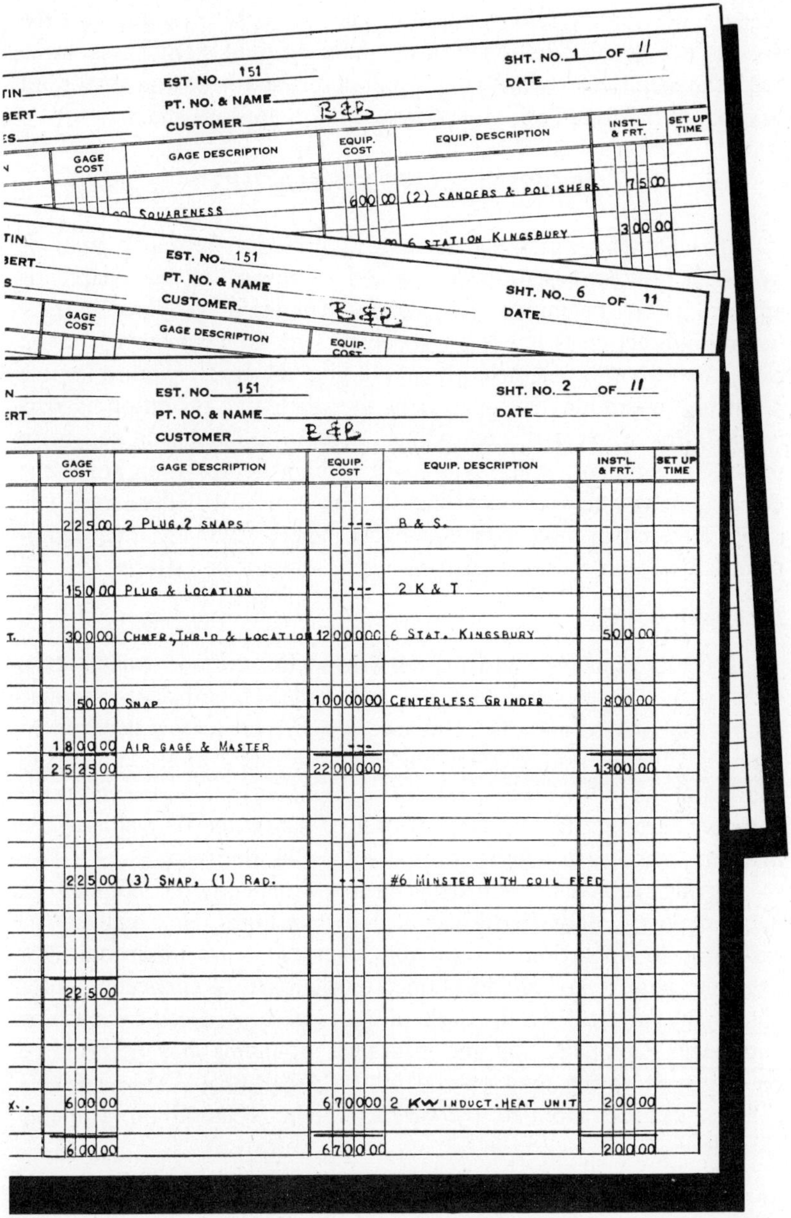

GAGE COST	GAGE DESCRIPTION	EQUIP. COST	EQUIP. DESCRIPTION	INST'L. & FRT.	SET UP TIME
225.00	2 PLUG, 2 SNAPS	---	B & S.		
150.00	PLUG & LOCATION	---	2 K & T		
300.00	CHMFR, THR'D & LOCATION	12000.00	6 STAT. KINGSBURY	500.00	
50.00	SNAP	10000.00	CENTERLESS GRINDER	800.00	
1800.00	AIR GAGE & MASTER	---			
2525.00		22000.00		1300.00	
225.00	(3) SNAP, (1) RAD.	---	#6 MINSTER WITH COIL FEED		
225.00					
600.00		6700.00	2 KW INDUCT. HEAT UNIT	200.00	
600.00		6700.00		200.00	

Fig. 9. These sheets were prepared for the cost estimate of a pump assembly used in an automatic transmission. Eleven sheets were necessary to show the complete estimate. Sheets 1, 2, and 6 are shown here.

because the lot is of long duration and the cost of setting up the process was absorbed directly in the labor cost. In many cases, however, the setup cost is indicated separately since it has an important bearing on the total cost, especially when lot sizes are small.

INDIRECT COST ESTIMATING

The chapter on manufacturing costs presents the major methods by which indirect costs are determined. A review of that chapter is advised before beginning this section. The main problem in estimating indirect costs is not the mechanics of the estimate itself, but rather choosing the method which will give the truest picture for the particular operation or department in which the operation is performed. For example, if a department contains a number of expensive units of equipment, which will result in high depreciation costs, the machine-hour rate method of distribution is used to advantage. The direct material method is recommended where relatively little equipment is used to process a relatively great amount of material.

Toolroom Costs

The toolroom must also be considered in overhead calculations. Most plants have separate rates established for their toolrooms. Indirect labor and material costs can be assigned to this department from existing payroll records and material requisitions. The fixed charges of the indirect expenses can be applied to the toolroom on the basis of the proportionate amount of floor space and the value of the machines, such as grinders and small lathes, in the room.

Having records of each department's direct payroll, numbers of men employed, floor space occupied by machines, etc., enables the estimator to apportion the variable charges to the toolroom. For example, power may be apportioned on the basis of connected motor load; light and heat, on the basis of floor space occupied by machine equipment. Compensation and insurance premiums may be prorated on the basis of the total payroll in the department. Other variable charges can be prorated by various methods based on available records.

Importance of Indirect Cost Estimates

Estimating indirect costs is an important part of the estimating scheme. Although it may seem like a cut-and-dried procedure, in reality each different manufacturing situation requires different indirect cost estimates. The various department heads cannot establish overhead rates for their departments and expect them to remain constant for a multitude of different operations. On the contrary, they must continually update their figures to meet changing situations. Experienced department heads keep meticulous records of indirect expenses so that for each new operation they will have a solid base on which to set a new overhead rate.

DETAILS OF ESTIMATING

The results of estimating have a number of side influences that are valuable to the production process as a whole. An estimate of the labor and material costs necessary to process a component of an assembly may reveal that it might be less expensive to purchase the component, if possible, from an outside source. For example, the seals in a valve are often purchased by the valve manufacturer since the seal and gasket manufacturer (the outside source) has the facilities and volume to produce seals cheaper, despite the profit factor the latter's price includes.

Estimates of labor and material often tend to stimulate cost reduction programs. Here the tool engineer may spot points in the process where costs are obviously too high. In this respect both the tool engineer and the estimator can make estimating a dynamic subject by introducing measures which will lower scrap losses, improve manufacturing methods, make equipment more efficient, etc.

As already mentioned, the wise estimator will learn to use old cost figures as a guide for his current estimate. This action will save time and needless research. He will learn to investigate the market with respect to material prices so that he can take advantage of bargains of short duration. He must also learn to recognize that future changes in costs, especially wages, must be taken into account now. If the margin of profit on a certain item is slim there is always the possibility a future wage increase will cancel that margin altogether.

Volume of parts has an effect on the overall cost. Computing the unit cost of a product and multiplying this figure by the total number of parts is a sound procedure. However, the overall cost will be less, up to a point, for a greater volume of parts. This, of course, is due mainly to the laws of supply and demand, but the result must be accounted for by the tool engineer and estimator.

Examples of Effective Cost Estimating

Fig. 10 shows the result of effective cost estimating combined with good tool engineering. Six operations were reduced to three in the production of a gear blank, as shown in Fig. 10 (and in insert). The old method of processing this part required drilling, round broaching, spline broaching, and three turning operations. The new method makes it possible for all operations except spline broaching to be combined into two chuckings, one on each of two machines, handled simultaneously by one operator.

Warner & Swasey Co.

Fig. 10. Effective cost estimating and tool engineering reduced the gear blanking costs of this machine by 42%. The chucking operations are performed on a single spindle automatic.

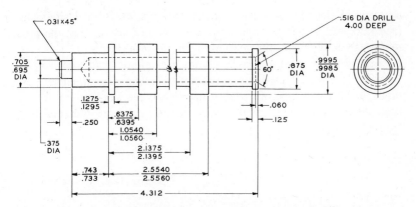

Fig. 11. This is a drawing of a control valve spool blank, the cost of which was reduced by changing the tooling to eliminate an operation.

The result was that gear-blanking costs dropped by 42%. After spline broaching, the blanks are ready for machining of gear teeth. Although lot sizes average about 200 parts with frequent runs of only 25 parts, costs are appreciably less no matter what size run.

Fig. 11 shows another example of effective cost estimating and tool engineering. The part, a control valve spool blank, shown in plan form in Fig. 11, was re-analyzed after the original cost estimate for the purpose of a possible cost reduction. By changing the tooling on the multiple-spindle automatic machine, used to produce the part, it was possible to make a direct savings of 5.4 cents per part. The tooling change permitted the part to be completed during the first operation. This change eliminated a second operation, which was formerly necessary to drill the blank to the required depth.

Formulas for Labor Estimating

Most manufacturing plants today have developed estimating to a very high degree, especially direct labor estimates. The following section shows and explains several formulas[1] used in labor estimating. The formulas were originally developed for purely technical purposes, but the estimator also finds them valuable in his work.

Engineering handbooks, manufacturer's data, and other sources of information recommend the cutting speeds for a great variety of machining operations. These speeds depend upon the material of the

---

[1] *A Treatise on Milling and Milling Machines,* THE CINCINNATI MILLING MACHINE CO., Cincinnati, Ohio, 1951, Third Ed.

part and of the tool, the depth of cut, the type of finish desired, the feed rate, etc. The important point to remember here is that the estimator can convert this information to suit his own purposes.

For example, let's assume that we are milling soft cast iron of 150-180 B.H.N. (Brinell hardness number). The recommended cutting speed for this type of metal, using high-speed steel cutters is 110 fpm. At this speed the spindle rpm is computed from the following formula:

$$V_c = \frac{\pi DN}{12}$$

where,

V_c = cutting velocity in feet per minute,

D = diameter of the milling cutter, which is 8 in.,

N = spindle rpm.

Therefore,

$$N = \frac{12V_c}{D}$$

$$= \frac{12 \times 110}{8}$$

$$= 53 \text{ rpm.}$$

This is the calculated rpm. The actual rpm may be somewhat different since there may be an incremental range of spindle speeds on the particular milling machine. Let us set the actual available rpm at 54.

Computing table feed rate. On a milling machine the table feed rate is usually computed from the given feed per tooth of cutter, commonly known as the *chip board*. Let us assume that for the above conditions the feed rate per tooth of cutter is 0.004 in. as recommended in tables in engineering handbooks. To insure a good finish and minimize corner breakout, a minimum feed per tooth of 0.003 in. is selected. The corresponding feed rate of the table per minute (F), calculated for a 48-tooth cutter operating at 54 rpm is:

$$F = 48 \times 54 \times 0.003 = 7.8 \text{ in. per minute.}$$

This value is frequently referred to as the *metal removal rate*. For our example let us establish a width and depth of cut of $1\frac{1}{4}$ in. The power required at the cutter may then be computed from the following formula:

$$Hp = aV^n$$

where,

Hp = horsepower at the cutter,

V = rate of stock removal (for our example, $7.8 \times 1\frac{1}{4} \times 1\frac{1}{4} = 12.2$ cu. in. per minute),

a = horsepower at the cutter when the rate of stock removal is one cu. in. per minute (for our example, $a = 1$ is recommended),

n = experimental fractional exponent obtained from tables in engineering handbooks. It depends upon the type of metal machined and the type of cutter employed. For our example, the value of n is $\frac{3}{4}$.

Therefore,

$$Hp = aV^n$$
$$= 1\,(12.2)^{\frac{3}{4}}$$
$$= 6.6.$$

The total horsepower input to the machine, assuming 80% efficiency of the spindle drive is:

$$\text{Hp(in)} = \frac{6.6}{.80}$$

$$= 8.25$$

Computing machine time. The figure 8.25 is used by the estimator in computing the burden of the machine. He may also use it in estimating machine tool costs. To calculate the machine time let us assume that the length of cut is $1\frac{11}{16}$ in., which includes cutter approach and overtravel. The machine time (T_m) is:

$$T_m = \frac{L}{F}$$

where,

   L = the total length of cut,

   F = the feed rate of the table per minute.

Then,

$$T_m = \frac{1\frac{11}{16}}{7.8}$$

$$= 0.22 \text{ minutes.}$$

This figure is used by the estimator in computing labor costs. It represents a unit of time, the actual machining time, of the entire operation. Totaling all the time units comprising the operation will give a sum that can readily be converted to labor cost by multiplying it by the operator's wage rate.

CHAPTER TWELVE

Economics of Machine Tool Replacement

In recent years a number of technical papers and manuals have been published concerning the economics of machine tool replacement. Among them, the *MAPI Replacement Manual* [1] has been widely accepted by industry as an authoritative source of information for estimating the useful life of machine tools. Among other manuals devoted exclusively to this subject, *Dynamic Equipment Policy* [2] and *Business Investment Policy* [3] are especially valuable. The information contained in this chapter is derived mainly from these references. Additional references are suitably credited.

THE GROWTH OF REPLACEMENT PROGRAMS

Manufacturers have always been confronted with three basic problems: (1) competition, which is becoming keener each year, (2) the high cost of obsolescence of machine tools, and (3) profitable operating conditions. Practical solutions to these problems are vital. Case histories of various manufacturing plants, large and small, show convincingly the economic soundness of planned machine tool replacement programs. Although each plant must plan a program to suit its own individual requirements, replacement programs, as we shall see, fall into general types.

Whenever we purchase anything, for ourselves, our family, or our

---

[1] *MAPI Replacement Manual*, published by MACHINERY AND ALLIED PRODUCTS INSTITUTE, Washington, D. C., 1950.

[2] *Dynamic Equipment Policy*, by George Terborgh, published by McGRAW-HILL BOOK CO., New York, N. Y., 1950.

[3] *Business Investment Policy*, George Terborgh, published by MACHINERY AND ALLIED PRODUCTS INSTITUTE, Washington, D. C., 1958.

business, we instinctively if not consciously, weigh certain factors that in proper balance make the purchase a "good buy." These factors are our need for a certain product, the value it offers, and its purchase price. No matter what we purchase, be it a single product or a whole line of capital goods, we first weigh the purchase in our minds by these standards.

Competitive Pricing

In the course of manufacturing, pricing situations are often encountered which are very similar to that of purchasing ordinary household items. As with these items, machined parts may also be offered at different prices, as demonstrated by the Jones and Lamson Machine Company in their film entitled, "The Price of Eggs." In the film a manufacturer is cited as being capable of offering a potential customer a machined part at three different prices, depending on how he processed the part and with what equipment. In this case, however, landing the customer meant a big contract, so the three different prices on the same part created a serious situation.

Based on the delivery of 20,000 parts per month for two years at a required selling price of $1.02 per unit, the manufacturer's cost analysis showed that, using two different machines presently in the shop, his cost-per-part was $1.32 on one machine and $1.24 on the other. After investigating a new machine, he found that the same part could be made for $0.93 per part, with further cost reductions readily attainable by adding automatic handling devices.

The manufacturer was faced with two alternatives: (1) missing out on a big order because his existing machines could not produce the part cheaply enough, or (2) investing in a new machine, which might not be able to return its initial cost in a reasonable time. The dilemma which faced this manufacturer is one similar to the problem that sooner or later every manufacturer faces. He must either expand to take care of increased production, or retool to lower his production cost, meet competition, and hold his business. Often the situation is critical, which requires close analysis.

The economic factors involved in a study of replacement and/or retooling are many, varied, and often complicated. They have challenged the best minds in industry. Since a major concern of management is profit, the true cost of manufacturing a product is of vital importance. An analysis of the factors which caused the cost variations in the Jones and Lamson example reveals some of the reasons for these variations. It also asserts the fact that the manufacturer who needs a new machine tool is already paying for it.

Typical Replacement Conditions

Fig. 1 shows a chart of the profit-point turning speed of the lathe

Example of PROFIT-POINT Turning		
Cost Item	Brazed Carbide	Throwaway Insert
Tool-change time	5 min.	2 min.
Cost per cutting edge	$1.27	$.25
Minimum cost tool life	40.4 min.	11 min.
Cutting speed for PROFIT-POINT turning	720 fpm 1000 rpm	980 fpm 1360 rpm
Machining time per piece	1 min.	.74 min.
Tool time per piece (including nonproductive time per piece)	2 min.	1.74 min.
Machining cost per piece	$.15	$.11
Total cost per piece	$.031	$.017
Nonproductive cost per piece	$.15	$.15
Pieces machined per hour	30	34
TOTAL COST PER PIECE	$.331	$.278

Barber-Colman Co.

Fig. 1. The turning speed at which tool and machining costs are in balance is called the profit-point speed.

of Fig. 2. The speed at which tool costs and machining costs are in balance is the profit point. Using throwaway tool inserts is covered in the Tool Design chapter. Pairing throwaway inserts with machines capable of only moderate speeds is liable to be wasteful. Depending upon costs, the alternative is to use high-speed machines and throwaway inserts. Although the machining time is reduced, there is no resharpening and resetting costs.

The lathe shown in Fig. 2 has a frame of rigid construction, a heavy cross slide, and a rugged tailstock, which are necessary features in high-speed machining. It is powered with a 25 HP motor and operates at spindle speeds up to 2500 RPM. An older machine may not have sufficient power to reach these speeds, nor the ruggedness of

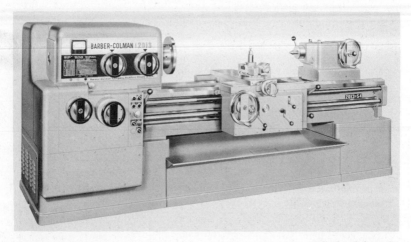

Barber-Colman Co.

Fig. 2. This is the lathe on which the profit-point turning speed of Fig. 1 is based.

design high-speed machining requires. In this situation the tool engineer is faced with two alternatives: (1) to use the older machine on hand, whose cutting tool has a longer tool life and lower cost, but higher resharpening-resetting costs and longer downtimes, or (2) a new, high-speed machine with throwaway inserts. Fig. 1 shows the total cost-per-part to be substantially less for the latter machine. If the initial investment can be paid off in a reasonable length of time, the wise tool engineer will advocate buying the high-speed machine.

Fig. 3 shows another machine tool of improved design to give greater productivity. Contrary to the machine of Fig. 2, this is a multiple tool machine with drill-and-tap spindles designed with a swivel head, which enables the swinging of the tool out of the work area, thereby providing greater accessibility for easier and faster tool changing.

Developing Replacement Programs

There are four major steps in developing a policy and program of machine tool replacement. The sequence of steps follow in logical order:

Step No. 1. A study of present conditions and what lies ahead, for industry and the economy as a whole. The charts in Figs. 4 and 5 will aid in the study. The chart in Fig. 4 indicates industrial production

The Cross Co.

Fig. 3. This multiple spindle machine is designed with a swivel head, which allows the swinging of the spindles out of the work area.

in terms of physical volume, and that in Fig. 5 shows output of electrical energy based upon the number of kilowatt hours.[4] Because these charts are in terms of physical volume rather than dollars, they indicate very definitely the true expansion in industrial productivity. The growth beyond the known data is shown by dotted lines in the charts.

[4] From *Setting Your Sights For Tomorrow,* a pamphlet published by NATIONAL MACHINE TOOL BUILDERS' ASSOCIATION, Feb., 1957.

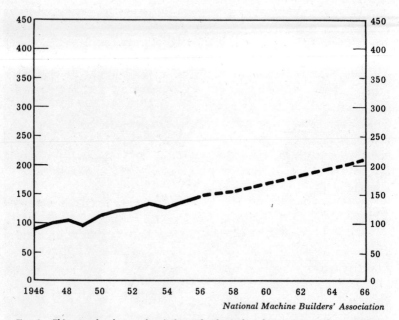

National Machine Builders' Association

Fig. 4. This graph shows the index of physical volume industrial production.
1947-49 = 100.

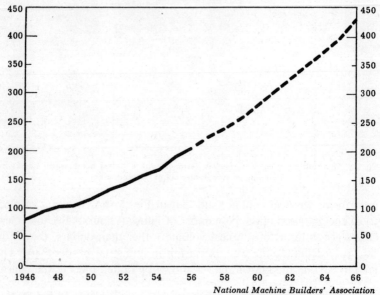

National Machine Builders' Association

Fig. 5. This graph shows the index of output of electrical energy. 1947-49 = 100.

Although speculative, this growth is still within the realm of probability.

Machine tool replacements should be considered in the light of ascending production requirements over a period of five to ten years. Such production requirements can be met only by the installation of new machines that turn out more work per man per hour.

Step No. 2. Knowledge of latest machine tool development. In the field of metal cutting and metal forming, more advances have been made in recent years than in the entire previous portion of this century. In planning modernization, the factor of ungoverned acceleration in machine tool development must be taken into account.

An engineering knowledge of the performance potential of modern machine tools indicates the nature and scope of results that may be achieved by replacement. It is essential that a manufacturing firm have in its organization a competent person who specializes in machine tool development. He can keep abreast of trends and possibilities by conversing with machine tool sales engineers, visiting up-to-date machine tool builders, subscribing to magazines in the field, and attending such exhibits as the National Machine Tool Show. In large plants this man may work with the tool engineer in machine tool replacement programs. In smaller plants the tool engineer may handle the duties of this position himself.

Step No. 3. Determination of replacement sequence. Some machines should obviously be replaced because of their age, their condition, their inability to hold tolerances. Other machines, although relatively new, should just as obviously be replaced because newer models have rendered them obsolete. Cases that are more critical than others should receive preference in the replacement program. In a program to be pursued over a period of time, studies should be made in order to determine the best sequence of replacement. All things being equal, the amount of reduction in cost realizable would determine the order of replacement.

Savings in direct labor cost constitute only one factor to be considered. Other factors are indirect labor costs, scrap reduction, maintenance, savings in floor space, possibility of combining operations, relation to the flow of work.

Various formulas are used for estimating the savings to be effected by replacement. One of the most widely accepted is the formula developed by the Machinery and Allied Products Institute. Called the MAPI formula, it endeavors to take into consideration all the factors mentioned in the previous paragraph, as will be shown. Other formulas of a simpler nature are also available.

A decision should not be made on the basis of a formula alone. It is very useful as a guide and a yardstick, but should be used along with good business judgment, and above all else, an eye to the future. A formula can only give an estimate as to the amount of savings realizable by immediate replacement. A good formula will give a good estimate. Using current data, no formula can indicate how much productive capacity may be required in the manufacturing plant at some future time. (See Fig. 6.)

Greenlee Bros. & Co.

Fig. 6. This is a modern, efficient transfer machine. Despite its modern design, however, there is no guarantee it will not soon become obsolete.

Step No. 4. Schedule replacement. At this stage of development a decision has already been made as to what should be replaced and the order in which replacement should be undertaken. The next step is to determine how fast the replacement should take place. This step involves finances since there are limits to what a firm can spend in one year. There is also a limit to the life of a firm that fails to spend enough on modernization to stay competitive, and a limit to the growth of a firm that fails to spend enough on modernization to allow it to expand.

Each firm must arrive at an answer in the light of its own circumstances. With this in mind, the following observations are pertinent:

1. In formulating a decision regarding a certain replacement program, a preliminary discussion is in order as to what this replacement will cost. How much it would cost the firm not to make the replacement should also be discussed. The annual savings revealed by the application of a replacement formula provide this figure.

2. Obsolete machines still remaining in a department in which new machines have been installed may hold back the output of the department and offset the benefits of the new machines. More and more manufacturing firms are viewing replacement not from the standpoint of individual machines, but from the standpoint of the entire department. It is wise to study what machines in a particular department should be replaced, but a study of the benefits to be gained by modernizing the entire department may be much more constructive. In this regard the tool engineer plays a valuable role, as his position enables him to see the operations of the entire department.

3. The time element is important in relation to competitive firms. The charts in Figs. 4 and 5 show the anticipated rate of industrial growth. How fast are competitive firms stepping up their plans to match this indicated pace? In the face of this situation, can a manufacturer afford to lag behind? In every decision the tool engineer makes, in every proposal he submits to management, he must always remember the consequences of underestimating the competition.

Terms Used in Replacement

As explained in Chapter Three, deterioration and obsolescence are terms that define a machine's capacity to operate economically. Deterioration may be defined as the gradual wearing out of a machine tool incident to its use and is reflected in increased operating costs

Fig. 7. If this installation is giving satisfactory and economical performance it has no operating inferiority.

resulting from repairs, spoilage of parts, and reduced production. Obsolescence occurs as the result of the marketing of an improved machine or manufacturing method, or because the present equipment cannot handle a change in design of the product being manufactured. Obsolescence, therefore, is defined in terms of a machine becoming out of date in relation to a particular job, while deterioration is defined in terms of the physical condition of a machine.

Operating inferiority. The relative importance of obsolescence and deterioration on operating cost may vary widely from machine to machine. However, for the purpose of a replacement analysis their combined values are considered as a single factor accumulating at a constant rate with the passage of time. This factor is known as the *operating inferiority*. It measures the gap between the performance of a machine in service and the performance which can be obtained from the best new machine available on the market. (See Fig. 7.)

A MAPI REPLACEMENT ANALYSIS

The essential principle of the MAPI replacement analysis can be shown in an approximate formula by representing in general terms the sum of the time-adjusted annual averages of operating inferiority and capital cost. The formula is:

$$L_a = \frac{g(n-1)}{2} + \frac{(c-s)}{n} + \frac{i(c+s)}{2}$$

where,

L_a = sum of the life average of capital cost and operating inferiority, in dollars,

g = annual operating inferiority gradient, in dollars,

c = acquisition and installation cost of a machine, in dollars,

s = salvage value of a machine, in dollars,

i = rate of interest, in decimals,

n = machine service, in years.

In this formula, the first term $g(n-1)/2$ is the life average operating inferiority of the machine, increasing at a constant rate after the first year's operation. A machine accumulates no operating inferiority in the first year of service. The factor g, which gives the annual constant rate of a machine's accumulation of deterioration and obsolescence, is the machine's *operating inferiority gradient.*

Together the second and third terms of the formula measure capital cost. The second term is the capital recovery of the difference between the acquisition cost of the machine and its salvage value. This capital must be recovered over a number of years which constitutes the service or useful life of the machine. When the service life n of a machine is known or closely estimated, it is then possible to determine the average amount of money to be set aside each year to recover the capital actually spent. The amount to be set aside each year decreases as the number of years of service increases.

The third term is the average interest to be paid. This amount is unaffected by the service life of the machine, remaining constant for any selected values of c (capital), s (salvage value), and i (the rate of interest).

The Adverse Minimum Concept

Operating inferiority and capital cost are not constant throughout the service life of a machine. With the passage of time, operating inferiority increases while capital cost decreases. However, there will be a certain number of years of service life for which the sum L_a of these factors will become a minimum. If a machine is kept in service beyond this number of years, the sum of these factors will increase.

The minimum simply indicates that the average cost per year of service will reach a minimum value when the machine has been in service a certain number of years, and is the lowest time-adjusted annual average of operating inferiority and capital cost obtainable from the machine in question. To this minimum value has been given the name *adverse minimum* in the MAPI replacement analysis.

The adverse minimum value is used as a yardstick to determine when an existing machine should be replaced with a prospective new machine of more advanced design. Whenever the adverse minimum of the existing machine exceeds that of the new machine, the existing machine should be replaced. The greater the difference, the more pressing is the need for replacement. Actually, the difference between the adverse minimum of the two machines is the excess cost of manufacturing which the user is paying by retaining the existing machine in operation when a better, more efficient machine has become available.

In developing a replacement analysis, MAPI assigns the names of *defender* and *challenger* to the machines being compared. The defender is the machine which is currently in use on a particular operation, and the challenger is the best possible machine that can be purchased as a replacement for the defender at the time of the analysis.

The information pertaining to the defender can be obtained from plant records, while the information on the challenger is obtained from the machine tool manufacturer. The choice of the challenger, of course, is arrived at through cost analyses of comparable machines available on the market. With this information the adverse minimum of the defender and challenger can be quickly and easily determined by a simple procedure.

In this procedure lies the advantage of the MAPI method of replacement analysis. In fact, the MAPI method has eliminated not only the use of complicated formulas for determining adverse minimums, but also the need for referring to highly complete sets of cost records for accurate information in the replacement problem. Obviously in cases where cost records are available they will help in arriving at a more accurate result. Even without them, however, the results which can be secured are precise enough to permit the tool engineer to make sound proposals to management on replacement.

Adverse Minimum of Defender

The adverse minimum of the defender is usually assumed to be the sum of: (1) the defender's next year's operating inferiority or the challenger's operating advantage, and (2) the defender's next year's capital cost. In replacement studies, we will consider the operating inferiority as the loss of operating income which results from not replacing a machine when replacement is indicated by a comparison of the adverse minimums of the challenger and defender.

The length *A* of the defender's bar shown in Fig. 8 represents the total operating cost of a machine, including all factors except capital cost. The defender's operating cost would include labor (direct and indirect), supplies, building and lighting, etc. The length of bar *C* represents the same factors for the challenger.

While these bars are shown with the defender's cost in excess of the challenger's cost, this is not necessarily true in all cases. The reverse is sometimes true, since a new machine may require more power and floor space, and even a more responsible and higher paid operator. In this event the actual operating cost of the challenger may be higher than that of the defender, although overall costs of the challenger may be lower.

The defender's operating cost does not include revenue advantages resulting from installation of the challenger, or advantages that may be

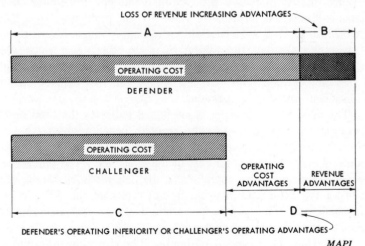

Fig. 8. Shown is the next year's operating inferiority of the defender, or the challenger's operating advantage.

due to the challenger's increased capacity. These revenue advantages should be included in the analysis because they are a credit to the challenger. When they are considered, the operating cost of the challenger may be less than that of the defender.

Charting the adverse minimum. In Fig. 8, the challenger's revenue advantages are represented as a loss for the defender by the additional length B of the defender's bar, since they are actually losses of revenue which are incurred for not replacing the defender with the challenger. For example, if the challenger produces twice as much work as the defender, this is obviously a credit to it and should be charged against the defender. If the challenger's hourly production is greater than actually required, the excess which is not immediately salable has a potential value which should be given a dollar evaluation. Both of these items are included in the extension B of bar A of the defender. If the new machine, by its characteristics, can eliminate operations required in using the present defender, then the cost of these operations is charged against the operating cost of the defender.

Similarly, when an operator is assigned a new machine, the improvement in morale, which has been shown to be true time and again, may result in a gain in production or quality of work. The corresponding value should then be estimated and included in B, making certain that this factor has not already been included, for instance, in the increased production mentioned previously. If the machine has some advertising value to the purchaser, that factor should also receive consideration and an approximate estimate made of the potential value. In addition, there are other items which would be included, depending upon circumstances. These should be added if they are deemed important enough by the tool engineer for the replacement analysis in question.

The defender's bar $A + B$ of Fig. 8 indicates the total cost of operating the defender, plus the revenue benefits which would be secured from its replacement by the challenger. The challenger's bar C indicates only the operating cost of the challenger. The difference D between these two bars, therefore, is the defender's operating inferiority, or the extra cost incurred by not replacing the defender with the challenger. This comparison should always be made under a definite set of output conditions.

Analyzing the adverse minimum. The operating inferiority of the defender is a comparative dollar value which can be obtained by adding all the estimated values operating against the defender, adding all the estimated values operating against the challenger, and then finding the difference between the two values. It is possible to estimate this difference for any factor of cost under consideration and credit it to either the challenger or the defender, as the case may be. For instance, labor cost will usually be a factor in favor of the challenger and consequently the difference is placed in the defender's column as an inferiority factor. On the other hand, taxes and insurance are

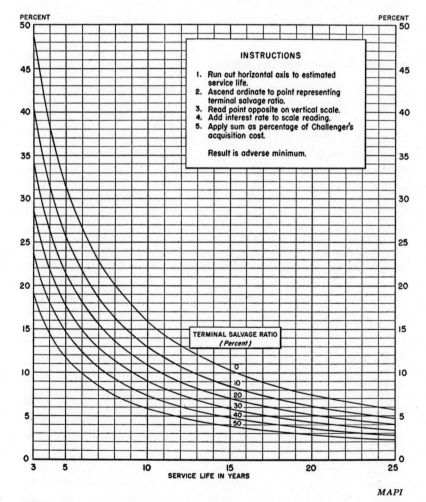

INSTRUCTIONS

1. Run out horizontal axis to estimated service life.
2. Ascend ordinate to point representing terminal salvage ratio.
3. Read point opposite on vertical scale.
4. Add interest rate to scale reading.
5. Apply sum as percentage of Challenger's acquisition cost.

Result is adverse minimum.

TERMINAL SALVAGE RATIO
(Percent)

SERVICE LIFE IN YEARS

MAPI

Fig. 9. This is a chart for deriving the challenger's adverse minimum by the MAPI formula.

usually greater on the challenger and in that case the differences are placed in the challenger's column as an inferiority factor.

It is not difficult to make a time study of the defender equipment and to obtain figures and cost estimates on the challenger from the machine tool manufacturer. It is also a relatively simple matter to compute the operating inferiority factor of the defender with reference to the challenger, which is taken as the standard at the time of the analysis. As previously noted, by adding the capital cost to the inferiority factor of the defender, the adverse minimum of the defender is obtained.

Adverse Minimum of Challenger

To determine the challenger's adverse minimum, it is necessary to know its operating inferiority. In his book, *Dynamic Equipment Policy,* Mr. Terborgh assumes that the challenger will be at par for the first year of its use and, therefore, have no accumulation of operating inferiority. The future value of operating inferiority of the challenger cannot be predicted with any certainty because it depends on the availability of future challengers. The only certainty is that both obsolescence and deterioration will develop in the future.

In order to avoid complications and simplify calculation of the challenger's adverse minimum, MAPI has developed a chart, which is reproduced in Fig. 9.[5] With very simple calculations this chart can be used to obtain the desired minimum by an approximation which is satisfactory for all practical purposes. The only data required is the interest rate on the capital, the acquisition cost of the challenger, its probable salvage value and service life. The adverse minimum of the challenger can then be obtained by following instructions in Fig. 9.

Application of the MAPI Analysis

The following is an example which applies the MAPI replacement analysis.[6] A company is confronted with the problem of increasing the

---

[5] Other charts of more recent origin have been developed by the MACHINERY AND ALLIED PRODUCTS INSTITUTE and the COUNCIL FOR TECHNOLOGICAL ADVANCEMENT, both situated in Washington, D.C. These charts are described and fully explained in the 1958 publication *Business Investment Policy,* by George Terborgh, published by MAPI. Also a pamphlet, *An Introduction To Business Investment Analysis,* was published by the same source in 1958.

[6] Adapted from *A Treatise On Milling and Milling Machines,* by the CINCINNATI MILLING MACHINE CO., 1951.

present production rate of 120 parts per hour to 160 parts per hour in a milling operation. These production figures are based on a fifty-one minute hour to take into account the operator's personal needs and normal changing time of cutters for resharpening.

The present equipment consists of three hand-controlled milling machines equipped with hand-operated fixtures and high-speed steel milling cutters, arranged for milling one part at a time. Each machine produces at a rate of 40 parts per hour, for a combined total of 120 parts per hour. A production rate of 160 parts per hour could be obtained by adding a similar machine from another department to the present group of machines. The conversion cost would amount to $300. All of these machines have the same age and are in satisfactory operating condition. Since the parts are polished after milling, an additional operator would be required to handle the increased production in the polishing and buffing department at no extra cost for equipment.

At first glance this solution seems the most advantageous economically, since production requirements could be met with practically no capital investment by this method. By comparison the new production requirements could also be met by purchasing one automatic fixture and six carbide-tipped cutters, arranged for an abreast milling operation. The new equipment was selected for purposes of analysis because it represented the most economical equipment currently available as determined after a cost analysis. The machine performs the same operation at a rate of 200 parts per hour, or 40 parts above the proposed requirements of 160 per hour. We see the new machine would require only part of a day's operation to fulfill the daily output, so the operator could be assigned to another job for the remaining time.

The apparent advantages in favor of the new machine are: (1) improved quality of finish of the milled surface resulting from the use of carbide cutters, which is made possible by the advanced design of this machine as compared with the existing machines, and (2) subsequent savings in the number of manhours expended in the polishing and buffing operations. The released floor space may also provide a definite advantage when it is utilized for other production equipment. On the other hand, the operator for the new machine will be paid at a higher rate than the operators of the existing machines because of the increased amount of skill required in changing cutters, making necessary adjustments, and attending to the operation of a more

TABLE I

DEFENDER	Present salvage value of four machines.....................	$4,000.00
	Next year's salvage value...............................	3,200.00
	Direct labor cost per hour, net..........................	1.75
	Indirect labor cost per hour, net........................	0.10
	Cost to convert one machine to this job..................	300.00
	Addition of one man in polishing dept. at................	1.40 per hr.
	Interest rate on capital.................................	10%
CHALLENGER	Acquisition cost of an automatic milling machine, installed........................	$25,500.00
	Tool cost (arbors, cutters and fixture)	3,540.00
	Direct labor cost per hour, net..........................	2.25
	Indirect labor cost per hour, net........................	0.10
	Prospective service life of machine......................	10 yrs.
	Prospective salvage value of machine	$510.00
	Salvage ratio (510/25,500)...............................	2%
	Production rate per hour.................................	200 parts
	Actual working hours yearly (2,000 × 160/200).............	1,600
	Saving of wages of one operator in the polishing and buffing dept. at..................	$1.40 per hr.
	Interest rate on capital.................................	10%

Cincinnati Milling Machine Co.

Operating and cost data on the defender and challenger machines.

complicated machine. Of course, overall operator wages for the new machine will be less than the combined wages of the others. All advantages and disadvantages are accounted for in this manner.

The new machine will cost $25,500 installed. With the required tooling (arbors, cutters, and fixture) costing $3,540, the investment totals $29,040. In order to determine whether it is advisable to purchase the new machine or to utilize the existing equipment, the MAPI replacement analysis is used; the new machine is considered the challenger, the three present machines plus the added machine, the defender. Available data for the analysis is the following:

TABLE II

		DEFENDER	CHALLENGER
LOSS OF REVENUE	1. Superiority of product	....	....
	2. Increased output	$50.00	....
	3. Sales promotion	....	....
	4. Other	....	....
OPERATING COST	1. Direct labor	$14,000.00	$ 3,600.00
	2. Indirect labor	200.00	160.00
	3. Labor for other operations	2,800.00	....
	4. Maintenance	600.00	250.00
	5. Spoilage of material	150.00	100.00
	6. Supplies	200.00	400.00
	7. Downtime	262.50	112.50
	8. Tools	1,100.00	4,260.00
	9. Fringe benefits	1,420.00	376.00
	10. Floor space	....	....
	11. Property taxes and insurance	200.00	1,275.00
	12. Power	200.00	100.00
	13. Other	....	....
		$21,182.50	$10,633.50
		-10,633.50	
	Defender's Operating Inferiority	$10,549.00	

Cincinnati Milling Machine Co.

Replacement analysis calculations to determine the defender's operating inferiority for the next year.

Present hourly production: 120 parts per hour
Required production: 160 parts per hour
Annual working time: 2,000 hours
Required annual production: 320,000 parts

TABLE III

DEFENDER'S ADVERSE MINIMUM	Operating inferiority.................................. $10,549.00
	Capital cost
	Salvage value now (4 machines) $4,000.00
	Salvage value next year............. 3,200.00
	Loss of salvage value........................... 800.00
	Interest on $4,000 at 10% 400.00
	$11,749.00
CHALLENGER'S ADVERSE MIN.	Acquisition cost........................ $25,500.00
	Operating inferiority and capital recovery cost factor from Fig. 9 ...... 15%
	Interest................................. 10%
	Total factor 25%
	Acquisition cost x total factor $6,375.00
	$6,375.00

Cincinnati Milling Machine Co.

Final calculations to determine the defender's and challenger's adverse minimums.

Tables I, II, and III show the figures necessary in the calculation of the comparative costs. The tables are related to one another and are self-explanatory.

From Table III we see the difference in the adverse minimums is in favor of the challenger ($11,749 — $6,375), or $5,374. Since the adverse minimum of the defender is substantially higher than that of the challenger, an immediate replacement with the new automatic milling machine is recommended.

Short-cut Methods of Replacement

Simplified formulas are sometimes used in industry for short-cut solutions of problems arising in the areas of equipment replacement. Caution must be exercised in the use of these formulas, since they give only approximate solutions. Whenever a thorough analysis is indicated, the methods outlined earlier should be employed.

Several manufacturing plants have used the following formulas for the solution of simple equipment replacement problems. The first formula is:

$$R = \frac{(S - D)\ (1 - X)}{P - P/n} \times 100$$

In this formula the rate of return on the average net investment, *R*, expressed as a percentage, equals the annual net saving divided by the average net investment, where:

$$
\begin{aligned}
P &= \text{cost of equipment, in dollars,} \\
n &= \text{life of equipment, in years,} \\
D &= \text{depreciation, in dollars per year,} \\
&= P/n, \\
S &= \text{savings, in dollars per year,} \\
S - D &= \text{gross savings, in dollars per year,} \\
X &= \text{tax rate, in percent,} \\
1 - X &= \text{tax factor to obtain net saving,} \\
(S - D)(1 - X) &= \text{net saving, in dollars per year,} \\
P - P/n &= \text{average net investment.}
\end{aligned}
$$

Out-of-pocket formula. Another simplified formula used for the same purpose is sometimes called an out-of-pocket formula. This formula is developed as follows (costs and savings are expressed in dollars):

$$M = \frac{CE + CT}{NS}$$

in which,

$$NS = GS - FT$$

and,

$$GS = (RP - RE)(ND \times DM) \pm S - T$$

For these equations the symbols are:

$M =$ time for equipment to pay for itself, in months,
$CE =$ cost of new equipment and installation,

CT = cost of tools, jigs, fixtures,
RP = cost-per-part on present equipment,
RE = cost-per-part on proposed equipment,
ND = parts produced per day,
DM = working days per month,
 S = increase or decrease (±) in total of all items of overhead per month,
 T = interest on investment,
GS = gross savings,
FT = federal tax,
NS = net cost savings.

The net cost savings are determined by the following steps:

1. Subtract the labor cost-per-part on the proposed method *RE* from the labor cost-per-part on the present method.

2. This saving is multiplied by the quantity produced per day *ND*, times the number of working days per month, *DM*. The resultant figure represents the monthly saving in labor.

3. The savings in labor are either increased or decreased by any changes in overhead *S*, thereby revealing the net operating advantage. (An operating advantage could result from an increase in labor and a decrease in overhead or raw material.)

4. This advantage is reduced by the interest on the investment *T*, to compute the gross savings *GS*.

5. Finally the federal income tax *FT* is deducted from the gross savings to arrive at the net savings *NS*, for the period computed. Depreciation on the proposed equipment is deducted from the gross saving before computing the federal income tax.

The time for the equipment to pay for itself is determined by dividing the net cost saving into the total capital cost of the proposed project. This value is *M* in the formula.

Typical replacement forms. Fig. 10 shows a form used by Allis-Chalmers Manufacturing Co. for what they term a "Capital Equipment Replacement Analysis." The proposed equipment is a 48 inch × 48 inch × 18 foot double housing, heavy duty planer, which is intended to replace the existing equipment consisting of two overaged planers. The form is self-explanatory; the results are clearly indicated and can be interpreted with ease. Note that the salvage value of the planer is 10%, a normal amount for durable equipment.

ALLIS-CHALMERS MANUFACTURING COMPANY
FORM NO. 5981-2-3
PRINTED 12-50

CAPITAL EQUIPMENT REPLACEMENT ANALYSIS

Date: 4-25-

WORKS West Allis-General Machinery

1 Subject of Analysis Purchase and install a new 48" x 48" x 18' Planer which will
2 replace two (2) Planers M.T. #1266 and M.T. #2587.
3 Anticipated Rate of Production Proposed equipment will produce all the work processed on existing equipment in 60% of present total time.

PROPOSED EQUIPMENT

4 Description: 48" x 48" x 18' Double
5 Housing Heavy Duty Planer
6 Est. Primary Service Life: 20 Years
7 Est. Terminal Salvage Value = (X) = $7,800.00
8 Est. Cost Installed = (Y) = $78,000.00
9 Terminal Salvage Factor = $\frac{x}{y}$ = 10 %

EXISTING EQUIPMENT

Purch. Date: 1906 Tool No. 1266 & 2587
Description: MT #1266 - 48" x 48" x 10' Planer
MT #2587 - 42" x 42" x 8' Planer
Years of life to Date: 47 yrs. each Installed Cost: $6,332.11
Location: 5 Shop Dept. No.: 1061
Intended Disposal: Sell
Resale, Salvage or Conversion Value $ 2500.00

	FACTOR	PROPOSED EQUIPMENT	EXISTING EQUIPMENT
10	Direct Labor (For Anticipated Production):	$ 9,885.00	$ 16,345.00
11	Indirect Labor (For Anticipated Production): *	-	-
12	Defective Material Labor & Works Expense: *	-	-
13	Down Time: *	-	204.00
14	Power Consumption:	1,024.00	779.00
15	Tooling: *	-	-
16	Supplies: *	-	-
17	Floor Space: (if usable)	640.00	480.00
18	Property Taxes & Insurance:	1,534.56	34.52
19	Normal Maintenance:	-	1,500.00
20	Special Repairs: *	-	-
21	Sub Contract Costs:	-	-
22	Other Items (explain on reverse side):	-	-
23			
24	Totals:	B $ 13,083.56	A $ 19,342.51
25			B $ 13,083.56
26	Next Yrs. Variance in Operating Cost: (A Minus B):		C $ 6,258.95
27	(Next Years Capital Cost of Retaining Existing Equipment)		
28	Restorative Repairs $ 27,000 / Years Effective 10 + (Restorative Repairs 27000 x 6%)		D $ 4,320.00
29	Resale, Salvage or Conversion Value of Existing Equipment $ 2500.00 X 6%		E $ 150.00
30	Salvage Value Loss, Next Year		F $ 500.00
31	Total Next Yrs. Cost for Existing Equipment (C + D + E + F)		G $ 11,288.95
32	Total Next Yrs. Cost for Proposed Equipment. Chart 6 % + Int. 6% Total 12 % X $ 78,000.00 Est. Cost Installed		H $ 9,360.00
33	First Years Gain (+) or Loss (—) thru replacing existing equipment (G-H) (taking into account Depreciation, Loss of Efficiency and 6% return on Investment)		Plus $1,928.95

Approved by: _____ Date: _____ Calculated by: _____ Date: 4-29-53

* Note:- Items indicated show difference in costs. (Use Reverse Side for Calculation)

Allis-Chalmers Mfg. Co.

Fig. 10. A replacement form for replacing two overaged planers with a single, heavy duty planer.

Fig. 11 shows a form used by the Cooper-Bessemer Corporation for what they term a "Re-equipment Analysis and Operational Comparison." The proposed equipment is a 54 inch × 68 inch × 20 foot three-head, Ingersoll milling machine, which is to replace the present equipment, two old Ingersoll slab mills.

THE COOPER-BESSEMER CORPORATION

RE-EQUIPMENT ANALYSIS AND OPERATIONAL COMPARISON

WILLIAM KELLY & Co. • CHICAGO 3 •

WORK SHEET — See Summarizing Report and Recommendations (Page 1 of 2). See reverse side for other calculations.

Dated 2-4-51
Number G-3

Line
1 Subject of Analysis Replacement of old Ingersoll Slab Mills with one new 1
2 and modern Duplex Mill of sufficient capacity to handle heavy duty 2
3 crankshafts and connecting rods. 3
4 Assumed rate of production 1951 Production Level 4

Line	A PRESENT EQUIPMENT - DEFENDER	B PROPOSED EQUIPMENT - CHALLENGER	Line
6A/B	Description 2 - Ingersoll Slab Mills	Description 54" x 68" x 20' Three Head Ingersoll Milling Machine	6A/B
7	Machine Number 523 & 740; Date Purchased 1919	Make and Source Ingersoll	7
8	Location 301; Installed Cost $ 4826.00	Cost of Unit $140,000; Installation $ 5,000.; Total $ 145,000.	8
9	Disposal Sale; Salvage or Conversion Value $ 3000.00	Estimated Primary Service Life 17 yrs.; Estimated Terminal Salvage $ 28,000.	9

Line	10 OPERATIONAL NEXT-YEAR ADVANTAGES (DIFFERENCES)	A DEFENDER Total	A DEFENDER Advantage	B CHALLENGER Total	B CHALLENGER Advantage	Line
11	Income Advantages-					11
12A/B	Superiority of Product	$	$	$	$	12A/B
13	Increased Output					13
14	Other					14
15	Operating Cost Advantages					15
16	Direct Labor, Incl. Overtime & Shift Premiums	32414.00		12965.00	19449.00	16
17	Set-Up Time					17
18	Indirect Labor	4482.00		1328.00	3154.00	18
19	"Fringe" Labor Costs	5534.00		2144.00	3390.00	19
20	Ordinary Maintenance					20
21	Special Repairs	1184.00			1184.00	21
22	Tool Costs		4000.00	4000.00		22
23	Supplies					23
24	Defective Material - Rework					24
25	Spoilage - Scrap					25
26	Downtime - Outage					26
27	Power Consumption	3185.00	1394.00	4579.00		27
28	Floor Space, If Usable	1764.00	574.00	2338.00		28
29	Property Taxes and Insurance		710.00	710.00		29
30	Sub Contract Costs	23216.00			23216.00	30
31	Other					31
32A/B	Totals	$71779.00	$6678.00	$28064.00	$50393.00	32A/B
33	Defender Operating Inferiority (Net Challenger Advantage) 32B — 32A				$43715.00	33

Line	A ADVERSE MINIMUM - DEFENDER		B ADVERSE MINIMUM - CHALLENGER		Line
35	Operating Inferiority (Line 33)	$43715.00	Cost Installed (Total 8B)	$145000.00	35
36	Salvage value loss, next year	$ 300.00	Primary service life (9B)	17 yrs.	36
37	Interest @ [8] % (x line 9A)	$ 240.00	Terminal salvage value (9B)	$ 28000.00	37
38	Capital additions, Total $		Salvage % (37B of 35B)	19 %	38
39	Next year proration	$	Chart 6 % Int. 8 % Total	14 %	39
40	Interest @ % (x line 38A)	$	Total % x Cost Installed (39B x 35B)	20300.00	40
41	Total, omitting line 38		Annual Average, Periodic Capital Additions	$	41
42	Adverse Minimum	$44255.00	Adverse Minimum (40B + 41B)	$ 20300.00	42

43 NEXT YEAR GAIN FROM REPLACEMENT (42A – 42B) $ 23955.00 43

Analysis by J. D. Harlan Approved ____________

The Cooper-Bessemer Corp.

Fig. 11. A replacement form for replacing two slab mills with a three head milling machine.

Fig. 12 shows a form used at Illinois Institute of Technology in courses in tool engineering and manufacturing processes.

ANALYSIS AND OPERATIONAL COMPARISON—MACHINERY OPERATION:

Day)
Present Production (Pieces per Mo.)
Yr.)

Day)
Anticipated Production (Pieces per Mo.)
Yr.)

	Present Equipment Machine No.	Proposed Equipment Machine No.
Rate Per Hour	_____	_____
Hours Per Day) Mo.) Yr.)	_____	_____
Machine Base Rate	____c/hr. $____	____c/hr. $____
Power & Supplies	____c/hr. $____	____c/hr. $____
Misc. Dir. Costs	____c/hr. $____	____c/hr. $____
Total Dir. Cost	____c/hr. $____	____c/hr. $____

Annual Savings (Direct Cost)	$_____
Less: Amortization, $____ @ ____%	$_____
Annual Savings	$_____
Less: Income Tax 52%	$_____
Net Annual Savings	$_____

Fig. 12. This is a replacement form used at Illinois Institute of Technology.

The form shown in Fig. 11 employs the adverse minimum concept presented earlier in this chapter. The operating inferiority (line 33) is computed as $43,715.00, which appears to be overwhelming evidence that replacement of the two slab mills is necessary. However, the "cost installed" of the new Duplex mill is $145,000 (line 8), a figure sufficiently high to warrant a complete analysis to determine whether or not the difference of the adverse minimums of defender and challenger will favor the challenger.

The adverse minimum of the defender is the operating inferiority plus the salvage loss for the coming year plus the interest for the coming year, or $43,715 + $300.00 + $240.00 = $44,255.00.

The adverse minimum of the challenger is the cost installed multiplied by a percentage based on the machine's primary service life of seventeen years. From a chart (not shown) this percentage is computed as 14%. The adverse minimum, then, is $145,000 \times 0.14 = $20,300. Since no capital additions are anticipated the value is the challenger's total adverse minimum.

The difference between the adverse minimums of defender and challenger is $44,255.00 − $20,300 = $23,955. This amount is enough to warrant immediate replacement of the slab mills with the Duplex mill. It represents the next year's gain that will be realized through the replacement of the old mills.

Index